PRACTICE MASTERS

Merrill

Algebra 2

With Trigonometry

Applications and Connections

GLENCOE

Macmillan/McGraw–Hill

Lake Forest, Illinois
Columbus, Ohio
Mission Hills, California
Peoria, Illinois

Send all inquiries to:
Glencoe Division, Macmillan/McGraw-Hill
936 Eastwind Drive
Westerville, OH 43081

ISBN: 0-675-13130-8

2 3 4 5 6 7 8 9 10 POH 00 99 98 97 96 95 94 93 92

CONTENTS

Glencoe Division, Macmillan/McGraw-Hill

CONTENTS

Glencoe Division, Macmillan/McGraw-Hill

NAME ______________________ DATE ____________

1-1

Practice Worksheet

Expressions and Formulas

Find the value of each expression.

1. $18 \div 2 \cdot 3$

2. $9 = 6 \div 2 + 1$

3. $(3 - 8)^2 \cdot 4 - 3$

4. $5 + 3 \cdot (2 - 12 \div 2)$

5. $1 + 2 - 3 \cdot 4 \div 5$

6. $12 - [20 - 2(6^2 \div 3 \cdot 2^2)]$

Evaluate each expression if $a = \frac{3}{4}$, $b = -8$, $c = -2$, $d = 3$, and $e = \frac{1}{3}$.

7. $ab^2 - d$

8. $(c + d)b$

9. $\frac{ae}{c} + d^2$

10. $\frac{d(b - c)}{ac}$

11. $(a - ce)c^2$

12. $a^2c^3 - be^2$

13. $-b[a + (c - d)^2]$

14. $\frac{a^3c^4}{d^3} - \frac{c}{e^2}$

Glencoe Division, Macmillan/McGraw-Hill

NAME ____________________ DATE __________

1-1 Practice Worksheet

Expressions and Formulas

Find the value of each expression.

1. $18 \div 2 \cdot 3$ **27**

2. $9 = 6 \div 2 + 1$ **13**

3. $(3 - 8)^2 \cdot 4 - 3$ **97**

4. $5 + 3 \cdot (2 - 12 \div 2)$ **−7**

5. $1 + 2 - 3 \cdot 4 \div 5$ $\mathbf{\frac{3}{5}}$

6. $12 - [20 - 2(6^2 \div 3 \cdot 2^2)]$ **88**

Evaluate each expression if $a = \frac{3}{4}$, $b = -8$, $c = -2$, $d = 3$, and $e = \frac{1}{3}$.

7. $ab^2 - d$ **45**

8. $(c + d)b$ **−8**

9. $\frac{ae}{c} + d^2$ $\mathbf{\frac{71}{8}}$

10. $\frac{d(b - c)}{ac}$ **12**

11. $(a - ce)c^2$ $\mathbf{\frac{17}{3}}$

12. $a^2c^3 - be^2$ $\mathbf{-\frac{65}{18}}$

13. $-b[a + (c - d)^2]$ **206**

14. $\frac{a^3c^4}{d^3} - \frac{c}{e^2}$ $\mathbf{\frac{73}{4}}$

NAME ______________________ DATE ____________

1-2 Practice Worksheet

Properties of Real Numbers

Name the sets of numbers to which each number belongs.

1. 6425 **2.** $\sqrt{7}$ **3.** π **4.** 0

5. $\sqrt{\frac{25}{36}}$ **6.** $-\sqrt{16}$ **7.** -35 **8.** -31.8

State the property illustrated in each equation.

9. $5x + (4y + 3x) = 5x + (3x + 4y)$

10. $7x + (9x + 8) = (7x + 9x) + 8$

11. $5(3x + y) = 5(3x + 1y)$

12. $7n + 2n = (7 + 2)n$

13. $3(2x)y = 3 \cdot 2(xy)$

14. $3x \cdot 2y = 3 \cdot 2 \cdot x \cdot y$

15. $(6 + -6)y = 0y$

16. $\frac{1}{4} \cdot 4y = 1y$

17. $5(x + y) = 5x + 5y$

18. $4n + 0 = 3n$

Simplify each expression.

19. $5x - 3y - 2x + 3y$

20. $-11a - 13b + 7a - 3b$

21. $8xy - 7y - (3 - 6y)$

22. $4c - 2c^2 - (4c + 2c^2)$

23. $3(r - 10s) - 4(7s + 2r)$

24. $\frac{1}{5}(10a - 4) + \frac{1}{2}(8 + 4a)$

25. $2x(4 - 2x + y) - 5x(y^2 + x - y)$

26. $\frac{5}{6}\left(\frac{3}{10}x + 12y\right) - \frac{1}{4}(2x - 3y)$

NAME ______________________ DATE ____________

1-2

Practice Worksheet

Properties of Real Numbers

Name the sets of numbers to which each number belongs.

1. 6425 N, W, Z, Q, R
2. $\sqrt{7}$ I, R
3. π I, R
4. 0 W, Z, Q, R
5. $\sqrt{\frac{25}{36}}$ Q, R
6. $-\sqrt{16}$ Z, Q, R
7. −35 Z, Q, R
8. −31.8 Q, R

State the property illustrated in each equation.

9. $5x + (4y + 3x) = 5x + (3x + 4y)$ commutative +
10. $7x + (9x + 8) = (7x + 9x) + 8$ associative +
11. $5(3x + y) = 5(3x + 1y)$ identity ×
12. $7n + 2n = (7 + 2)n$ distributive
13. $3(2x)y = 3 \cdot 2(xy)$ associative ×
14. $3x \cdot 2y = 3 \cdot 2 \cdot x \cdot y$ associative ×
15. $(6 + -6)y = 0y$ inverse +
16. $\frac{1}{4} \cdot 4y = 1y$ inverse ×
17. $5(x + y) = 5x + 5y$ distributive
18. $4n + 0 = 3n$ identity +

Simplify each expression.

19. $5x - 3y - 2x + 3y$ $3x$
20. $-11a - 13b + 7a - 3b$ $-4a - 16b$
21. $8xy - 7y - (3 - 6y)$ $8xy - y - 3$
22. $4c - 2c^2 - (4c + 2c^2)$ $-4c^2$
23. $3(r - 10s) - 4(7s + 2r)$ $-30rs - 5r - 28s$
24. $\frac{1}{5}(10a - 4) + \frac{1}{2}(8 + 4a)$ $4a + \frac{16}{5}$
25. $2x(4 - 2x + y) - 5x(y^2 + x - y)$ $-5xy^2 + 7xy - 9x^2 + 8x$
26. $\frac{5}{6}\left(\frac{3}{10}x + 12y\right) - \frac{1}{4}(2x - 3y)$ $\frac{-x + 43y}{4}$

Glencoe Division, Macmillan/McGraw-Hill

NAME ________________________ DATE ____________

Practice Worksheet

Solving Equations

State the property illustrated in each statement.

1. If $\frac{n}{6} + 4 = 3 - 13$, then $\frac{n}{6} + 4 = -10$.

2. If $-5 = 4n - 8$, then $3 = 4n$.

3. If $17x + y = z$ and $z = 2k - 1$, then $17x + y = 2k - 1$.

4. If $\frac{2}{3}x = \frac{3}{5}y$, then $10x = 9y$.

5. If $5 - (2x - y) = 3$, then $3 = 5 - (2x - y)$.

6. $3m - n + 7 = 3m - n + 7$

Solve each equation.

7. $13 = 8 - 6r$

8. $9 + 4n = -59$

9. $\frac{3}{8}y = 2\frac{3}{4}$

10. $-6 = \frac{4x}{7} + 2$

11. $\frac{3}{4} - \frac{1}{2}n = \frac{4}{5}$

12. $\frac{5}{6}s + \frac{3}{8} = \frac{2}{3}$

13. $-1.6r + 5 = -7.8$

14. $6x - 5 = 7 - 9x$

15. $5(6 - 4v) = v + 21$

16. $-4(6y - 5) = 23 - 3(8y + 1)$

Glencoe Division, Macmillan/McGraw-Hill

NAME ____________________ DATE ____________

1-3

Practice Worksheet

Solving Equations

State the property illustrated in each statement.

1. If $\frac{n}{6} + 4 = 3 - 13$, then $\frac{n}{6} + 4 = -10$. **substitution**

2. If $-5 = 4n - 8$, then $3 = 4n$. **addition**

3. If $17x + y = z$ and $z = 2k - 1$, then $17x + y = 2k - 1$.
transitive

4. If $\frac{2}{3}x = \frac{3}{5}y$, then $10x = 9y$. **multiplication**

5. If $5 - (2x - y) = 3$, then $3 = 5 - (2x - y)$. **symmetric**

6. $3m - n + 7 = 3m - n + 7$ **reflexive**

Solve each equation.

7. $13 = 8 - 6r$ $-\frac{5}{6}$

8. $9 + 4n = -59$ -17

9. $\frac{3}{8}y = 2\frac{3}{4}$ $\frac{22}{3}$

10. $-6 = \frac{4x}{7} + 2$ -14

11. $\frac{3}{4} - \frac{1}{2}n = \frac{4}{5}$ $-\frac{1}{10}$

12. $\frac{5}{6}s + \frac{3}{8} = \frac{2}{3}$ $\frac{7}{20}$

13. $-1.6r + 5 = -7.8$ 8

14. $6x - 5 = 7 - 9x$ $\frac{4}{5}$

15. $5(6 - 4v) = v + 21$ $\frac{3}{7}$

16. $-4(6y - 5) = 23 - 3(8y + 1)$
all reals

NAME ____________________ DATE ____________

1-4 Practice Worksheet

Applications of Equations

Write an equation and solve each problem. Be sure to identify the variable.

1. Fourteen less than twice some number is 154. Find the number.

2. Craig is 24 years younger than his father. In 10 years, Craig's father will be three times as old as Craig will be. Find their ages now.

3. The length of a rectangle is 9 centimeters more than half the width. Find the length if the perimeter is 60 centimeters.

4. It takes Kay 20 minutes to drive to work traveling 45 mph. Two minutes after she left home this morning, her husband, Dan, started out with her briefcase, which she had forgotten. If Dan arrived at Kay's office just as she did, how fast did he drive?

5. In an evening, a sporting goods store sold twice as many T-shirts as shorts. T-shirts are $9 each, and shorts are $14 each. The total amount of money taken in for both items was $256. Find the number of each that was sold.

NAME ______________________________ DATE ______________

1-4 Practice Worksheet

Applications of Equations

Write an equation and solve each problem. Be sure to identify the variable.

1. Fourteen less than twice some number is 154. Find the number. **84**

2. Craig is 24 years younger than his father. In 10 years, Craig's father will be three times as old as Craig will be. Find their ages now. **Craig: 2 years old; father: 26 years old**

3. The length of a rectangle is 9 centimeters more than half the width. Find the length if the perimeter is 60 centimeters. **16 cm**

4. It takes Kay 20 minutes to drive to work traveling 45 mph. Two minutes after she left home this morning, her husband, Dan, started out with her briefcase, which she had forgotten. If Dan arrived at Kay's office just as she did, how fast did he drive? **50 mph**

5. In an evening, a sporting goods store sold twice as many T-shirts as shorts. T-shirts are $9 each, and shorts are $14 each. The total amount of money taken in for both items was $256. Find the number of each that was sold. **8 shorts, 16 T-shirts**

Glencoe Division, Macmillan/McGraw-Hill

NAME ____________________ DATE ____________

1-5

Practice Worksheet

Problem Solving Strategy: List the Possibilities

Use the strategy of listing possibilities to answer these questions.

1. In how many ways can a clerk give a customer 25¢ in change?

2. Fred sent birthday cards to four friends. Only after he had dropped them in the mailbox did he realize that he had not checked to see whether he had put the right cards in the right envelopes. How many ways of putting the cards in the envelopes could result in at least one person's getting the wrong birthday card?

3. In how many ways can you select three numbers from the set {1, 2, 3, 4, 5, 6, 7, 8} so that the numbers could represent the measures of the sides of a triangle? Remember that the sum of the measures of any two sides of a triangle must be greater than the measure of the other side.

4. The president of a student council wants to select three of the other five members for a special committee. In how many ways can the members of the committee be chosen?

Glencoe Division, Macmillan/McGraw-Hill

NAME ____________________ DATE ____________

1-5 Practice Worksheet

Problem Solving Strategy: List the Possibilities

Use the strategy of listing possibilities to answer these questions.

1. In how many ways can a clerk give a customer 25¢ in change? **13 ways**

2. Fred sent birthday cards to four friends. Only after he had dropped them in the mailbox did he realize that he had not checked to see whether he had put the right cards in the right envelopes. How many ways of putting the cards in the envelopes could result in at least one person's getting the wrong birthday card? **23 ways**

3. In how many ways can you select three numbers from the set {1, 2, 3, 4, 5, 6, 7, 8} so that the numbers could represent the measures of the sides of a triangle? Remember that the sum of the measures of any two sides of a triangle must be greater than the measure of the other side. **22 ways**

4. The president of a student council wants to select three of the other five members for a special committee. In how many ways can the members of the committee be chosen? **10 ways**

Glencoe Division, Macmillan/McGraw-Hill

NAME ______________________ DATE ____________

1-6 Practice Worksheet

Solving Absolute Value Equations

Solve each equation.

1. $|n - 4| = 13$

2. $7|x + 3| = 42$

3. $|2y - 3| = 29$

4. $\left|x - \frac{3}{8}\right| = 2$

5. $\left|\frac{2}{3}u - 6\right| = 42$

6. $|5x - 4| = -6$

7. $-3|4x - 9| = 24$

8. $-6|5 - 2y| = -9$

9. $|1 - 3x| = x + 5$

10. $|9 + 4x| = 5x + 18$

11. $|8 + p| = 2p - 3$

12. $5|4w - 1| = 5w + 40$

13. $4|2y - 7| + 5 = 9$

14. $-2|7 - 3y| - 6 = -14$

NAME ______________________ DATE ____________

1-6 Practice Worksheet

Solving Absolute Value Equations

Solve each equation.

1. $|n - 4| = 13$ **−9, 17**

2. $7|x + 3| = 42$ **−9, 3**

3. $|2y - 3| = 29$ **−13, 16**

4. $\left|x - \frac{3}{8}\right| = 2$ $-\frac{13}{8}, \frac{19}{8}$

5. $\left|\frac{2}{3}u - 6\right| = 42$ **−54, 72**

6. $|5x - 4| = -6$ **no solution**

7. $-3|4x - 9| = 24$ **no solution**

8. $-6|5 - 2y| = -9$ $\frac{7}{4}, \frac{13}{4}$

9. $|1 - 3x| = x + 5$ **−1, 3**

10. $|9 + 4x| = 5x + 18$ **−3**

11. $|8 + p| = 2p - 3$ **11**

12. $5|4w - 1| = 5w + 40$ $-\frac{7}{5}, 3$

13. $4|2y - 7| + 5 = 9$ **3, 4**

14. $-2|7 - 3y| - 6 = -14$ $1, \frac{11}{3}$

NAME ______________________ DATE ____________

1-7 Practice Worksheet

Solving Inequalities

Solve each inequality. Graph the solution set.

1. $8x - 6 \geq 10$

2. $23 - 4u < 3$

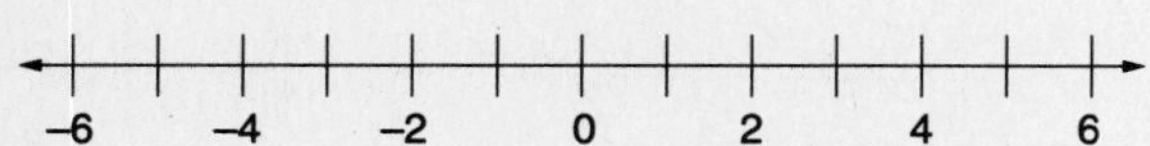

3. $-3(4w - 1) > -12$

4. $5(2x + 3) \leq 4$

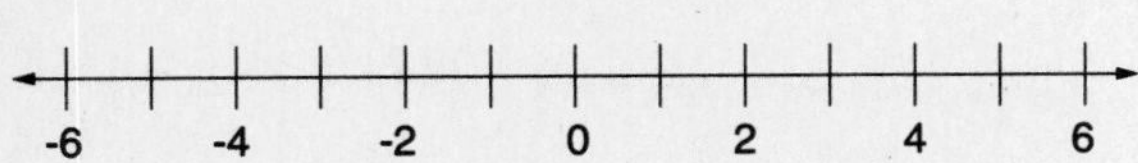

Solve each inequality.

5. $9x - 11 > 4x + 12$

6. $1 - 8u \leq 3u - 10$

7. $16 - 10r \geq 0$

8. $9(2r - 5) - 3 < 7r - 4$

9. $1 + 5(x - 8) \leq 2 - (x + 5)$

10. $4n - 5(n - 3) > 3(n + 1) - 20$

11. $17.5 < 19 - 2.5x$

12. $\frac{5x}{8} - \frac{3}{4} < \frac{1}{5}$

13. $-6\left(\frac{1}{2} + \frac{2w}{3}\right) > 2w$

14. $\frac{4x - 3}{2} \geq -1.9$

Glencoe Division, Macmillan/McGraw-Hill

NAME ______________________ DATE ____________

1-7 Practice Worksheet

Solving Inequalities

Solve each inequality. Graph the solution set.

1. $8x - 6 \geq 10$ $\{x|x \geq 2\}$

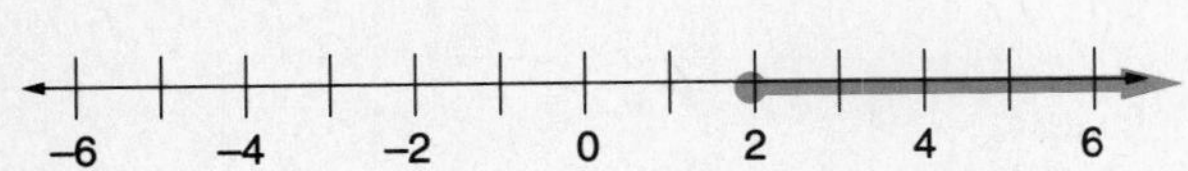

2. $23 - 4u < 3$ $\{u|u > 5\}$

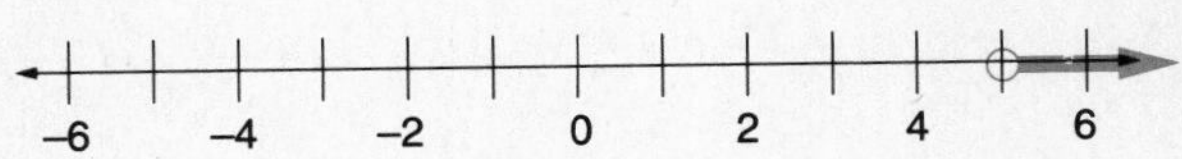

3. $-3(4w - 1) > -12$ $\left\{w|w < \frac{5}{4}\right\}$

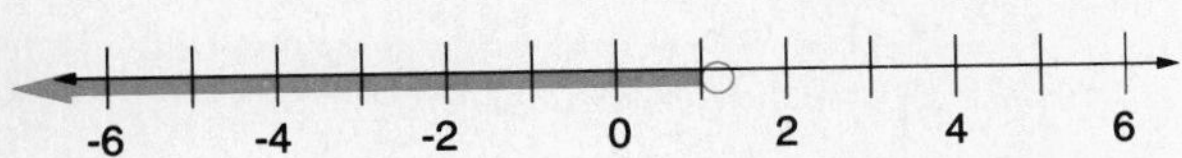

4. $5(2x + 3) \leq 4$ $\left\{x|x \leq -\frac{11}{10}\right\}$

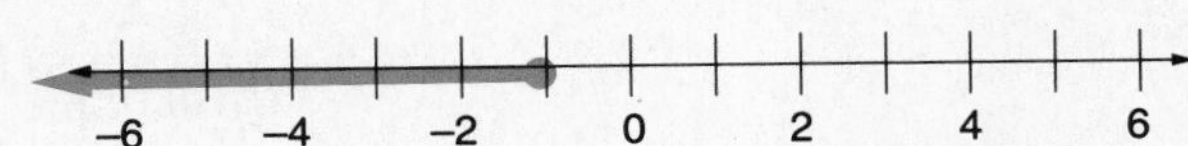

Solve each inequality.

5. $9x - 11 > 4x + 12$ $\left\{x|x > \frac{23}{5}\right\}$

6. $1 - 8u \leq 3u - 10$ $\{u|u \geq 1\}$

7. $16 - 10r \geq 0$ $\left\{r|r \leq \frac{8}{5}\right\}$

8. $9(2r - 5) - 3 < 7r - 4$ $\{r|r < 4\}$

9. $1 + 5(x - 8) \leq 2 - (x + 5)$ $\{x|x \leq 6\}$

10. $4n - 5(n - 3) > 3(n + 1) - 20$ $\{n|n < 8\}$

11. $17.5 < 19 - 2.5x$ $\left\{x|x < \frac{3}{5}\right\}$

12. $\frac{5x}{8} - \frac{3}{4} < \frac{1}{5}$ $\left\{x|x < \frac{38}{25}\right\}$

13. $-6\left(\frac{1}{2} + \frac{2w}{3}\right) > 2w$ $\left\{w|w < -\frac{1}{2}\right\}$

14. $\frac{4x - 3}{2} \geq -1.9$ $\{x|x \geq 0.2\}$

NAME ______________________ DATE ______________

1-8 Practice Worksheet

Solving Compound Sentences and Absolute Value Inequalities

Solve each compound sentence. Graph each solution set.

1. $-8 \leq 3y - 20 < 52$

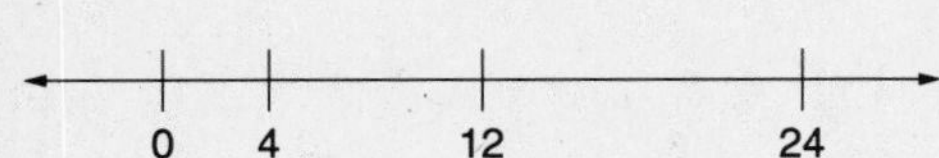

2. $3(5x - 2) < 24$ or $6x - 4 > 9 + 5x$

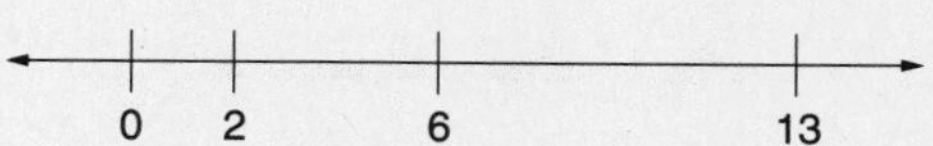

3. $2x - 3 > 15$ or $3 - 7x < 17$

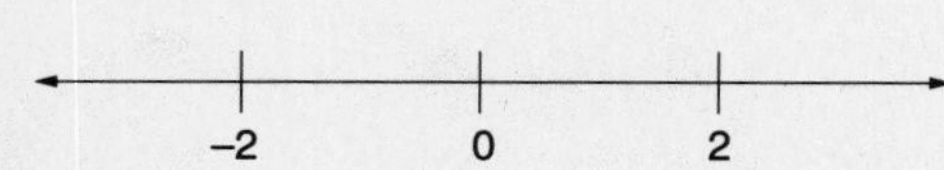

4. $35 - 5x \leq 0$ and $5x + 6 \geq -14$

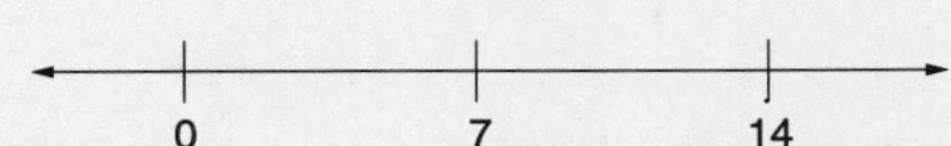

Solve each inequality. Graph each solution set.

5. $|2w| \geq 5$

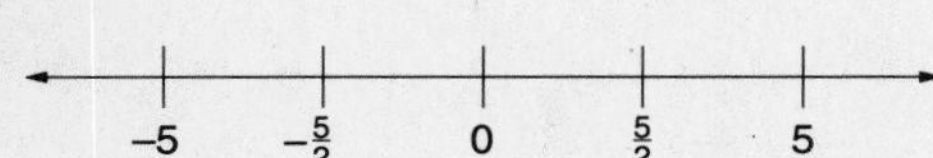

6. $|y + 5| < 2$

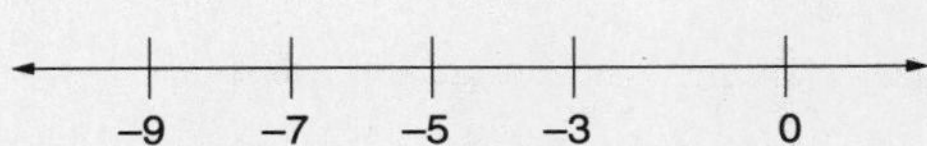

7. $|x - 8| \geq 3$

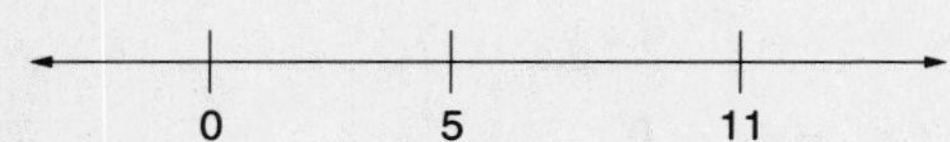

8. $|3x - 2| \leq -2$

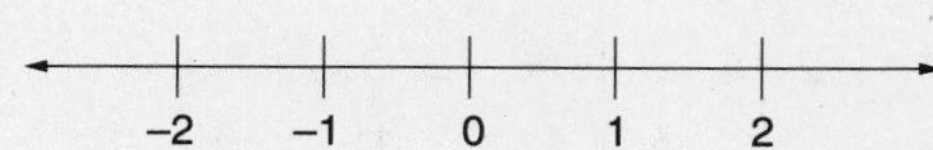

9. $|x + 2| \leq 2x + 7$

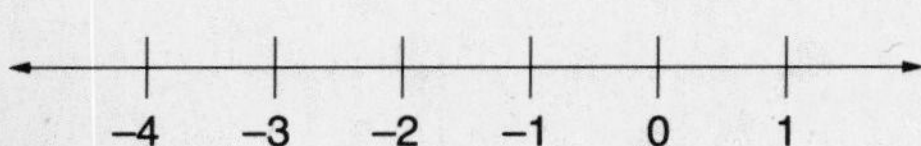

10. $|x| > x - 1$

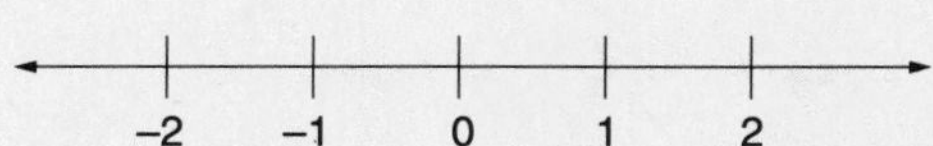

NAME ______________________ DATE ______________

1-8 Practice Worksheet

Solving Compound Sentences and Absolute Value Inequalities

Solve each compound sentence. Graph each solution set.

1. $-8 \leq 3y - 20 < 52$

$\{y|4 \leq y < 24\}$

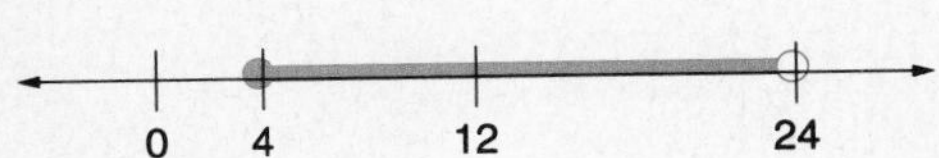

2. $3(5x - 2) < 24$ or $6x - 4 > 9 + 5x$

$\{x|x < 2 \text{ or } x > 13\}$

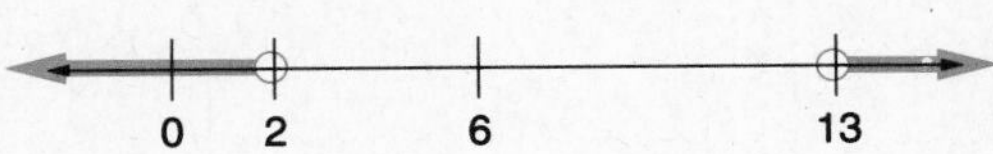

3. $2x - 3 > 15$ or $3 - 7x < 17$

$\{x|x > -2\}$

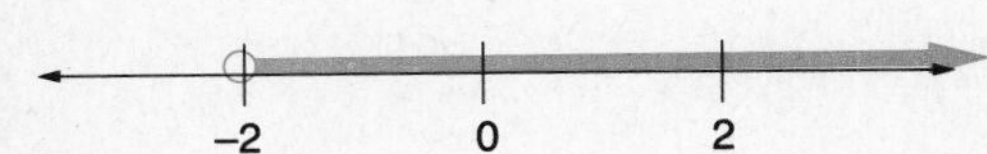

4. $35 - 5x \leq 0$ and $5x + 6 \geq -14$

$\{x|x \geq 7\}$

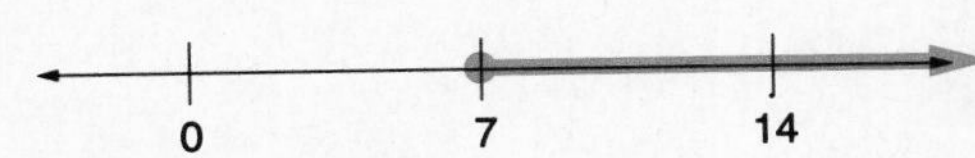

Solve each inequality. Graph each solution set.

5. $|2w| \geq 5$

$\left\{w|w \leq -\frac{5}{2} \text{ or } w \geq \frac{5}{2}\right\}$

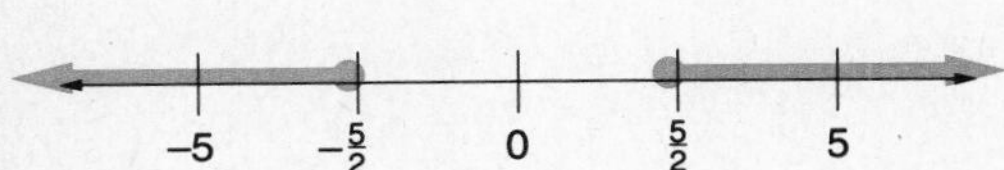

6. $|y + 5| < 2$

$\{y| -7 < y < -3\}$

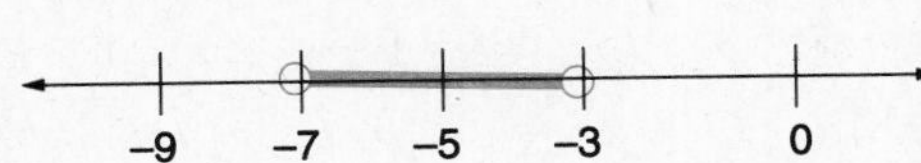

7. $|x - 8| \geq 3$

$\{x|x \leq 5 \text{ or } x \geq 11\}$

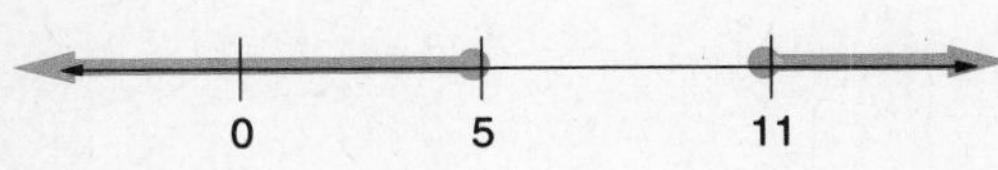

8. $|3x - 2| \leq -2$

$\varnothing$

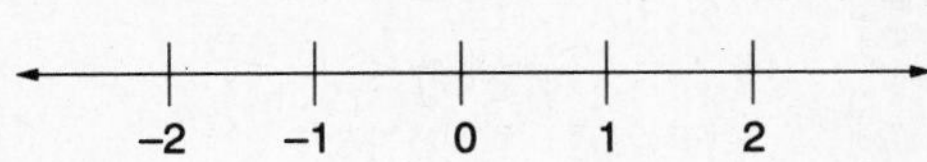

9. $|x + 2| \leq 2x + 7$

$\{x|x \geq -3\}$

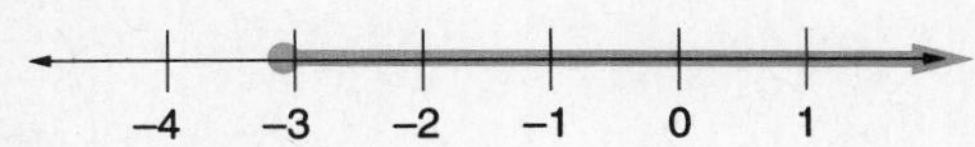

10. $|x| > x - 1$

all reals

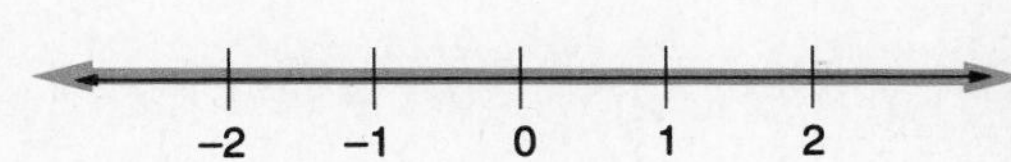

Glencoe Division, Macmillan/McGraw-Hill

NAME ______________________ DATE ____________

2-1

Practice Worksheet

Relations and Functions

Graph each set of ordered pairs on the same coordinate plane.

1. $\{(0.75, 0.5), (0.75, -0.5), (-0.75, 0.5)\}$

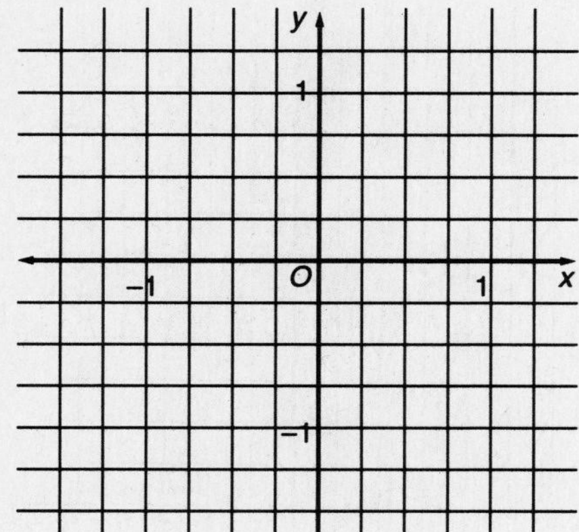

2. $\{(-20, -7), (20, 0), (0, 15), (10, 0)\}$

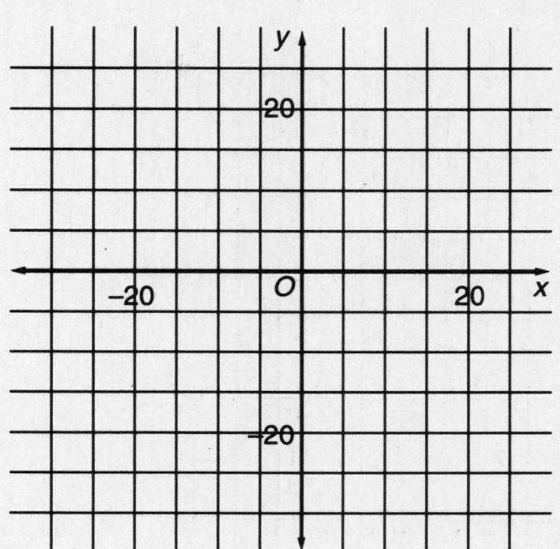

State the domain and range of each relation. Is the relation a function?

3. $\{(3, 2), (3, 5), (3, 8)\}$

4. $\{(2, 6), (6, 2)\}$

5. $\{(4, 1), (3, 1), (2, 1), (0, 1)\}$

6. $\{(1, 6), (1, 4), (1, 2), (1, 0)\}$

Use the vertical line test to determine if each relation is a function.

7.

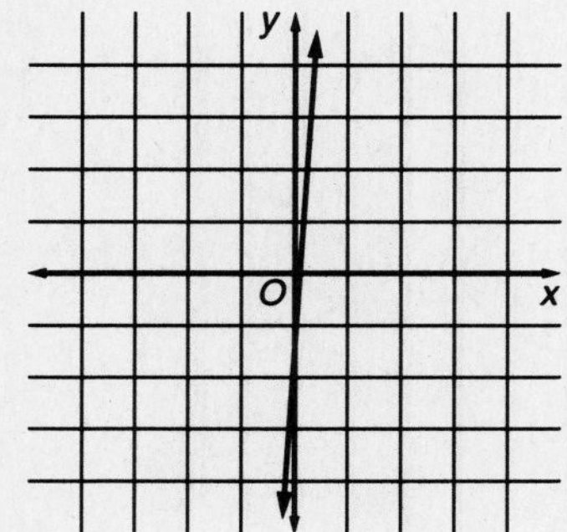

8.

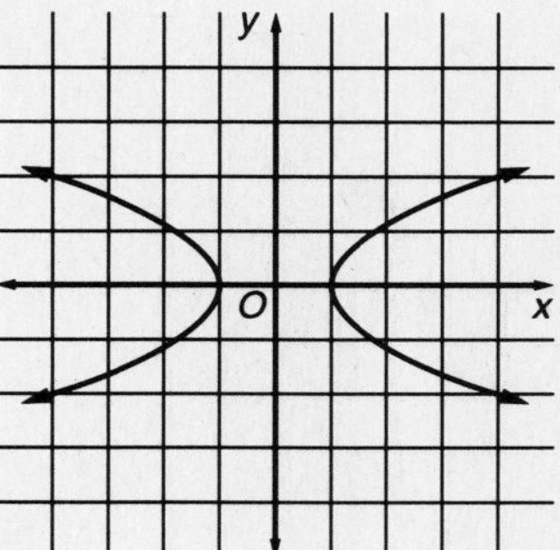

Find each value if $f(x) = \dfrac{5}{x+2}$.

9. $f(3)$

10. $f(-4)$

11. $f\left(\frac{1}{2}\right)$

12. $f(-2)$

13. $f(0)$

14. $f(m - 2)$

Glencoe Division, Macmillan/McGraw-Hill

NAME ______________________ DATE ______________

2-1 Practice Worksheet

Relations and Functions

Graph each set of ordered pairs on the same coordinate plane.

1. {(0.75, 0.5), (0.75, −0.5), (−0.75, 0.5)}

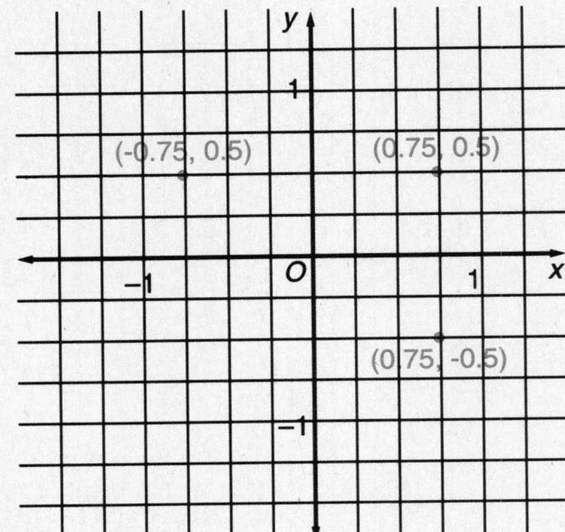

2. {(−20, −7), (20, 0), (0, 15), (10, 0)}

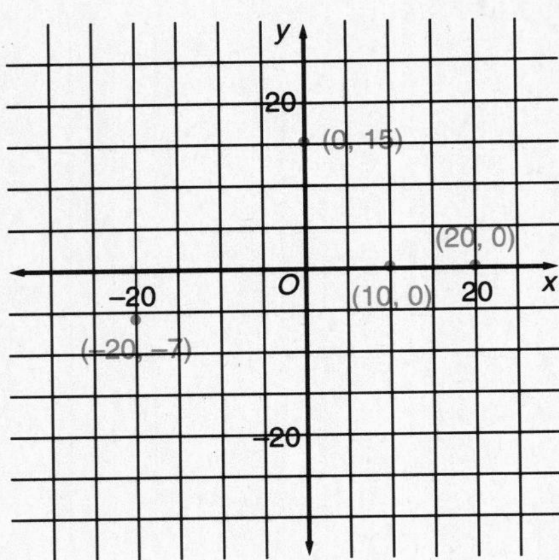

State the domain and range of each relation. Is the relation a function?

3. {(3, 2), (3, 5), (3, 8)} *d*: {3}, r: {2, 5, 8}, not a function

4. {(2, 6), (6, 2)} *d*: {2, 6}, r: {2, 6}, function

5. {(4, 1), (3, 1), (2, 1), (0, 1)} *d*: {0, 2, 3, 4}, *r*: {1}, function

6. {(1, 6), (1, 4), (1, 2), (1, 0)} *d*: {1}, r: {6, 4, 2, 6}, not a function

Use the vertical line test to determine if each relation is a function.

7.

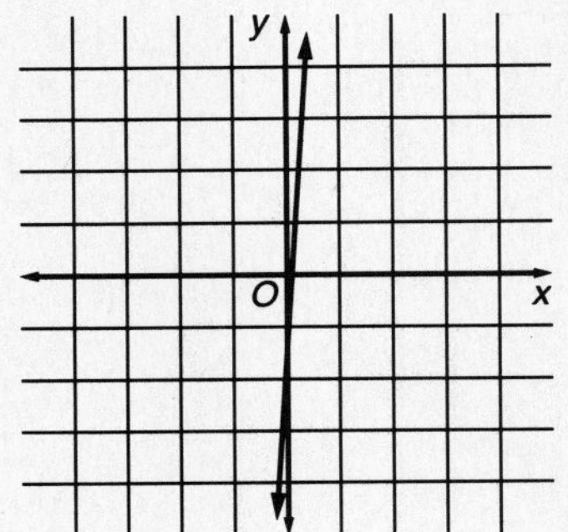

function

8.

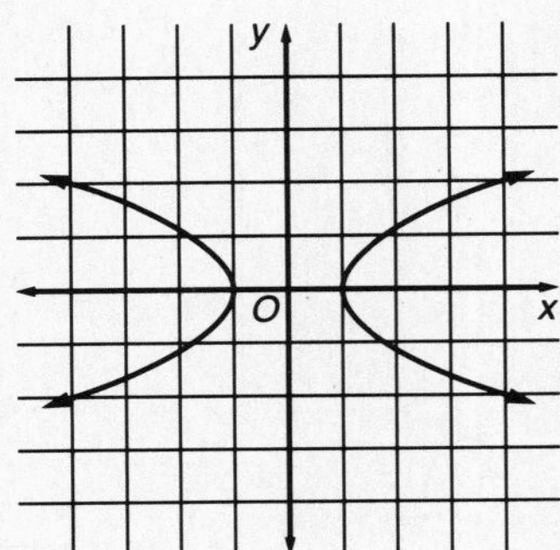

not a function

Find each value if f(x) = $\frac{5}{x + 2}$.

9. $f(3)$ 1

10. $f(-4)$ $-\frac{5}{2}$

11. $f\left(\frac{1}{2}\right)$ 2

12. $f(-2)$ undefined

13. $f(0)$ $\frac{5}{2}$

14. $f(m - 2)$ $\frac{5}{m}$

NAME ______________________ DATE ____________

2-2 Practice Worksheet

Linear Functions

Write each equation in standard form.

1. $y = 7x - 5$

2. $y = \frac{3}{8}x + 5$

3. $x = -\frac{2}{7}y + \frac{3}{4}$

4. $3y - 5 = 0$

Solve each equation for the specified variable.

5. $2x - y = 5$ for y

6. $3a = 4b - 5$ for b

7. $3m - 5 = n$ for m

8. $5a + 2b = 6$ for b

Graph each equation.

9. $y = 3x - 1$

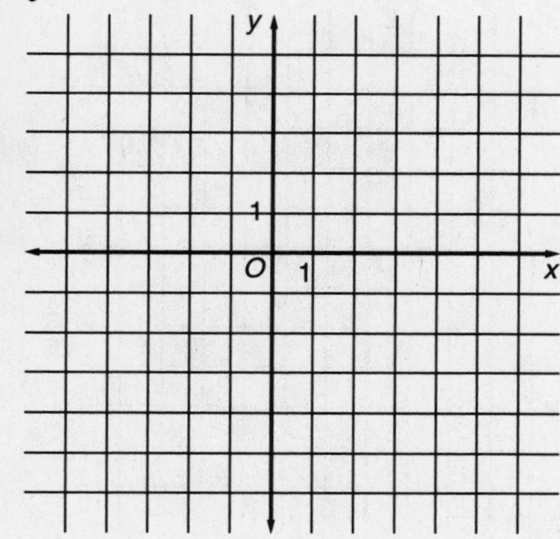

10. $f(x) = -2x + 3$

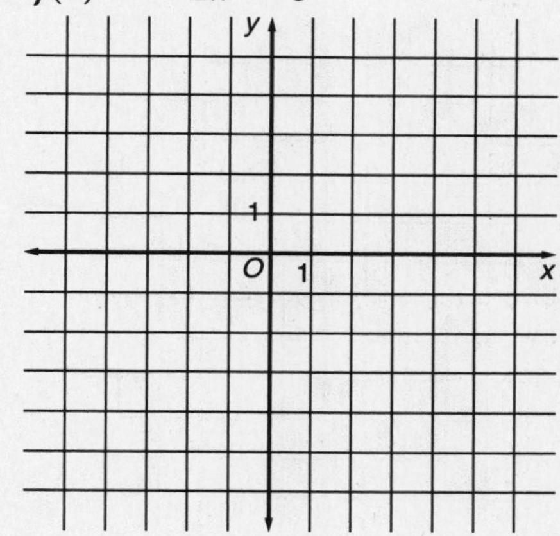

11. $2x + 7y = 14$

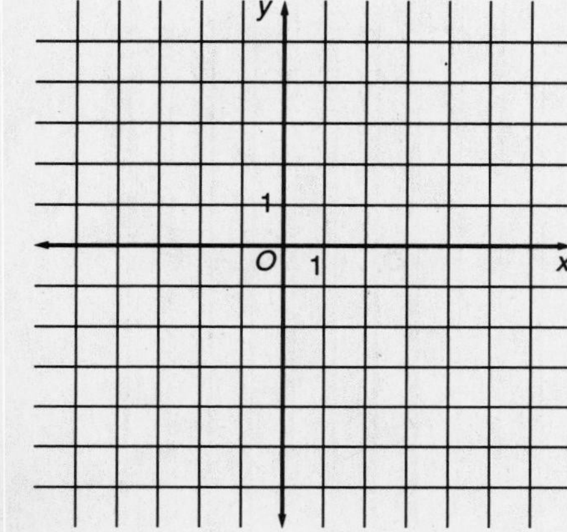

12. $\frac{2}{5}x + \frac{y}{4} = 1$

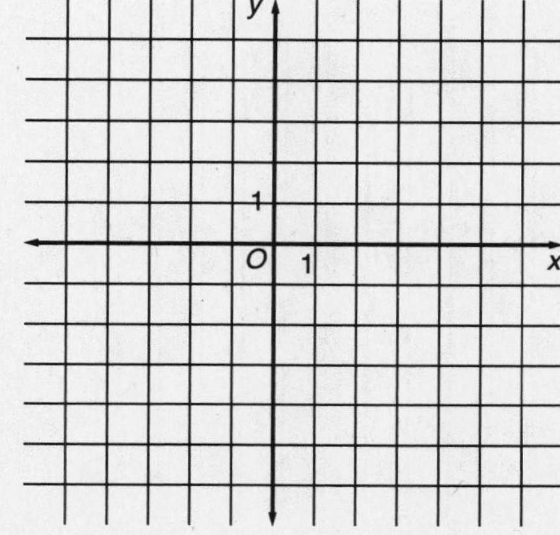

NAME ______________________ DATE ____________

2-2 Practice Worksheet

Linear Functions

Write each equation in standard form.

1. $y = 7x - 5$
   $7x - y = 5$

2. $y = \frac{3}{8}x + 5$
   $-3x + 8y = 40$

3. $x = -\frac{2}{7}y + \frac{3}{4}$
   $28x + 8y = 21$

4. $3y - 5 = 0$
   $3y = 5$

Solve each equation for the specified variable.

5. $2x - y = 5$ for y
   $y = 2x - 5$

6. $3a = 4b - 5$ for b $b = \frac{3a + 5}{4}$

7. $3m - 5 = n$ for m
   $m = \frac{n + 5}{3}$

8. $5a + 2b = 6$ for b $b = \frac{6 - 5a}{2}$

Graph each equation.

9. $y = 3x - 1$

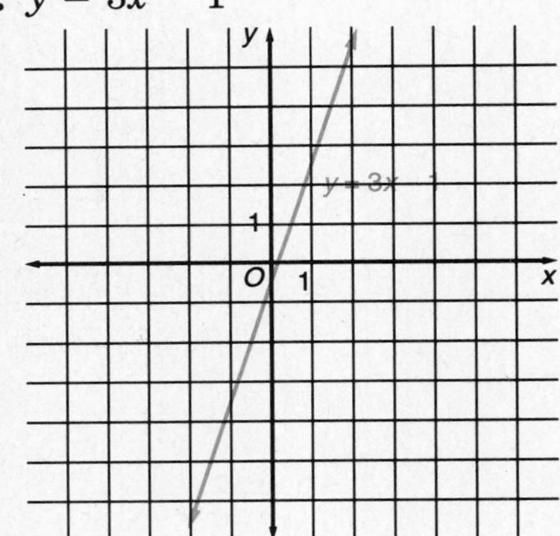

10. $f(x) = -2x + 3$

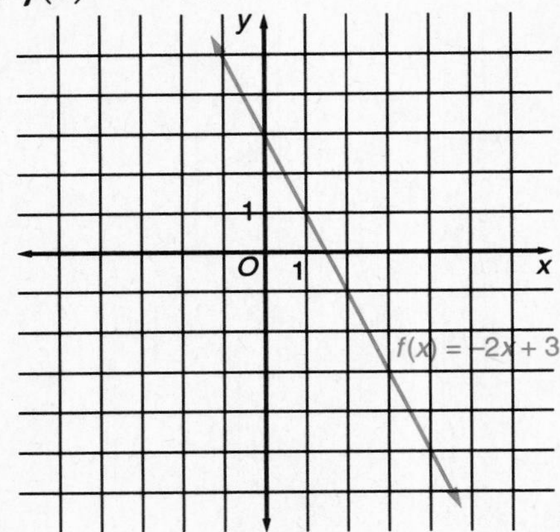

11. $2x + 7y = 14$

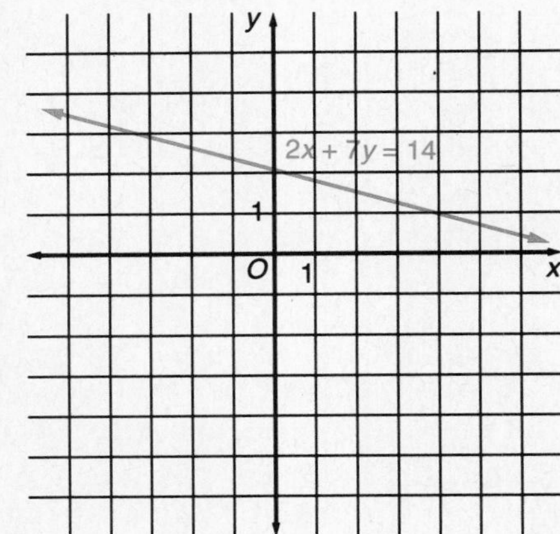

12. $\frac{2}{5}x + \frac{y}{4} = 1$

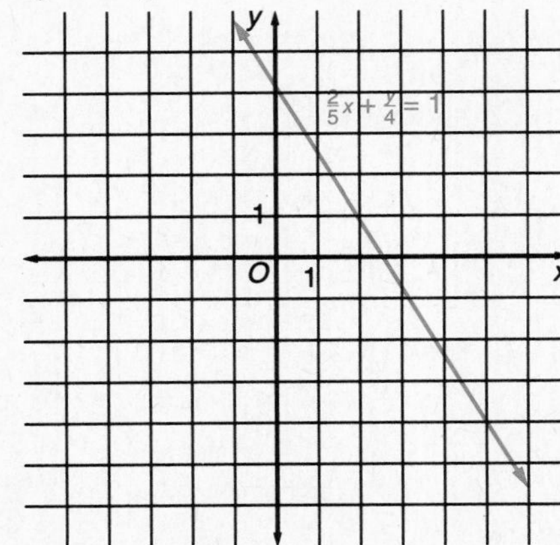

NAME ______________________ DATE ____________

2-3

Practice Worksheet

Problem Solving Strategy: Look for a Pattern

Solve. Look for a pattern.

1. How many shaded triangles will there be in the tenth figure?

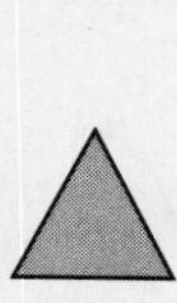
1

2

3

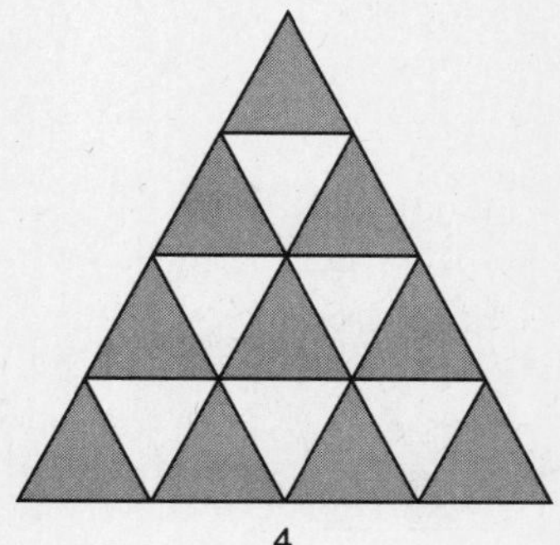
4

2. How many shaded squares will there be in the tenth figure?

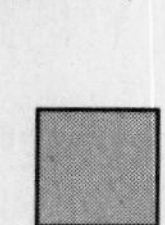
1

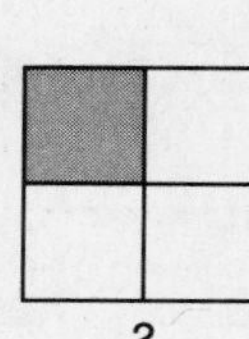
2

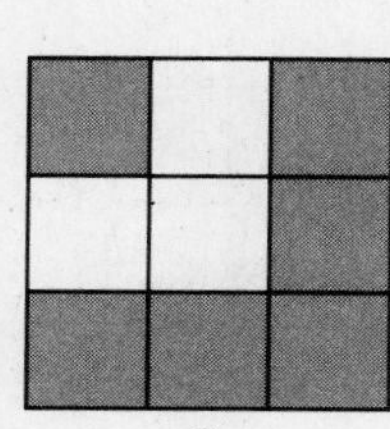
3

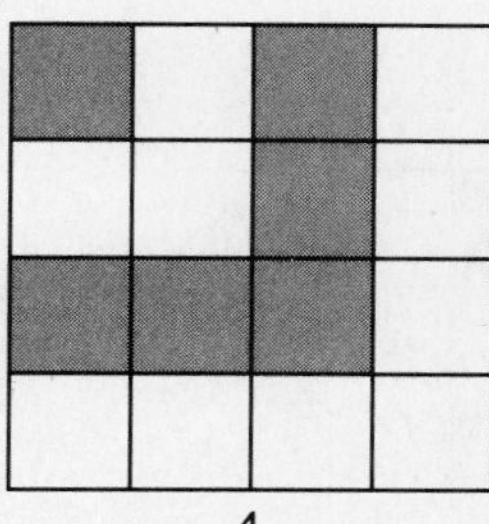
4

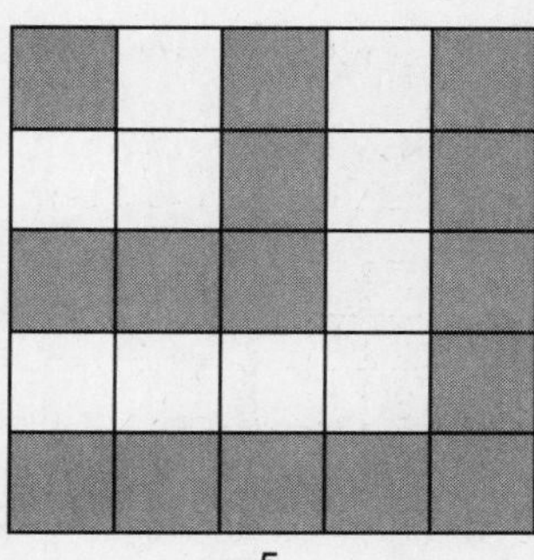
5

Solve. Use any strategy.

3. Can you trace the figure at the right without lifting your pencil or tracing over any line you have already drawn?

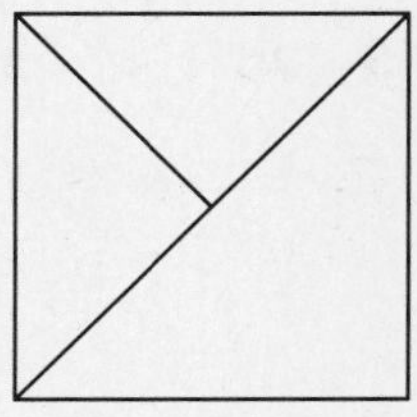

4. A pyramid of aluminum cans is built against a wall so that there are two cans in the top row, four cans in the second row, six cans in the third row, and so on. How many rows are there if the pyramid contains 1190 cans?

2-3

NAME ______________________ DATE ____________

Practice Worksheet

Problem Solving Strategy: Look for a Pattern

Solve. Look for a pattern.

1. How many shaded triangles will there be in the tenth figure? 55

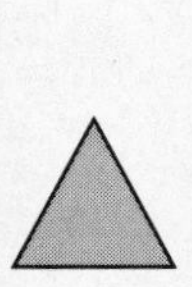
1

2

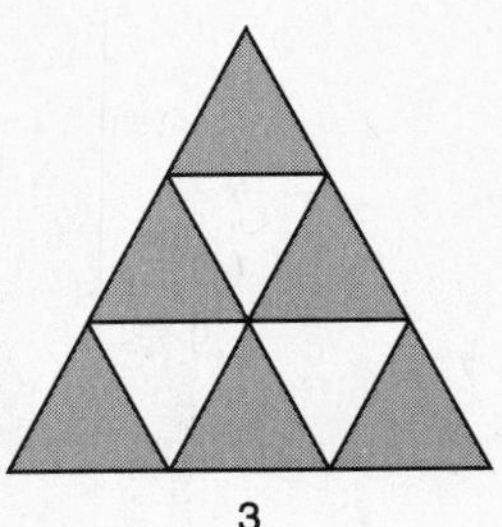
3

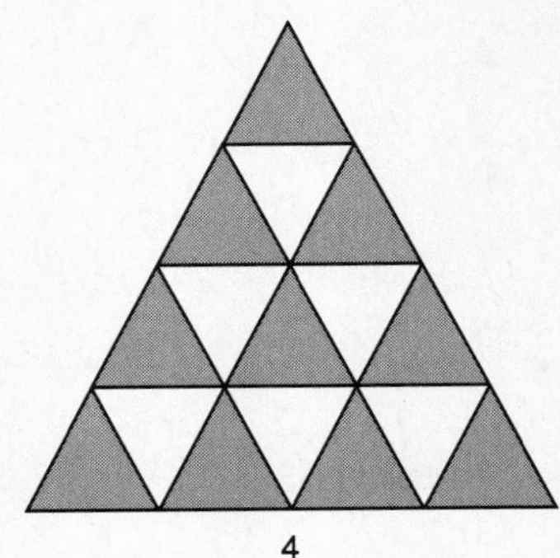
4

2. How many shaded squares will there be in the tenth figure? 45

1

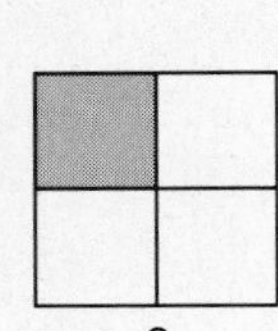
2

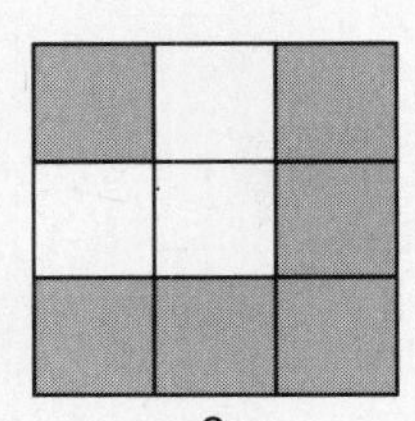
3

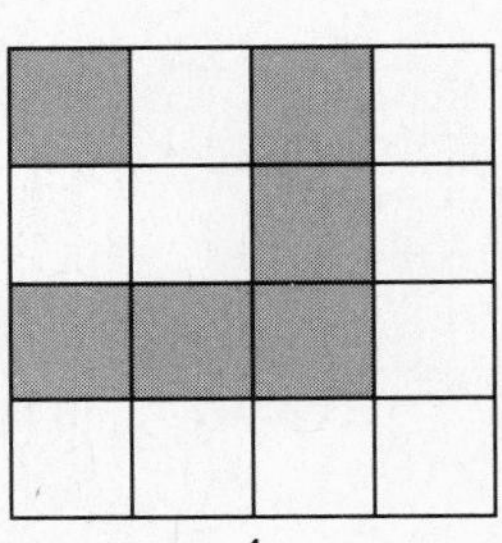
4

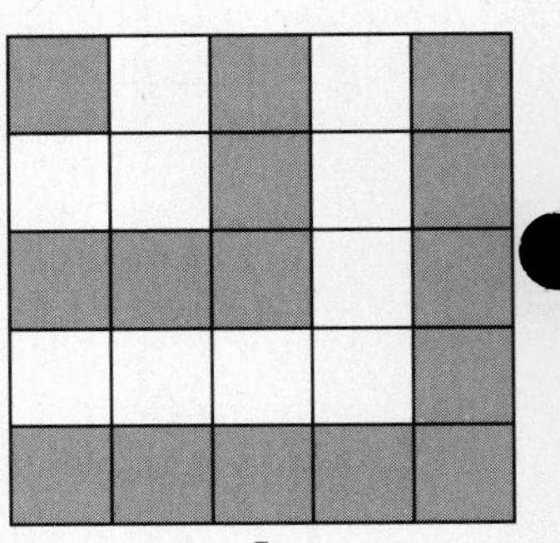
5

Solve. Use any strategy.

3. Can you trace the figure at the right without lifting your pencil or tracing over any line you have already drawn? no

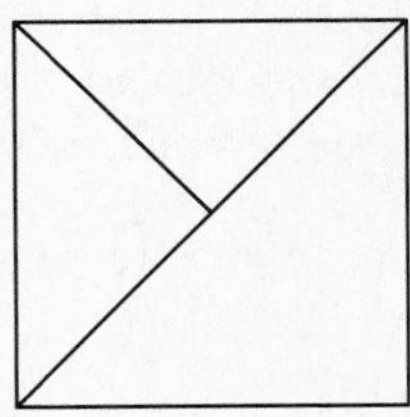

4. A pyramid of aluminum cans is built against a wall so that there are two cans in the top row, four cans in the second row, six cans in the third row, and so on. How many rows are there if the pyramid contains 1190 cans? 34

Glencoe Division, Macmillan/McGraw-Hill

NAME ____________________ DATE ____________

2-4 Practice Worksheet

Slopes and Intercepts

Determine the slope of the line passing through each pair of points.

1. (3, −8) and (−5, 2)

2. (−10, −3) and (7, 2)

3. (−7, −6) and (3, −6)

4. (8, 2) and (8, −1)

Find the y-intercept and the x-intercept of the graph of each equation.

5. $y = 7x + 5$

6. $y = -9x + 15$

Graph a line that passes through the given point and has the given slope.

7. (1, −3), $m = 3$

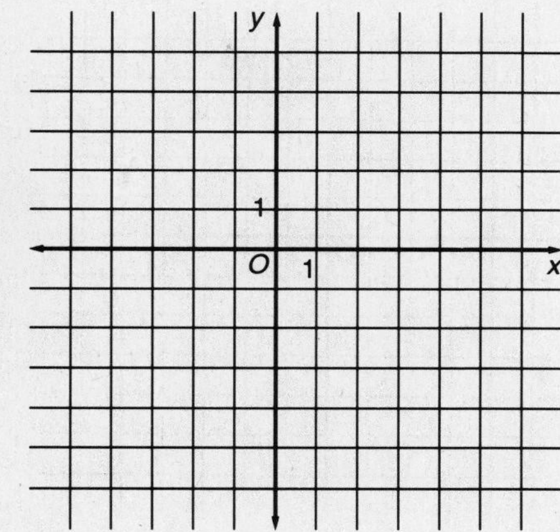

8. (2, 1), $m = -\frac{3}{4}$

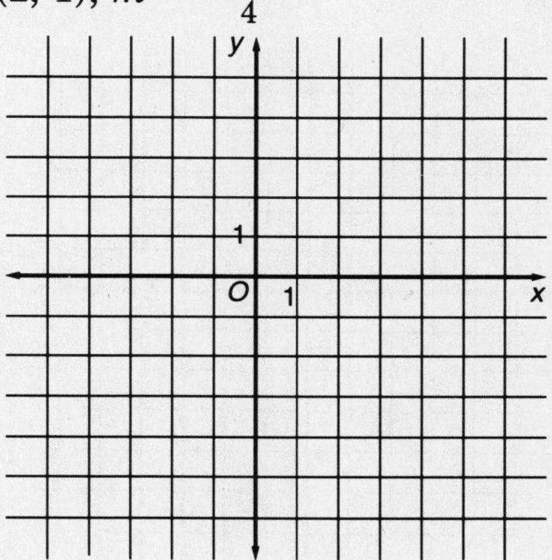

State whether the graphs of the following equations are parallel, perpendicular, or neither.

9. $2x + 3y = 4$
$3x + 2y = 6$

10. $\frac{1}{2}x + 2y = 1$
$4x - y = 3$

11. $6x - 9y = 4$
$\frac{2}{3}x - y = 11$

12. $y - 7 = 0$
$3x = 5$

Glencoe Division, Macmillan/McGraw-Hill

NAME ______________________ DATE ____________

2-4 Practice Worksheet

Slopes and Intercepts

Determine the slope of the line passing through each pair of points.

1. (3, −8) and (−5, 2) $-\frac{5}{4}$

2. (−10, −3) and (7, 2) $\frac{5}{17}$

3. (−7, −6) and (3, −6) 0

4. (8, 2) and (8, −1) undefined

Find the y-intercept and the x-intercept of the graph of each equation.

5. $y = 7x + 5$ x: $-\frac{5}{7}$, y: 5

6. $y = -9x + 15$ x: $\frac{5}{3}$, y: 15

Graph a line that passes through the given point and has the given slope.

7. (1, −3), $m = 3$

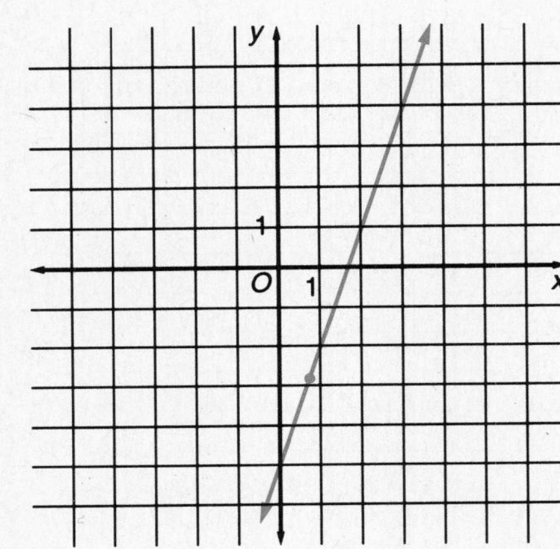

8. (2, 1), $m = -\frac{3}{4}$

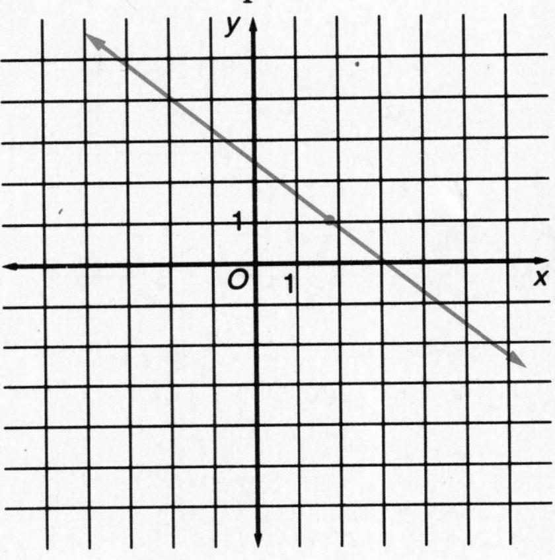

State whether the graphs of the following equations are parallel, perpendicular, or neither.

9. $2x + 3y = 4$
$3x + 2y = 6$
neither

10. $\frac{1}{2}x + 2y = 1$
$4x - y = 3$
perpendicular

11. $6x - 9y = 4$
$\frac{2}{3}x - y = 11$
parallel

12. $y - 7 = 0$
$3x = 5$
perpendicular

Glencoe Division, Macmillan/McGraw-Hill

NAME ______________________ DATE ____________

2-5

Practice Worksheet

Writing Linear Equations

State the slope and y-intercept of the graph of each equation.

1. $5x - 4y = 8$

2. $3x - y = -11$

3. $\frac{2}{3}x + \frac{4}{7}y = 1$

4. $3y = 7$

Find the slope-intercept form of each equation.

5. $3x - 5y = 15$

6. $4x + 7y = 12$

7. $7y = -15$

8. $2x = -8$

Write an equation for the line that satisfies each of the given conditions in slope-intercept form and in standard form.

9. slope $= -5$, passes through $(-3, -8)$

10. *slope* $= \frac{4}{5}$, *passes through* $(10, -3)$

11. *passes through* $(4, 3)$ *and* $(7, -2)$

12. *passes through* $(-6, -3)$ *and* $(-8, 4)$

13. *passes through* $(3, 11)$ *and* $(-6, 5)$

14. *passes through* $(7, 2)$ *and* $(3, -5)$

15. x-intercept $= 3$, y-intercept $= 2$

16. x-intercept $= -5$, y-intercept $= 7$

17. x-intercept $= -5$, y-intercept $= -5$

18. x-intercept $= \frac{1}{2}$, y-intercept $= 4$

Glencoe Division, Macmillan/McGraw-Hill

NAME ____________________ DATE ____________

2-5 Practice Worksheet

Writing Linear Equations

State the slope and y-intercept of the graph of each equation.

1. $5x - 4y = 8$ $m = \frac{5}{4}, b = -2$

2. $3x - y = -11$ $m = 3, b = 11$

3. $\frac{2}{3}x + \frac{4}{7}y = 1$ $m = -\frac{7}{6}, b = \frac{7}{4}$

4. $3y = 7$ $m = 0, b = \frac{7}{3}$

Find the slope-intercept form of each equation.

5. $3x - 5y = 15$ $y = \frac{3}{5}x - 3$

6. $4x + 7y = 12$ $y = -\frac{4}{7}x + \frac{12}{7}$

7. $7y = -15$ $y = -\frac{15}{7}$

8. $2x = -8$
no slope-intercept form

Write an equation for the line that satisfies each of the given conditions in slope-intercept form and in standard form.

9. slope $= -5$, passes through $(-3, -8)$
$y = -5x - 23, 5x + y = -23$

10. *slope* $= \frac{4}{5}$, *passes through* $(10, -3)$
$y = \frac{4}{5}x - 11, 4x - 5y = 55$

11. *passes through* $(4, 3)$ *and* $(7, -2)$
$y = -\frac{5}{3}x + \frac{29}{3}, 5x + 3y = 29$

12. *passes through* $(-6, -3)$ *and* $(-8, 4)$
$y = -\frac{7}{2}x - 24,$
$7x + 2y = -48$

13. *passes through* $(3, 11)$ *and* $(-6, 5)$
$y = \frac{2}{3}x + 9, 2x - 3y = -27$

14. *passes through* $(7, 2)$ *and* $(3, -5)$
$y = \frac{7}{4}x - \frac{41}{4}, 7x - 4y = 41$

15. x-intercept $= 3$, y-intercept $= 2$
$y = -\frac{2}{3}x + 2, 2x + 3y = 6$

16. x-intercept $= -5$, y-intercept $= 7$
$y = \frac{7}{5}x + 7, 7x - 5y = -35$

17. x-intercept $= -5$, y-intercept $= -5$
$y = -x - 5, x + y = -5$

18. x-intercept $= \frac{1}{2}$, y-intercept $= 4$
$y = -8x + 4, 8x + y = 4$

NAME ____________________ DATE ____________

2-6 Practice Worksheet

Scatter Plots and Prediction Equations

According to a certain linear prediction equation, a person 25 years old needs 2400 calories of food intake a day. A person 30 years old needs 2300 calories. Let x stand for age in years and y stand for calories.

1. Find the slope of the prediction equation.

2. Find the y-intercept of the prediction equation. What does it measure?

3. Find the prediction equation.

4. Predict the caloric needs of a person who is 34 years old.

The Cody Company ran a study on its sales force and learned that the average number of years of experience for each sales team was in direct relation to annual sales volume. Use the data below to answer the following.

Annual Sales (in thousands)	46	35	51	42	33	50	30
Average Years of Experience	6	4	8	5.5	3	7	2.5

5. Draw a scatter diagram to show how years of experience per sales team and annual sales are related.

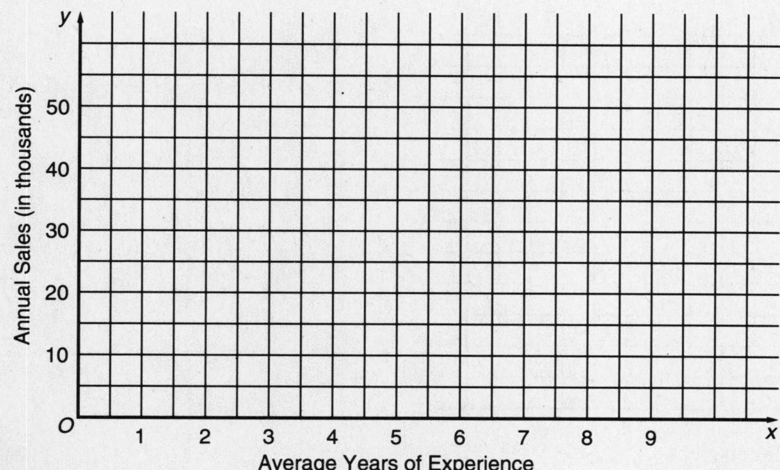

6. Find a prediction equation to show how years of experience and annual sales are related.

Glencoe Division, Macmillan/McGraw-Hill

NAME ________________________ DATE ____________

2-6 Practice Worksheet

Scatter Plots and Prediction Equations

According to a certain linear prediction equation, a person 25 years old needs 2400 calories of food intake a day. A person 30 years old needs 2300 calories. Let x stand for age in years and y stand for calories.

1. Find the slope of the prediction equation. -20

2. Find the y-intercept of the prediction equation. What does it measure? 2900; the calories needed by a newborn

3. Find the prediction equation. $y = -20x + 2900$

4. Predict the caloric needs of a person who is 34 years old. 2220 calories

The Cody Company ran a study on its sales force and learned that the average number of years of experience for each sales team was in direct relation to annual sales volume. Use the data below to answer the following.

Annual Sales (in thousands)	46	35	51	42	33	50	30
Average Years of Experience	6	4	8	5.5	3	7	2.5

5. Draw a scatter diagram to show how years of experience per sales team and annual sales are related.

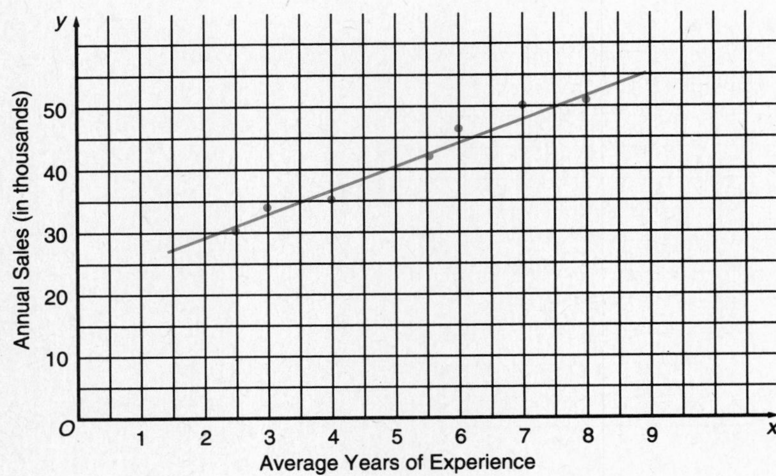

6. Find a prediction equation to show how years of experience and annual sales are related. Typical answer: $y = 3.6x + 22.2$

NAME ______________________ DATE ____________

2-7

Practice Worksheet

Special Functions

If $g(x) = |-3x + 1|$ ***and*** $h(x) = \left[\frac{1}{2}x\right]$***, find each value.***

1. $g\left(\frac{1}{3}\right)$

2. $h\left(\frac{1}{3}\right)$

3. $g(-7)$

4. $h(-7)$

Graph each function.

5. $y = |-3x|$

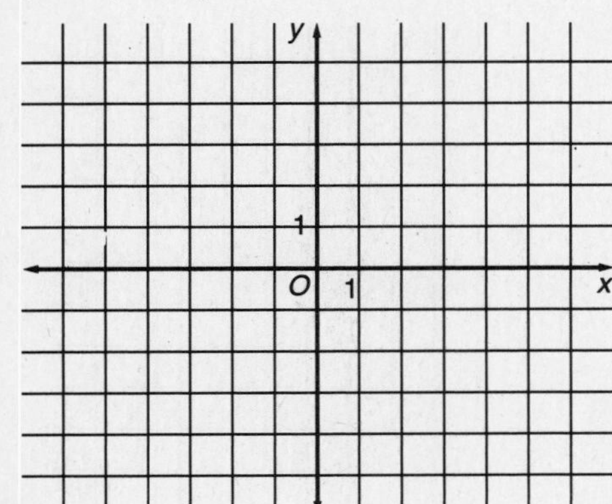

6. $y + 2 = |x + 1|$

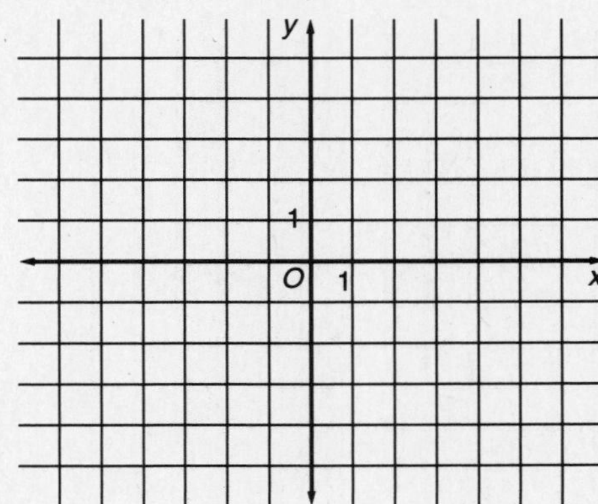

7. $y = |3x - 6|$

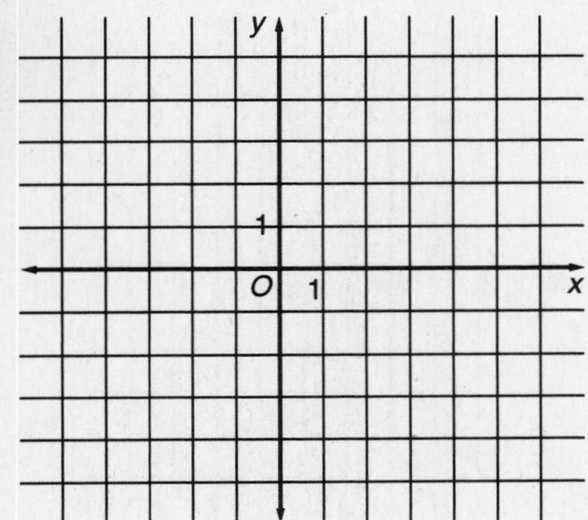

8. $y = [-5x]$

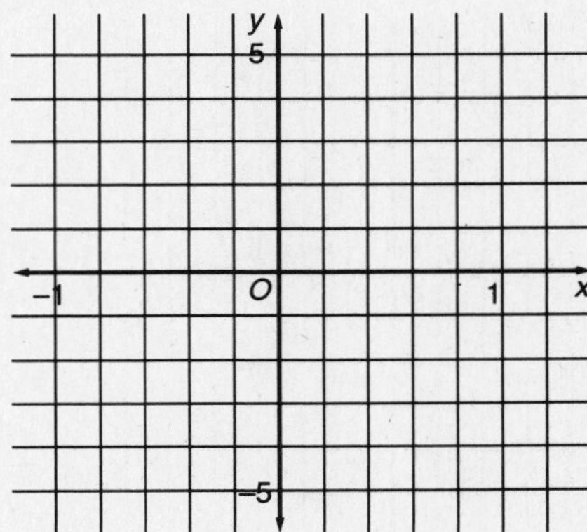

9. $y - 2 = [x + 3]$

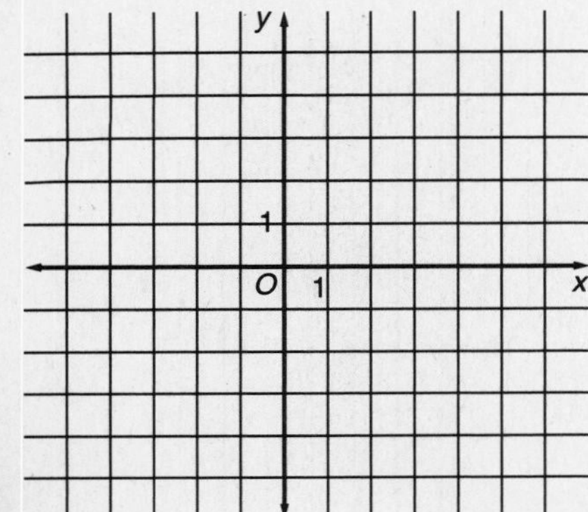

10. $y = [2x - 1]$

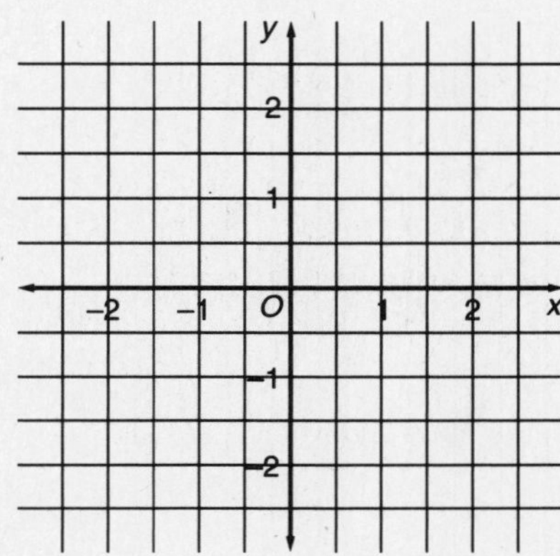

Glencoe Division, Macmillan/McGraw-Hill

NAME ______________________ DATE __________

2-7

Practice Worksheet

Special Functions

If $g(x) = |-3x + 1|$ and $h(x) = \left[\frac{1}{2}x\right]$, find each value.

1. $g\left(\frac{1}{3}\right)$ **0** **2.** $h\left(\frac{1}{3}\right)$ **0** **3.** $g(-7)$ **22** **4.** $h(-7)$ **−4**

Graph each function.

5. $y = |-3x|$

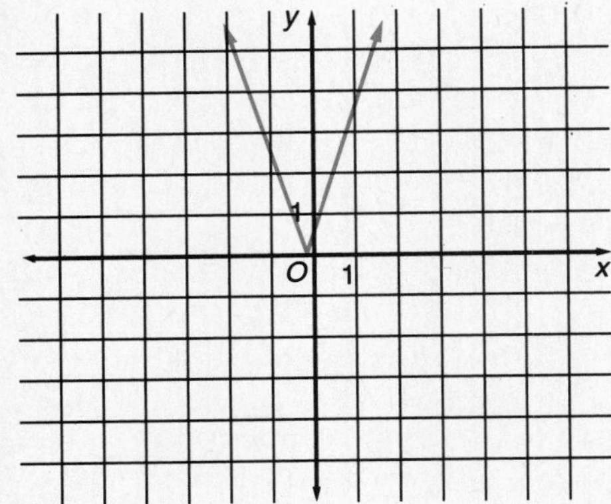

6. $y + 2 = |x + 1|$

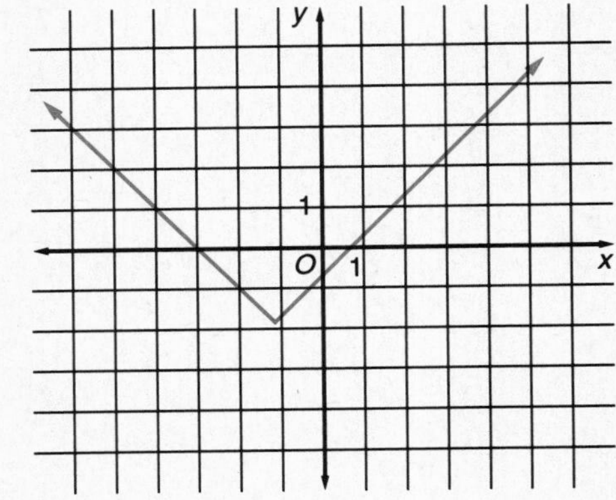

7. $y = |3x - 6|$

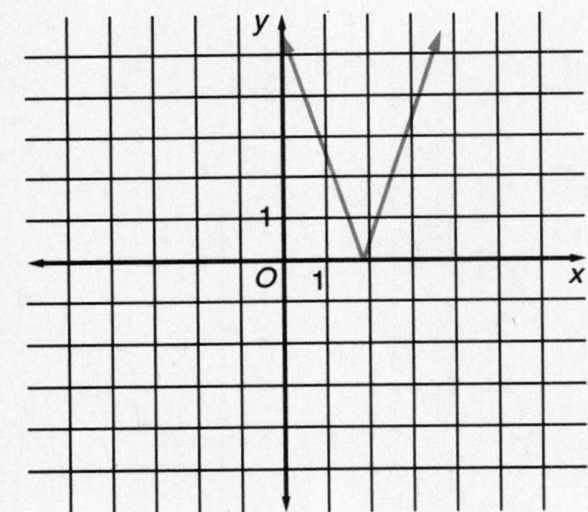

8. $y = [-5x]$

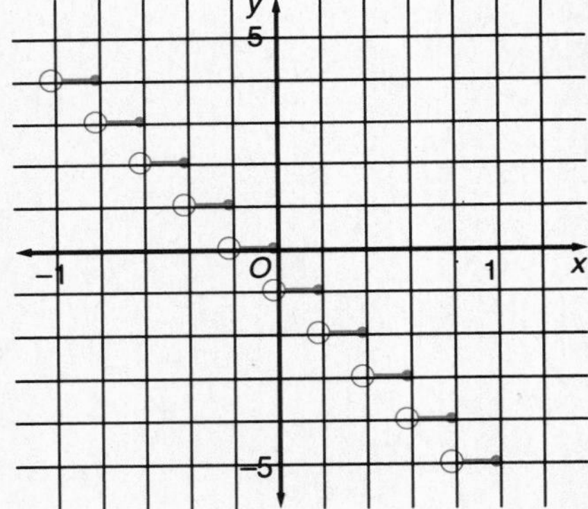

9. $y - 2 = [x + 3]$

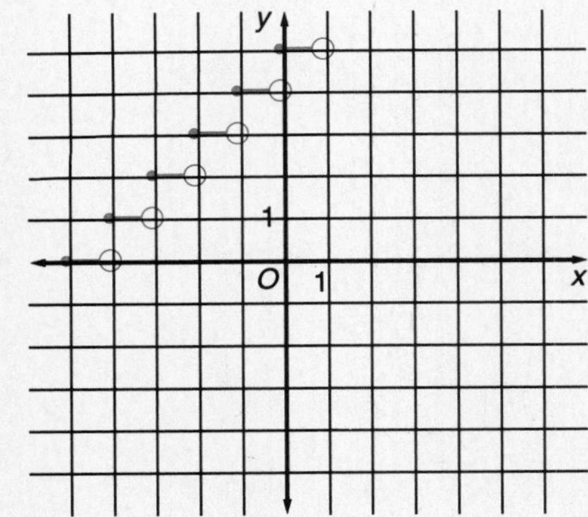

10. $y = [2x - 1]$

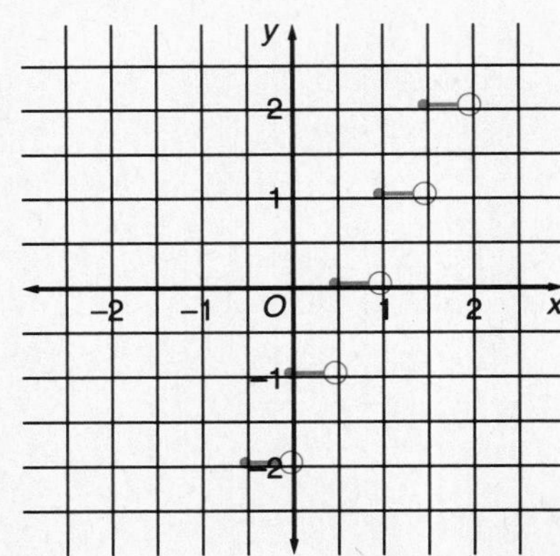

Glencoe Division, Macmillan/McGraw-Hill

NAME ________________________ DATE ____________

2-8

Practice Worksheet

Graphing Linear Inequalities

Graph each inequality.

1. $3 - x > 0$

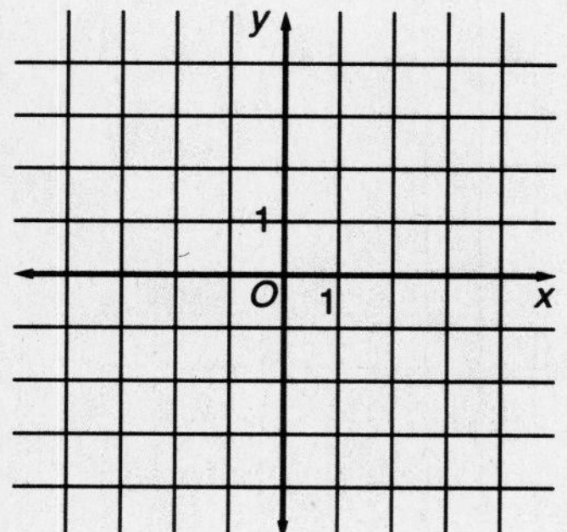

2. $y < -4x - 2$

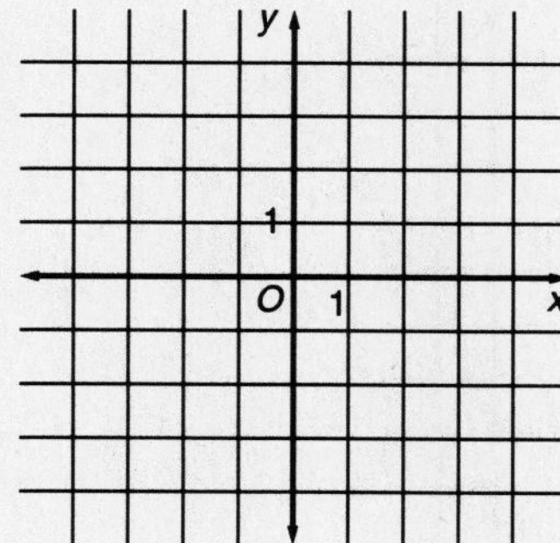

3. $y \geq 2x + 5$

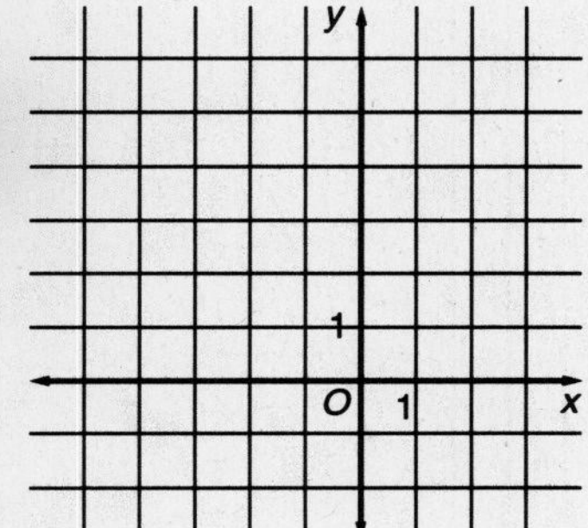

4. $x - 3y \leq 6$

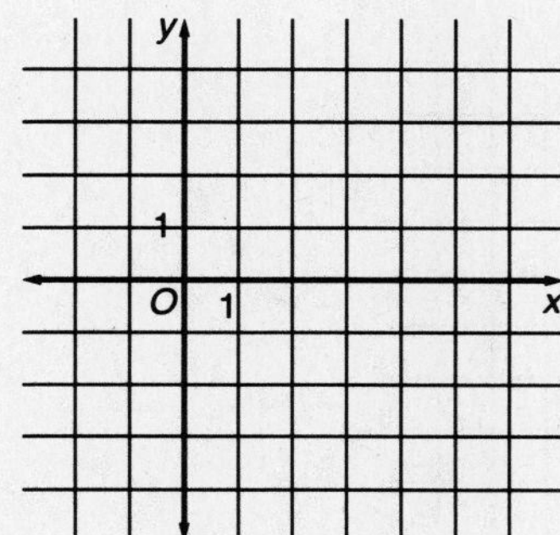

5. $y > |x| - 1$

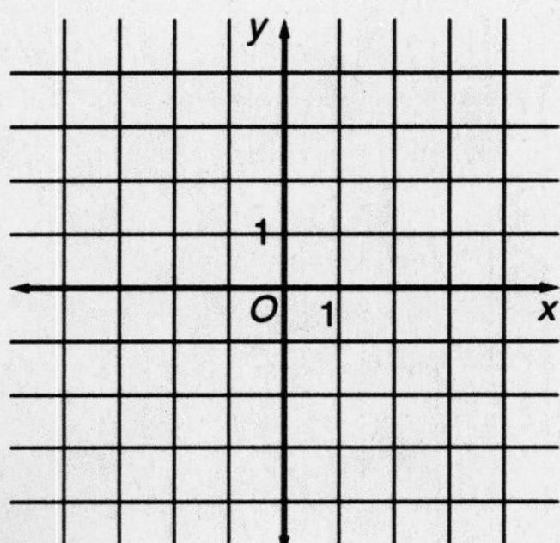

6. $y > -3|x + 1| - 2$

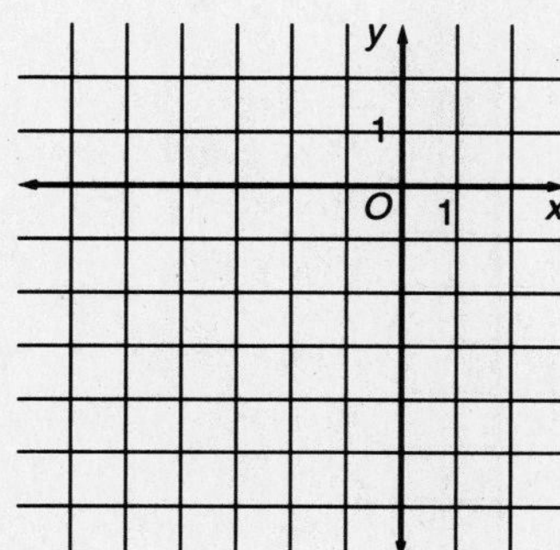

Glencoe Division, Macmillan/McGraw-Hill

NAME ________________________ DATE ____________

2-8 Practice Worksheet

Graphing Linear Inequalities

Graph each inequality.

1. $3 - x > 0$

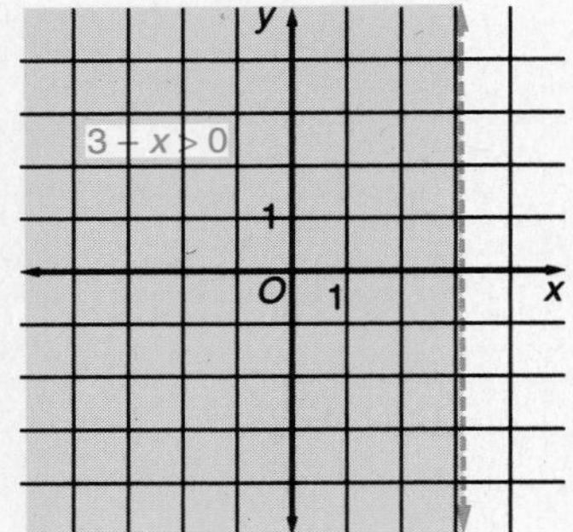

2. $y < -4x - 2$

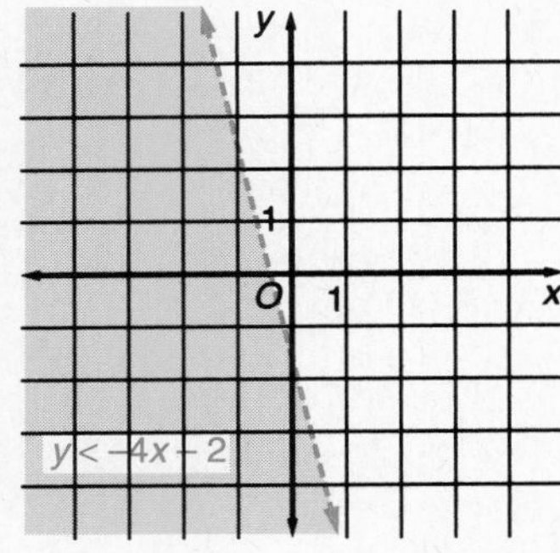

3. $y \geq 2x + 5$

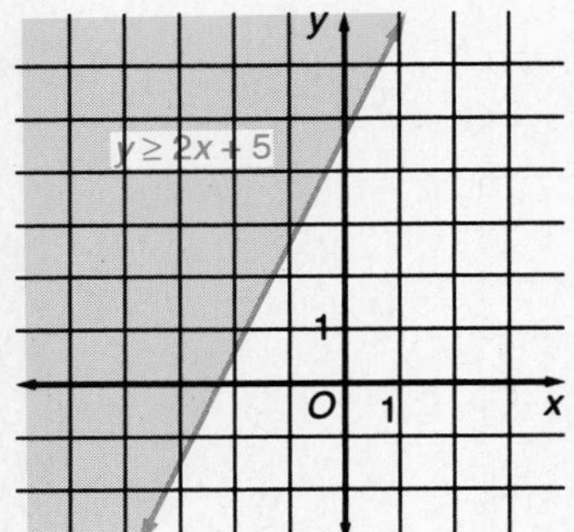

4. $x - 3y \leq 6$

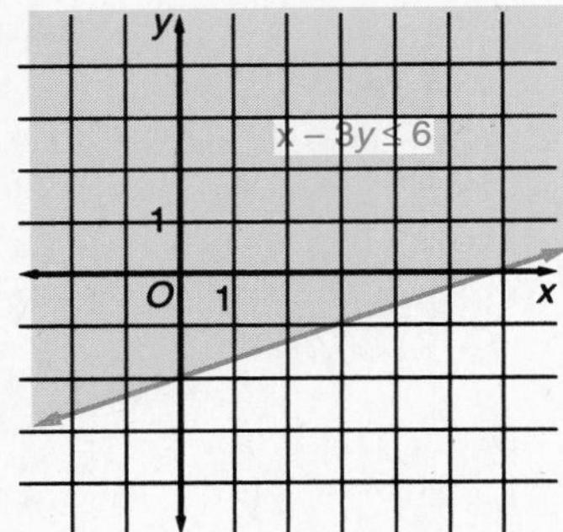

5. $y > |x| - 1$

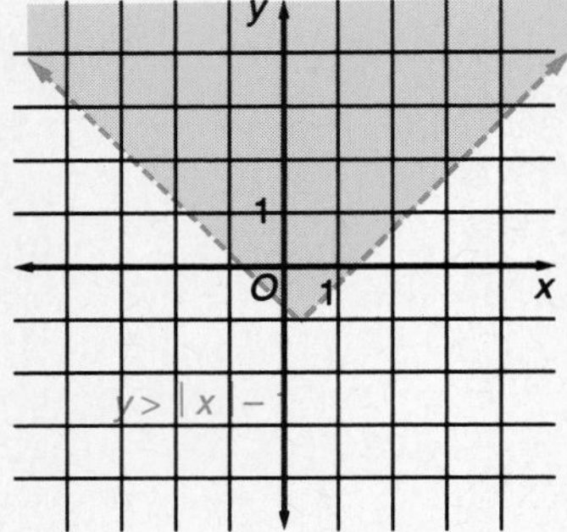

6. $y > -3|x + 1| - 2$

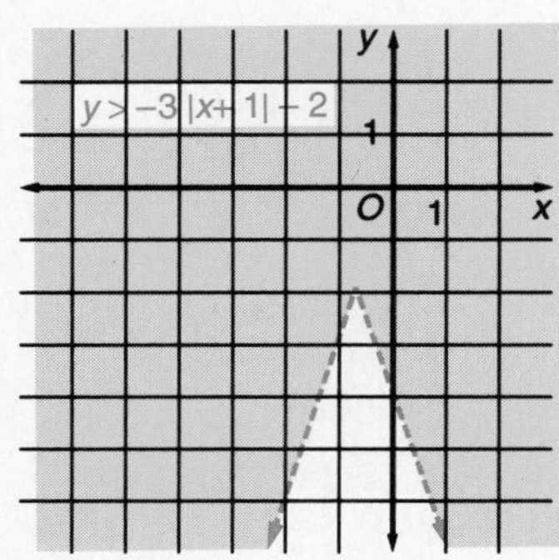

Glencoe Division, Macmillan/McGraw-Hill

NAME ______________________ DATE ____________

3-1 Practice Worksheet

Graphing Systems of Equations

Graph each system of equations and state its solution. Also, state whether the system is consistent and independent, consistent and dependent, or inconsistent.

1. $2x + y = 4$
$x - y = 2$

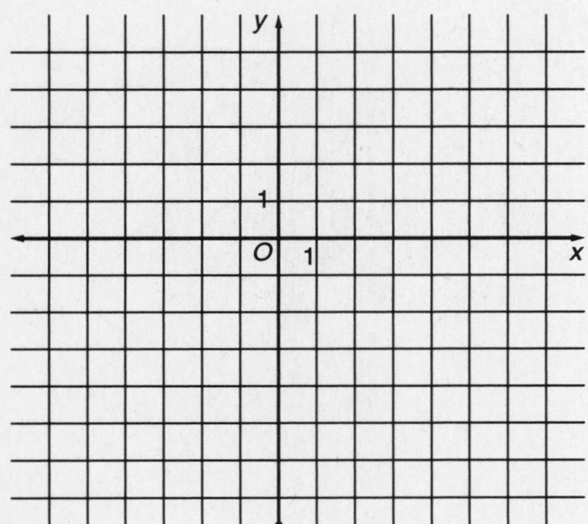

2. $x + y = 2$
$x + y = 6$

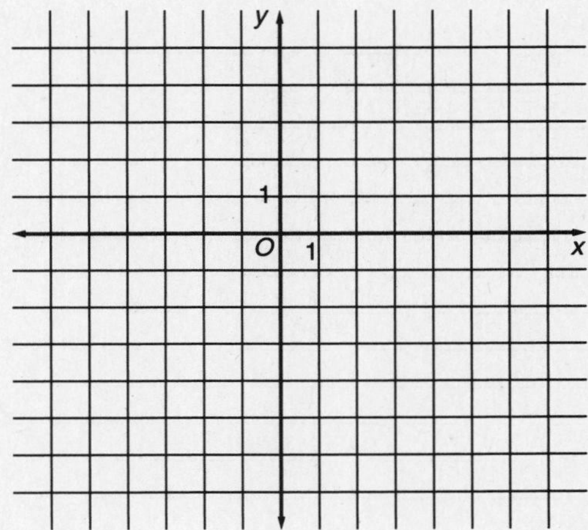

3. $2y - 8 = x$
$y = \frac{1}{2}x + 4$

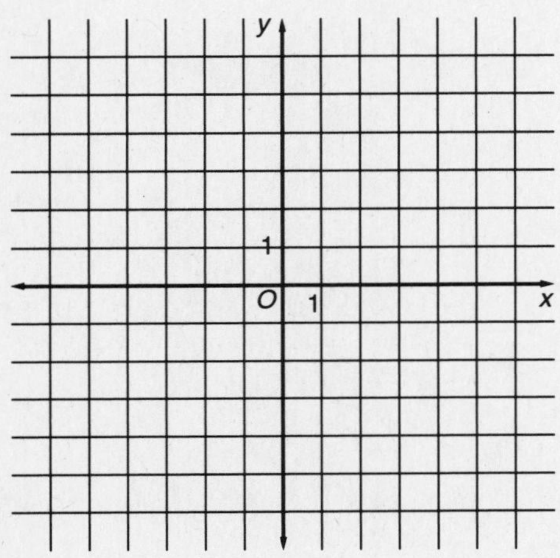

4. $x - 2y = 0$
$y = 2x - 3$

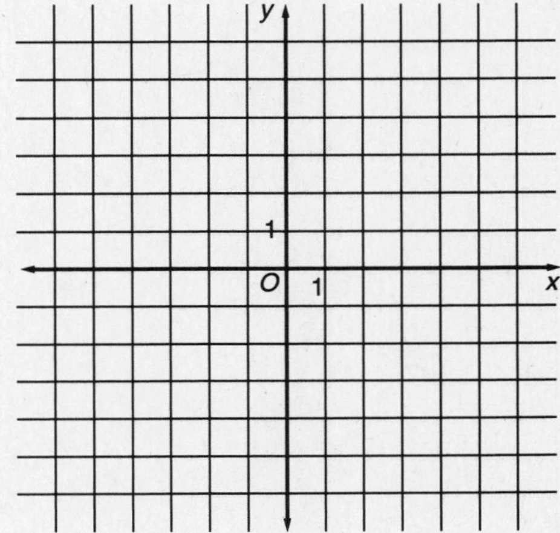

Glencoe Division, Macmillan/McGraw-Hill

NAME ______________________ DATE ____________

3-1 Practice Worksheet

Graphing Systems of Equations

Graph each system of equations and state its solution. Also, state whether the system is consistent and independent, consistent and dependent, or inconsistent.

1. $2x + y = 4$ **(2, 0); consistent**
$x - y = 2$ **and independent**

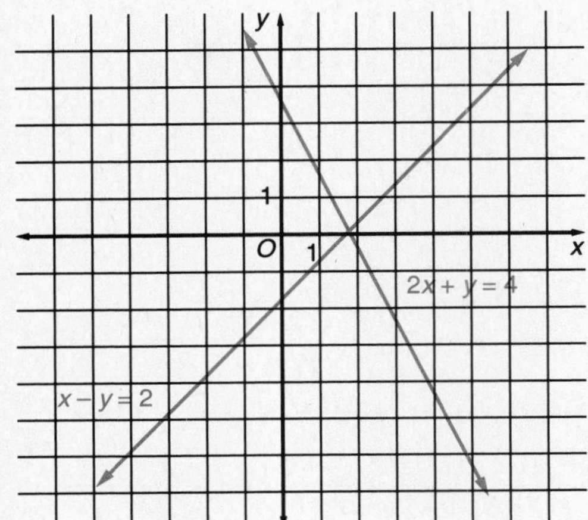

2. $x + y = 2$ **no solutions;**
$x + y = 6$ **inconsistent**

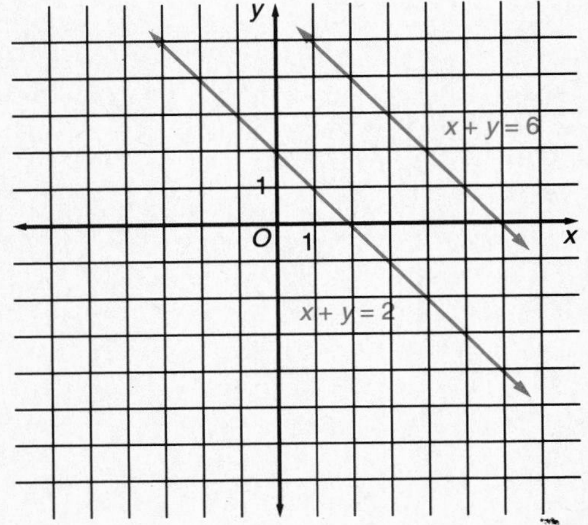

3. $2y - 8 = x$ **all points on the**
$y = \frac{1}{2}x + 4$ **line; consistent and dependent**

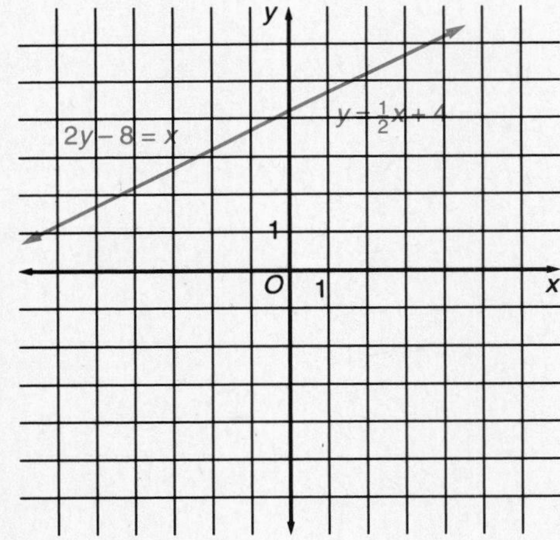

4. $x - 2y = 0$ **(2, 1); consistent**
$y = 2x - 3$ **and independent**

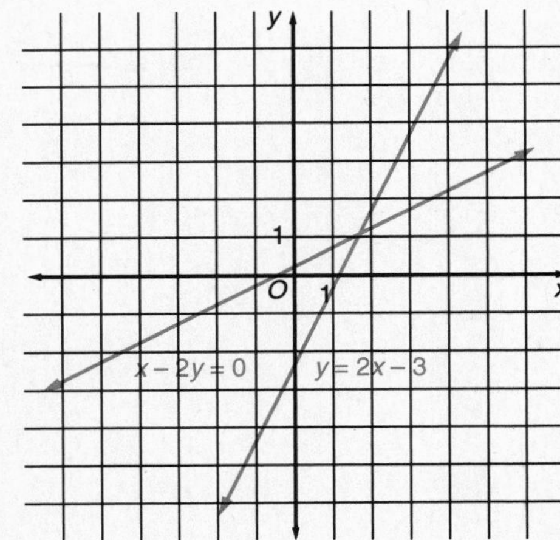

Glencoe Division, Macmillan/McGraw-Hill

NAME ________________________ DATE ____________

3-2 Practice Worksheet

Solving Systems of Equations Algebraically

Solve each system of equations using the substitution method.

1. $2x + y = 4$
$3x + 2y = 1$

2. $x - 9 = 3y$
$x + 2y = -1$

3. $x + 3y = 8$
$\frac{1}{3}x + y = 9$

4. $2x - 3y = 6$
$-\frac{2}{3}x + y = -2$

Solve each system of equations using the elimination method.

5. $2x + y = 1$
$3x - y = 14$

6. $2x - y = -1$
$3x + 2y = 30$

7. $6x + 3y = 6$
$8x + 5y = 12$

8. $\frac{3x - y}{2} = 5$
$\frac{4x - y}{4} = 4$

Solve each system of equations. (Use either algebraic method.)

9. $8x + 3y + 5 = 0$
$10x + 6y + 13 = 0$

10. $\frac{2x}{5} - \frac{3y}{4} = -2$
$\frac{x}{2} + \frac{y}{4} = 7$

11. $\frac{x}{4} - \frac{y}{3} = 1$
$\frac{1}{3}x - \frac{4y}{9} = \frac{4}{3}$

12. $4x - 2y = 5$
$2x = y - 1$

NAME ______________________ DATE ______________

3-2 Practice Worksheet

Solving Systems of Equations Algebraically

Solve each system of equations using the substitution method.

1. $2x + y = 4$
$3x + 2y = 1$ (7, −10)

2. $x - 9 = 3y$
$x + 2y = -1$ (3, −2)

3. $x + 3y = 8$
$\frac{1}{3}x + y = 9$ no solutions

4. $2x - 3y = 6$
$-\frac{2}{3}x + y = -2$ $\{(x, y) | 2x - 3y = 6\}$

Solve each system of equations using the elimination method.

5. $2x + y = 1$
$3x - y = 14$ (3, −5)

6. $2x - y = -1$
$3x + 2y = 30$ (4, 9)

7. $6x + 3y = 6$
$8x + 5y = 12$ (−1, 4)

8. $\frac{3x - y}{2} = 5$
$\frac{4x - y}{4} = 4$ (6, 8)

Solve each system of equations. (Use either algebraic method.)

9. $8x + 3y + 5 = 0$
$10x + 6y + 13 = 0$ $\left(\frac{1}{2}, -3\right)$

10. $\frac{2x}{5} - \frac{3y}{4} = -2$
$\frac{x}{2} + \frac{y}{4} = 7$ (10, 8)

11. $\frac{x}{4} - \frac{y}{3} = 1$
$\frac{1}{3}x - \frac{4y}{9} = \frac{4}{3}$ $\left\{(x, y) \middle| \frac{x}{4} - \frac{y}{3} = 1\right\}$

12. $4x - 2y = 5$
$2x = y - 1$ no solutions

Glencoe Division, Macmillan/McGraw-Hill

3-3 NAME ______________________ DATE ______________

Practice Worksheet

Cramer's Rule

Find the value of each determinant.

1. $\begin{vmatrix} 3 & 8 \\ 4 & 5 \end{vmatrix}$

2. $\begin{vmatrix} -6 & 5 \\ -4 & 9 \end{vmatrix}$

3. $\begin{vmatrix} -7 & -3 \\ -2 & -6 \end{vmatrix}$

4. $\begin{vmatrix} 5 & 10 \\ -6 & 8 \end{vmatrix}$

Solve each system of equations by using Cramer's Rule.

5. $4x - 3y = -6$
$x + 2y = -7$

6. $5s + 6u = 1$
$-2s - u = -6$

7. $2w - 5z = 13$
$6w + 3z = 10$

8. $m + 3p = -6$
$2m - 5p = 7$

9. $2x - 4y = 1$
$-x + 2y = 5$

10. $3c + 9d = 2$
$c + 3d = \frac{2}{3}$

Glencoe Division, Macmillan/McGraw-Hill

NAME ____________________ DATE ____________

3-3 **Practice Worksheet**

Cramer's Rule

Find the value of each determinant.

1. $\begin{vmatrix} 3 & 8 \\ 4 & 5 \end{vmatrix}$ **−17**

2. $\begin{vmatrix} -6 & 5 \\ -4 & 9 \end{vmatrix}$ **−34**

3. $\begin{vmatrix} -7 & -3 \\ -2 & -6 \end{vmatrix}$ **36**

4. $\begin{vmatrix} 5 & 10 \\ -6 & 8 \end{vmatrix}$ **100**

Solve each system of equations by using Cramer's Rule.

5. $4x - 3y = -6$
$x + 2y = -7$ **(−3, −2)**

6. $5s + 6u = 1$
$-2s - u = -6$ **(5, −4)**

7. $2w - 5z = 13$
$6w + 3z = 10$ $\left(\frac{89}{36}, -\frac{29}{18}\right)$

8. $m + 3p = -6$
$2m - 5p = 7$ $\left(-\frac{9}{11}, -\frac{19}{11}\right)$

9. $2x - 4y = 1$
$-x + 2y = 5$ **no solutions**

10. $3c + 9d = 2$
$c + 3d = \frac{2}{3}$ $\{(c, d) | 3c + 9d =$ [illegible]

NAME ______________________ DATE ____________

3-4 Practice Worksheet

Graphing Systems of Inequalities

Solve each system by graphing.

1. $y + 1 < -x$
$y \geq 1$

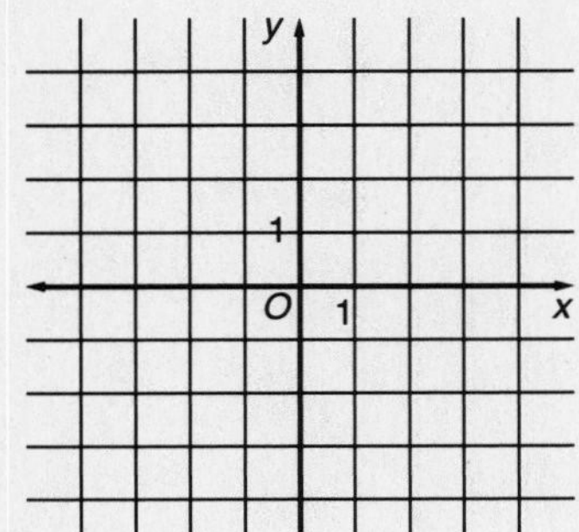

2. $x > -2$
$2y \geq 3x + 6$

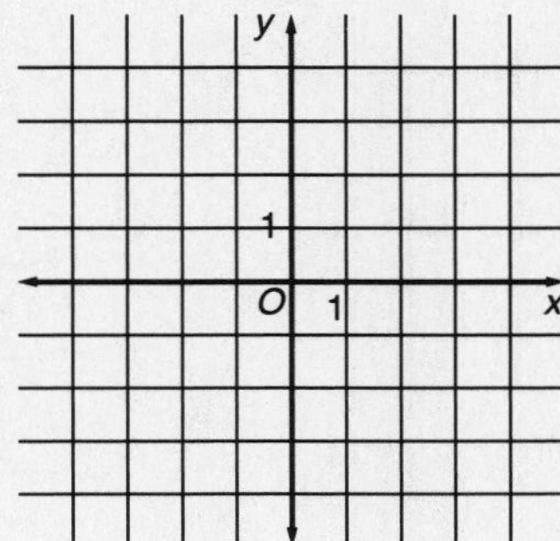

3. $y \leq 2x - 3$
$y \leq -\frac{1}{2}x + 2$

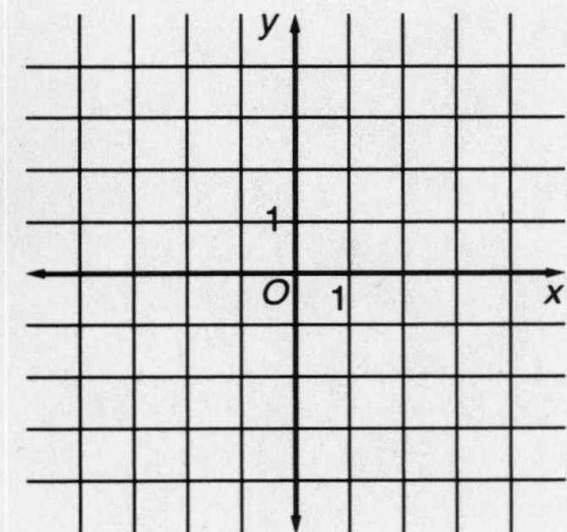

4. $y > -x - 2$
$y \leq 3x + 2$

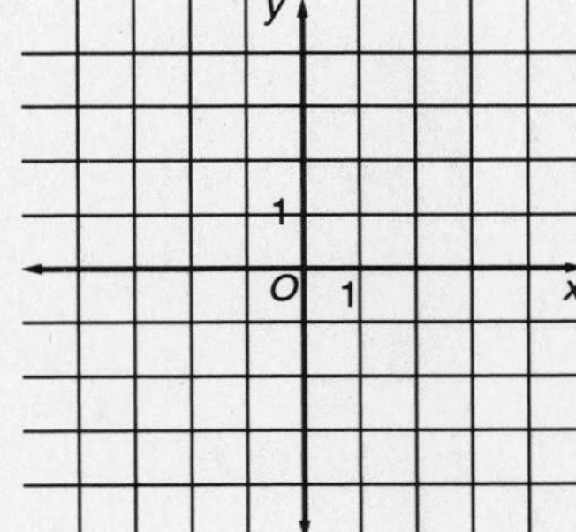

5. $|y| \leq 1$
$y \leq |x| - 1$

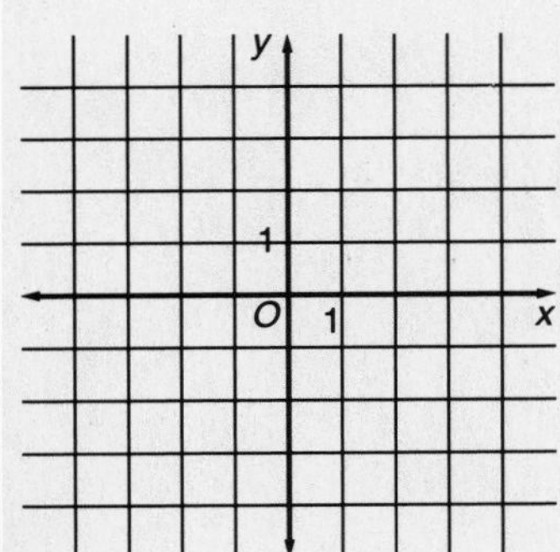

6. $x > -1$
$y < \frac{2}{3}x + 2$
$3y > 4x$

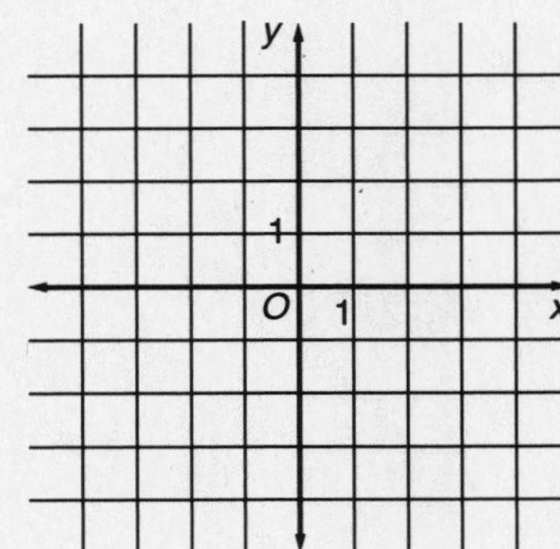

Glencoe Division, Macmillan/McGraw-Hill

NAME ______________________________ DATE ______________

3-4

Practice Worksheet

Graphing Systems of Inequalities

Solve each system by graphing.

1. $y + 1 < -x$
$y \geq 1$

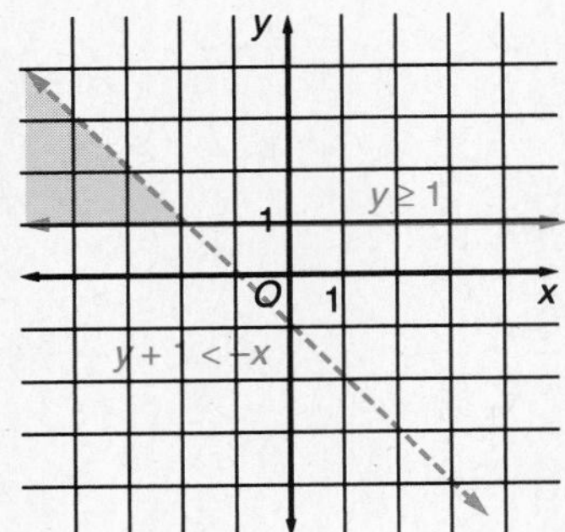

2. $x > -2$
$2y \geq 3x + 6$

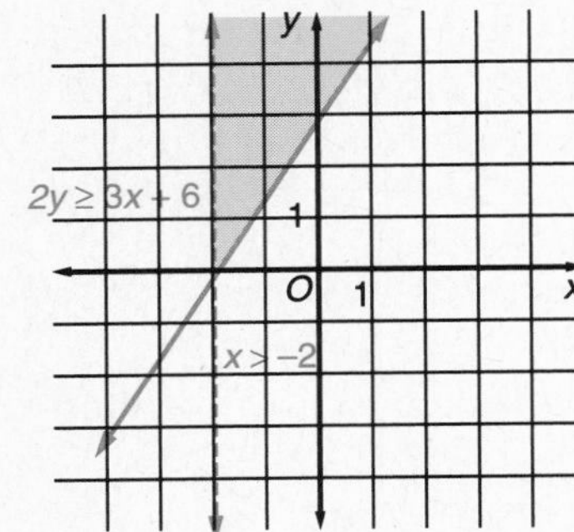

3. $y \leq 2x - 3$
$y \leq -\frac{1}{2}x + 2$

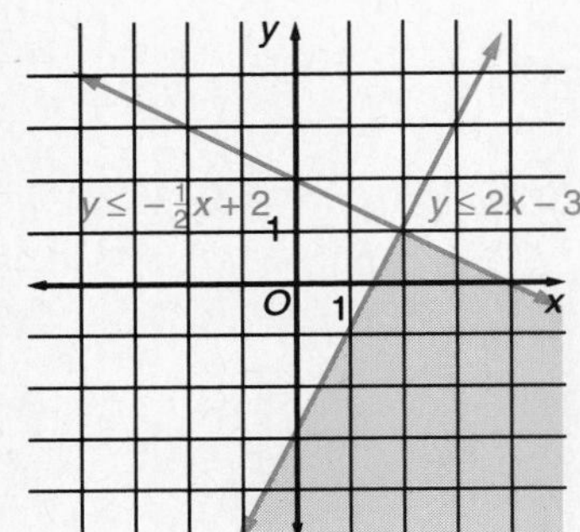

4. $y > -x - 2$
$y \leq 3x + 2$

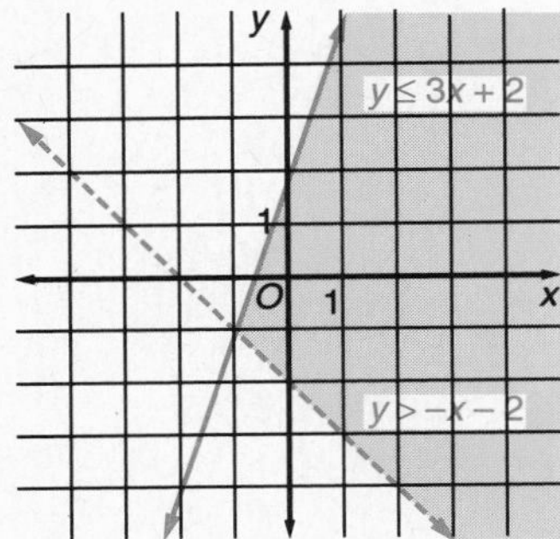

5. $|y| \leq 1$
$y \leq |x| - 1$

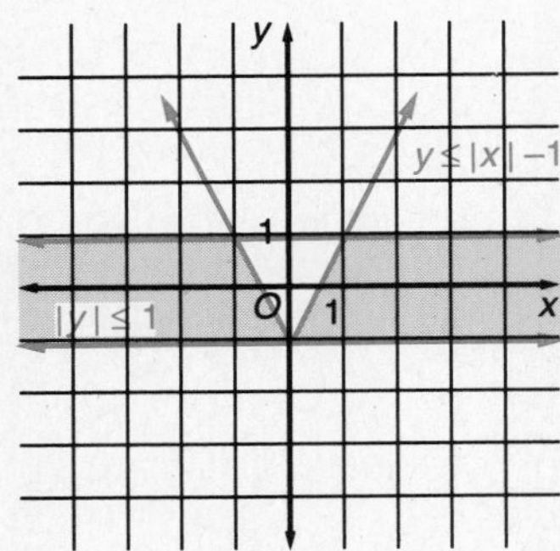

6. $x > -1$
$y < \frac{2}{3}x + 2$
$3y > 4x$

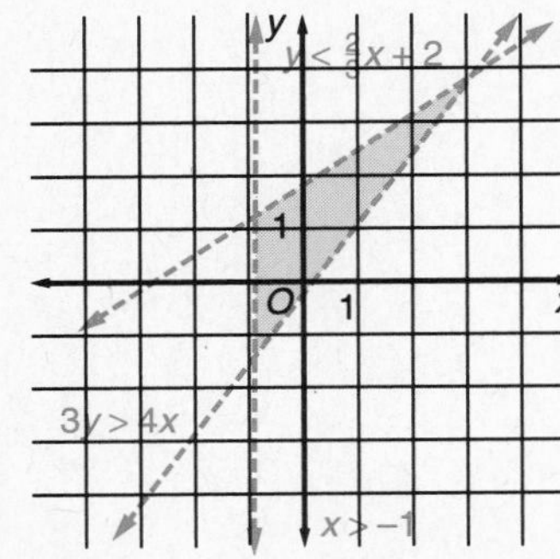

NAME ______________________ DATE ______________

3-5 Practice Worksheet

Problem Solving Strategy: Solve a Simpler Problem

Use any strategy.

1. Thirty people are at a party. If each person shakes hands exactly once with every other person, how many handshakes will there be?

2. Runners in a marathon must wear a sign that contains their entry numbers. The signs are numbered consecutively, beginning with 1. A total of 432 contestants entered the marathon. If one felt-tip marker can write 35 digits, how many markers will be needed to complete all of the signs?

3. A snail is at the bottom of a well that is 24 feet deep. The snail can climb 2 inches each hour, but then falls back 1 inch. How many hours will it take the snail to crawl out of the well?

4. What is the sum of the first 5000 counting numbers?

Glencoe Division, Macmillan/McGraw-Hill

NAME ______________________ DATE ______________

3-5 Practice Worksheet

Problem Solving Strategy: Solve a Simpler Problem

Use any strategy.

1. Thirty people are at a party. If each person shakes hands exactly once with every other person, how many handshakes will there be? **435 handshakes**

2. Runners in a marathon must wear a sign that contains their entry numbers. The signs are numbered consecutively, beginning with 1. A total of 432 contestants entered the marathon. If one felt-tip marker can write 35 digits, how many markers will be needed to complete all of the signs? **34 markers**

3. A snail is at the bottom of a well that is 24 feet deep. The snail can climb 2 inches each hour, but then falls back 1 inch. How many hours will it take the snail to crawl out of the well? **287 hours**

4. What is the sum of the first 5000 counting numbers? **12,502,500**

Glencoe Division, Macmillan/McGraw-Hill

NAME ______________________ DATE ____________

3-6 Practice Worksheet

Linear Programming

Graph each system of inequalities. Name the coordinates of the vertices of the polygon formed. Find the maximum and minimum values of the given function.

1. $2x - 4 \le y$
$-2x - 4 \le y$
$2 \ge y$
$f(x, y) = -2x + y$

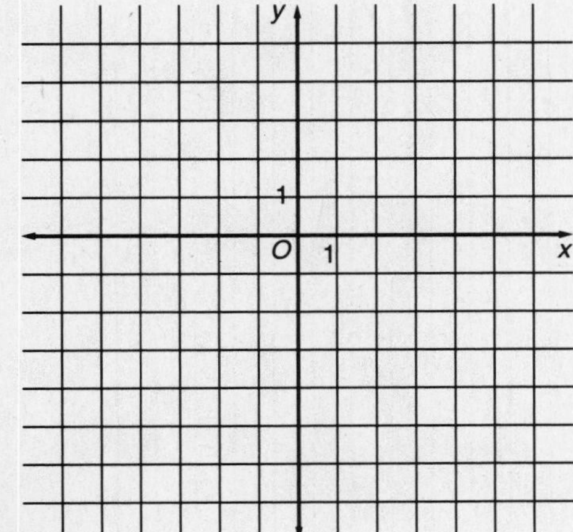

2. $3x - y \le 7$
$2x - y \ge 3$
$y \ge x - 3$
$f(x, y) = x - 4y$

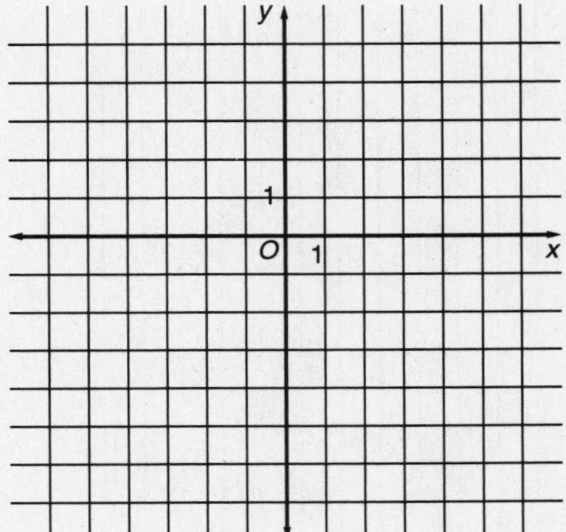

3. $x \ge 0$
$y \ge 0$
$3x + y \le 15$
$y \le 6$
$f(x, y) = 3x + y$

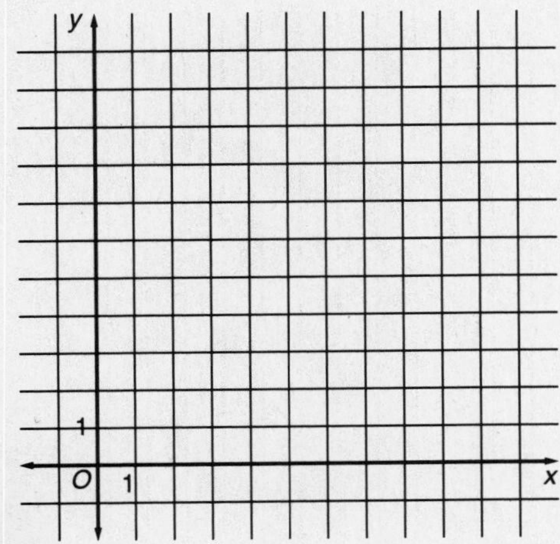

4. $x \le 0$
$y \le 0$
$4x + y \ge -7$
$f(x, y) = -x - 4y$

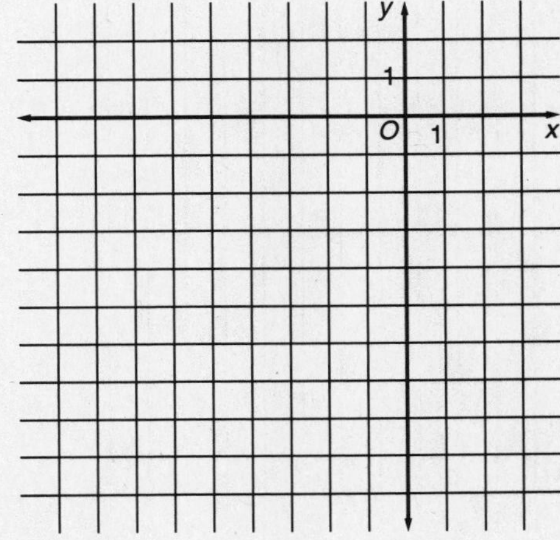

Glencoe Division, Macmillan/McGraw-Hill

NAME ____________________ DATE __________

3-6 Practice Worksheet

Linear Programming

Graph each system of inequalities. Name the coordinates of the vertices of the polygon formed. Find the maximum and minimum values of the given function.

1. $2x - 4 \leq y$
$-2x - 4 \leq y$
$2 \geq y$
$f(x, y) = -2x + y$

vertices: (3, 2), (−3, 2), (0, −4); max = 8, min = −4

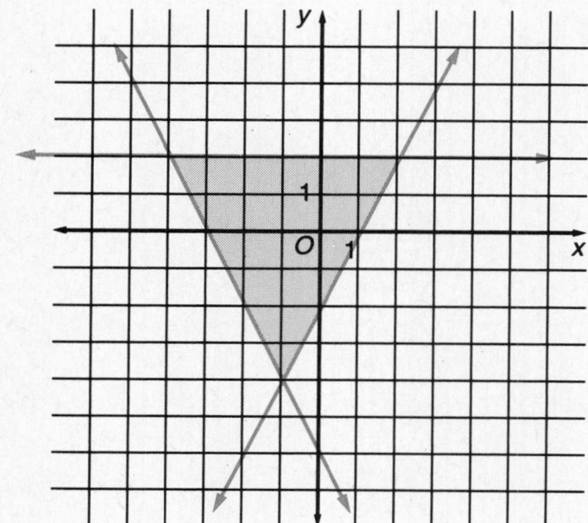

2. $3x - y \leq 7$
$2x - y \geq 3$
$y \geq x - 3$
$f(x, y) = x - 4y$

vertices: (4, 5), (2, −1), (0, −3); max = 12, min = −16

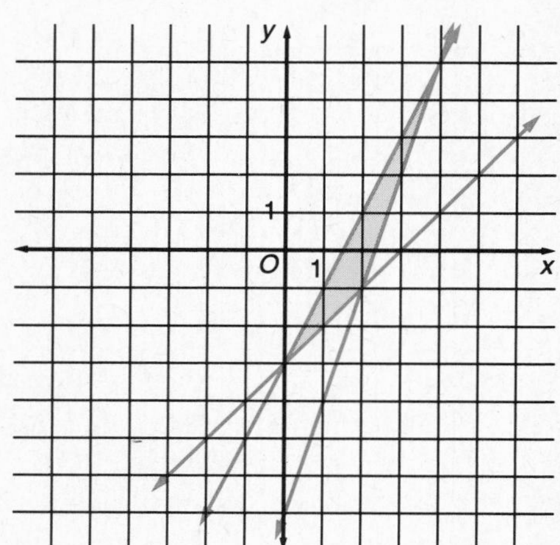

3. $x \geq 0$
$y \geq 0$
$3x + y \leq 15$
$y \leq 6$
$f(x, y) = 3x + y$

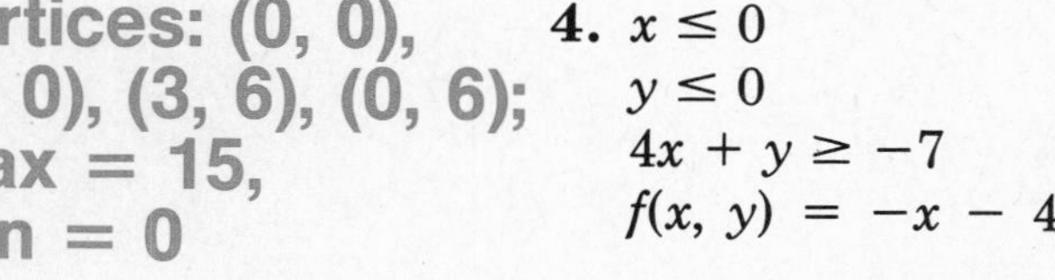

vertices: (0, 0), (5, 0), (3, 6), (0, 6); max = 15, min = 0

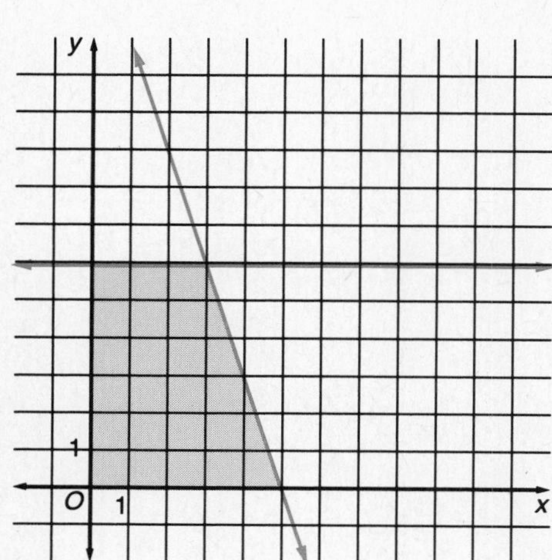

4. $x \leq 0$
$y \leq 0$
$4x + y \geq -7$
$f(x, y) = -x - 4y$

vertices: (0, 0), (0, −7), $\left(-\frac{7}{4}, 0\right)$; max = 28, min = 0

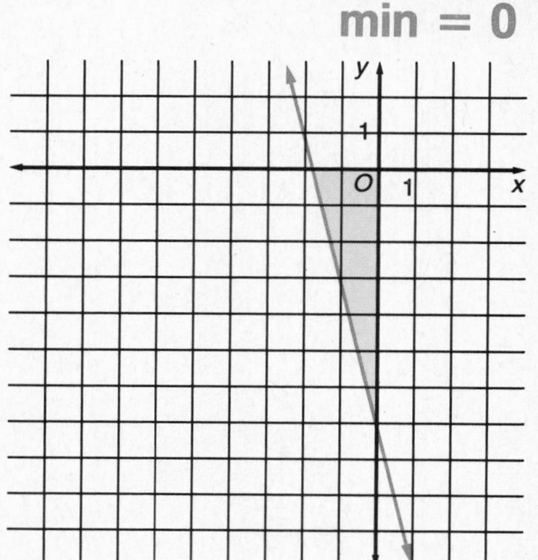

NAME ______________________ DATE ____________

3-7 **Practice Worksheet**

Applications of Linear Programming

Solve.

1. The area of a parking lot is 600 square meters. A car requires 6 square meters. A bus requires 30 square meters. The attendant can handle only 60 vehicles. If a car is charged $2.50 and a bus $7.50, how many of each should be accepted to maximize income?

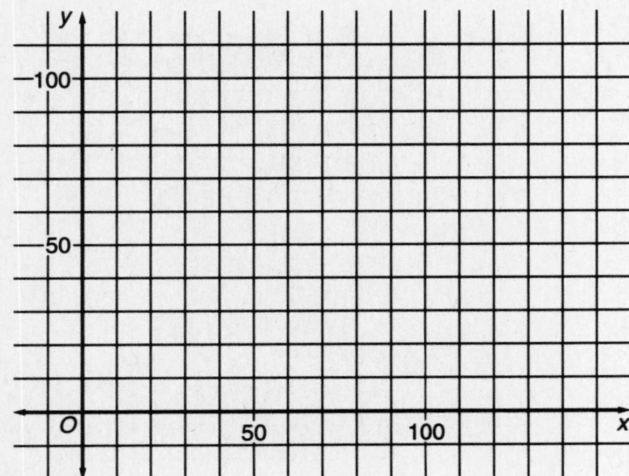

2. The cost to run Machine 1 for an hour is $2. During that hour, Machine 1 produces 240 bolts and 100 nuts. The cost to run Machine 2 for an hour is $2.40. During that hour, Machine 2 produces 160 bolts and 160 nuts. With a combined running time of no more than 30 hours, how long should each machine run to produce an order of at least 2080 bolts and 1520 nuts at the minimum operating cost?

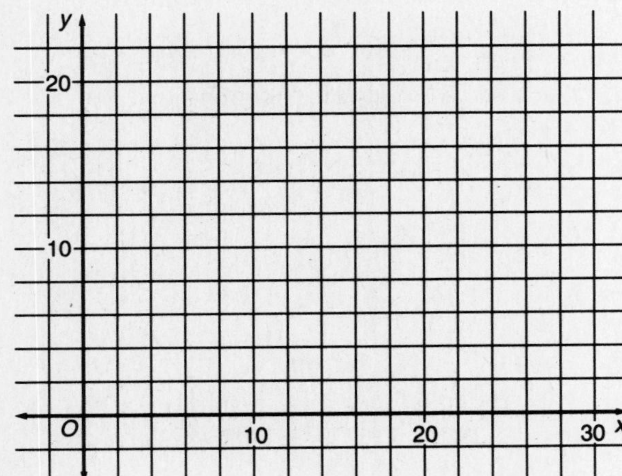

Glencoe Division, Macmillan/McGraw-Hill

NAME ____________________ DATE __________

3-7 Practice Worksheet

Applications of Linear Programming

Solve.

1. The area of a parking lot is 600 square meters. A car requires 6 square meters. A bus requires 30 square meters. The attendant can handle only 60 vehicles. If a car is charged \$2.50 and a bus \$7.50, how many of each should be accepted to maximize income?

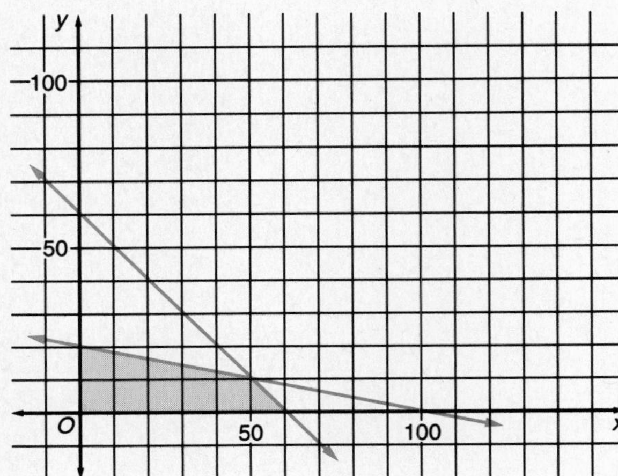

50 cars, 10 buses

2. The cost to run Machine 1 for an hour is \$2. During that hour, Machine 1 produces 240 bolts and 100 nuts. The cost to run Machine 2 for an hour is \$2.40. During that hour, Machine 2 produces 160 bolts and 160 nuts. With a combined running time of no more than 30 hours, how long should each machine run to produce an order of at least 2080 bolts and 1520 nuts at the minimum operating cost?

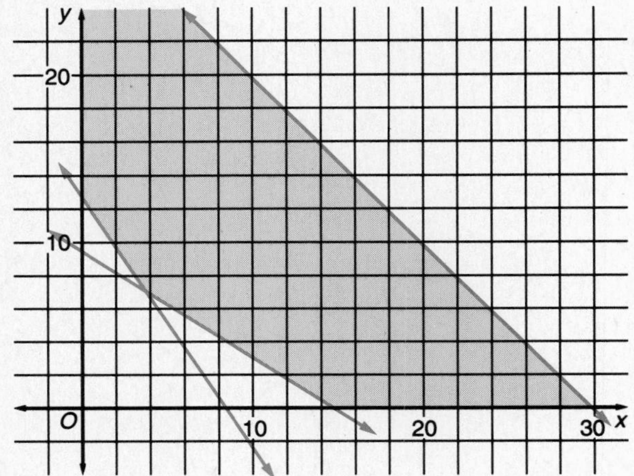

Machine 1: 4 hours
Machine 2: 7 hours

Glencoe Division, Macmillan/McGraw-Hill

NAME ________________ DATE ________

3-8 Practice Worksheet

Graphing Equations in Three Variables

In which octant does each point lie?

1. $(3, -1, 4)$ **2.** $(-8, 2, 7)$ **3.** $x < 0, y \geq 5, z = -4$ **4.** $x > 0, y = 7, z < -3$

Graph each equation.

5. $15x - 5y + 6z = 30$

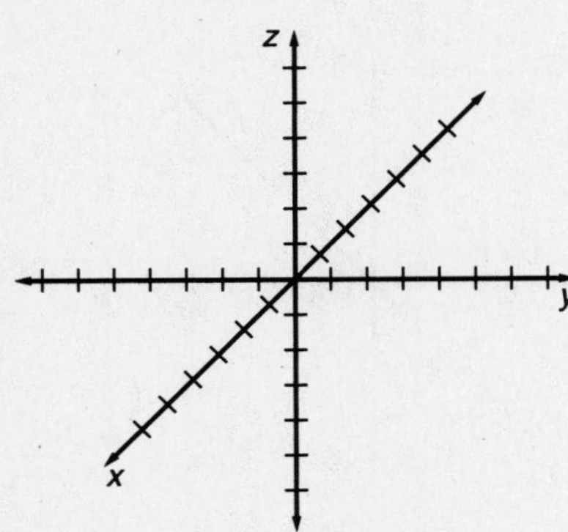

6. $-4x + 2y - z = 4$

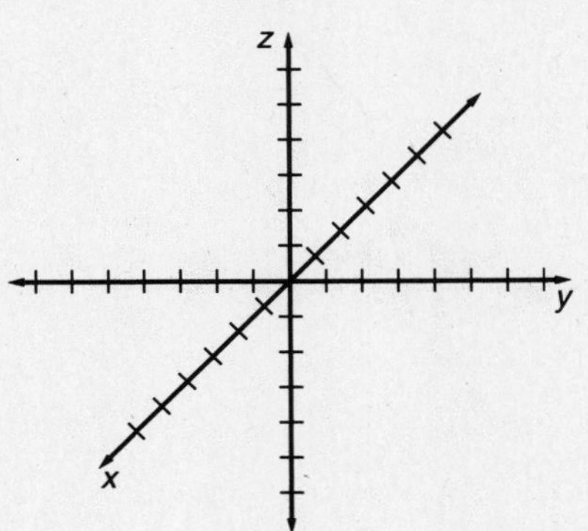

Find the x-, y-, and z-intercepts and the traces in the coordinate planes.

7. $-3x + 2y + 4z = 6$

8. $5x - 4z = 10$

Write an equation of the plane given its x-, y-, and z-intercepts.

9. $3, -7, 2$

10. $-5, 2, 4$

Write an equation of the plane given two of its traces in the coordinate planes.

11. $5x - 2y = 10; 5x + 4z = 10$

12. $2y + 9z = 4; 7x - 18z = -8$

Glencoe Division, Macmillan/McGraw-Hill

NAME ______________________ DATE ____________

3-8

Practice Worksheet

Graphing Equations in Three Variables

In which octant does each point lie?

1. (3, −1, 4)
2

2. (−8, 2, 7)
5

3. $x < 0, y \geq 5, z = -4$
8

4. $x > 0, y = 7, z < -3$
4

Graph each equation.

5. $15x - 5y + 6z = 30$

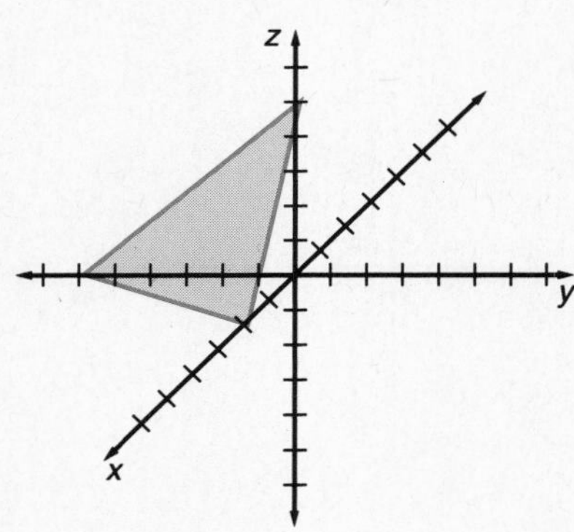

6. $-4x + 2y - z = 4$

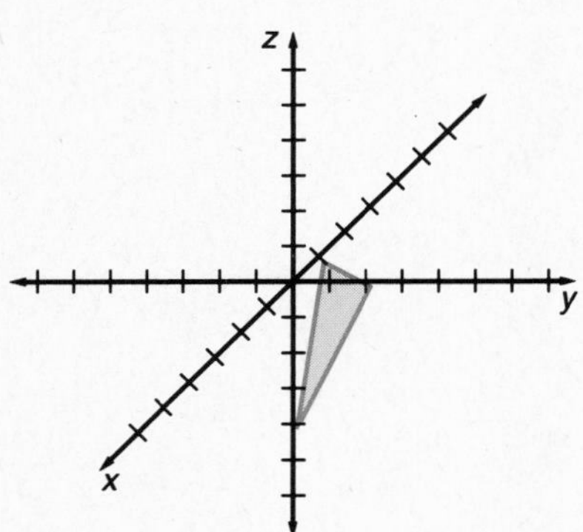

Find the x-, y-, and z-intercepts and the traces in the coordinate planes.

7. $-3x + 2y + 4z = 6$

x-intercept: −2
y-intercept: 3
z-intercept: $\frac{3}{2}$
xy-trace: $-3x + 2y = 6$
yz-trace: $y + 2z = 3$
xz-trace: $-3x + 4z = 6$

8. $5x - 4z = 10$

x-intercept: 2
y-intercept: none
z-intercept: $-\frac{5}{2}$
xy-trace: $x = 2$
xy-trace: $2z = -5$
xz-trace: $5x - 4z = 10$

Write an equation of the plane given its x-, y-, and z-intercepts.

9. 3, −7, 2
$14x - 6y + 21z = 42$

10. −5, 2, 4
$-4x + 10y + 5z = 20$

Write an equation of the plane given two of its traces in the coordinate planes.

11. $5x - 2y = 10;\ 5x + 4z = 10$
$5x - 2y + 4z = 10$

12. $2y + 9z = 4;\ 7x - 18z = -8$
$7x - 4y - 18z = -8$

Glencoe Division, Macmillan/McGraw-Hill

3-9

NAME ______________________ DATE ____________

Practice Worksheet

Solving Systems of Equations in Three Variables

Solve each system of equations.

1. $2x - y + 2z = 15$
$-x + y + z = 3$
$3x - y + 2z = 18$

2. $x - 4y + 3z = -27$
$2x + 2y - 3z = 22$
$4z = -16$

3. $a + b = 3$
$-b + c = 3$
$a + 2c = 10$

4. $3x - 2y + 4z = 15$
$x - y + z = 3$
$x + 4y - 5z = 0$

5. $2x + 3y + 4z = 2$
$5x - 2y + 3z = 0$
$x - 5y - 2z = -4$

6. $2x + y - z = -8$
$4x - y + 2z = -3$
$-3x + y + 2z = 5$

7. $2x - 5y + z = 5$
$3x + 2y - z = 17$
$4x - 3y + 2z = 17$

8. $p + 4r = -7$
$p - 3q = -8$
$q + r = 1$

9. The sum of three numbers is 6. The third number is the sum of the first and second number. The first number is one more than the third number. Find the numbers.

10. The sum of three numbers is −4. The second number decreased by the third is equal to the first. The sum of the first and second number is −5. Find the numbers.

Glencoe Division, Macmillan/McGraw-Hill

NAME ____________________ DATE __________

3-9

Practice Worksheet

Solving Systems of Equations in Three Variables

Solve each system of equations.

1. $2x - y + 2z = 15$
$-x + y + z = 3$
$3x - y + 2z = 18$ **(3, 1, 5)**

2. $x - 4y + 3z = -27$
$2x + 2y - 3z = 22$
$4z = -16$ **(1, 4, −4)**

3. $a + b = 3$
$-b + c = 3$
$a + 2c = 10$ **(2, 1, 4)**

4. $3x - 2y + 4z = 15$
$x - y + z = 3$
$x + 4y - 5z = 0$ **(3, 3, 3)**

5. $2x + 3y + 4z = 2$
$5x - 2y + 3z = 0$
$x - 5y - 2z = -4$ **(2, 2, −2)**

6. $2x + y - z = -8$
$4x - y + 2z = -3$
$-3x + y + 2z = 5$ **(−2, −3, 1)**

7. $2x - 5y + z = 5$
$3x + 2y - z = 17$
$4x - 3y + 2z = 17$ **(5, 1, 0)**

8. $p + 4r = -7$
$p - 3q = -8$
$q + r = 1$ **(1, 3, −2)**

9. The sum of three numbers is 6. The third number is the sum of the first and second number. The first number is one more than the third number. Find the numbers.
first = 4, second = −1, third = 3

10. The sum of three numbers is −4. The second number decreased by the third is equal to the first. The sum of the first and second number is −5. Find the numbers.
first = −3, second = −2, third = 1

NAME ______________________ DATE ____________

4-1

Practice Worksheet

Problem Solving Strategy: Using Matrix Logic

Use matrix logic to solve these problems.

1. Four friends—Bill, Lalo, Nellie, and April—have different favorite colors (blue, green, yellow, and red). Use the clues to find each person's favorite color.

- Bill likes either blue or yellow.
- Lalo likes either yellow or red.
- The girl who likes red is a freshman.
- Nellie is a senior.

2. The Peterson children are 13, 14, and 15 years old. One collects stamps, one collects coins, and one collects shells. From the clues, find each child's age and what he or she collects.

- The oldest collects stamps.
- Bart collects coins.
- Annette is older than Cassie.
- The 14-year-old does not collect coins.

Glencoe Division, Macmillan/McGraw-Hill

NAME ______________________ DATE ____________

4-1

Practice Worksheet

Problem Solving Strategy: Using Matrix Logic

Use matrix logic to solve these problems.

1. Four friends—Bill, Lalo, Nellie, and April—have different favorite colors (blue, green, yellow, and red). Use the clues to find each person's favorite color.

   - Bill likes either blue or yellow.
   - Lalo likes either yellow or red.
   - The girl who likes red is a freshman.
   - Nellie is a senior.

	blue	green	yellow	red
Bill	✓			
Lalo			✓	
Nellie		✓		
April				✓

2. The Peterson children are 13, 14, and 15 years old. One collects stamps, one collects coins, and one collects shells. From the clues, find each child's age and what he or she collects.

   - The oldest collects stamps.
   - Bart collects coins.
   - Annette is older than Cassie.
   - The 14-year-old does not collect coins.

	13	14	15	stamps	coins	shells
Annette			✓	✓		
Bart	✓				✓	
Cassie		✓				✓

NAME ____________________ DATE ____________

4-2 Practice Worksheet

An Introduction to Matrices

Solve for the variables.

1. $\begin{bmatrix} 3x & 4y \\ -48 & 49 \end{bmatrix} = \begin{bmatrix} 27 & -16 \\ -3w & 7z \end{bmatrix}$

2. $\begin{bmatrix} 3x \\ y + 4 \end{bmatrix} = \begin{bmatrix} y + 8 \\ 17 \end{bmatrix}$

3. $x\begin{bmatrix} 2 & -5 \\ 7 & y \end{bmatrix} = \begin{bmatrix} 8 & -20 \\ z & 24 \end{bmatrix}$

4. $5\begin{bmatrix} x & y + 2 \\ 6 & z \end{bmatrix} = \begin{bmatrix} 10 & 25 \\ 2z & 30x + 5y \end{bmatrix}$

5. $\begin{bmatrix} a^2 & -9 & 15 \\ 2 & 16 & 18 \end{bmatrix} = \begin{bmatrix} 36 & -9 & -5b \\ 2 & 2c & 18 \end{bmatrix}$

6. $\begin{bmatrix} 2x + y \\ x - 3y \end{bmatrix} = \begin{bmatrix} 23 \\ 15 \end{bmatrix}$

Perform the indicated operations.

7. $3\begin{bmatrix} 2 & 5 & -1 & 9 \\ 4 & 0 & 8 & -6 \end{bmatrix}$

8. $\begin{bmatrix} 2 & -1 \\ 3 & 7 \\ 14 & -9 \end{bmatrix} + \begin{bmatrix} -6 & 9 \\ 7 & -11 \\ -8 & 17 \end{bmatrix}$

9. $6\begin{bmatrix} 1 \\ -3 \\ 0 \end{bmatrix} + 5\begin{bmatrix} 2 \\ 7 \\ -8 \end{bmatrix} - 3\begin{bmatrix} -1 \\ 4 \\ 12 \end{bmatrix}$

10. $6\begin{bmatrix} 2 & 3 \\ -1 & 4 \\ 8 & -6 \end{bmatrix} + 5\begin{bmatrix} 7 & -4 \\ 3 & 2 \\ 0 & -1 \end{bmatrix}$

11. $7\begin{bmatrix} 2 & -1 & 8 \\ 4 & 7 & 9 \end{bmatrix} - 2\begin{bmatrix} -1 & 4 & -3 \\ 7 & 2 & -6 \end{bmatrix}$

12. $\frac{3}{4}\begin{bmatrix} 8 & 12 \\ -16 & 20 \end{bmatrix} + \frac{2}{3}\begin{bmatrix} 27 & -9 \\ 54 & -18 \end{bmatrix}$

NAME ______________________ DATE ______________

4-2 Practice Worksheet

An Introduction to Matrices

Solve for the variables.

1. $\begin{bmatrix} 3x & 4y \\ -48 & 49 \end{bmatrix} = \begin{bmatrix} 27 & -16 \\ -3w & 7z \end{bmatrix}$

x = 9, y = −4, w = 16, z = 7

2. $\begin{bmatrix} 3x \\ y + 4 \end{bmatrix} = \begin{bmatrix} y + 8 \\ 17 \end{bmatrix}$

x = 7, y = 13

3. $x\begin{bmatrix} 2 & -5 \\ 7 & y \end{bmatrix} = \begin{bmatrix} 8 & -20 \\ z & 24 \end{bmatrix}$

x = 4, y = 6, z = 28

4. $5\begin{bmatrix} x & y + 2 \\ 6 & z \end{bmatrix} = \begin{bmatrix} 10 & 25 \\ 2z & 30x + 5y \end{bmatrix}$

x = 2, y = 3, z = 15

5. $\begin{bmatrix} a^2 & -9 & 15 \\ 2 & 16 & 18 \end{bmatrix} = \begin{bmatrix} 36 & -9 & -5b \\ 2 & 2c & 18 \end{bmatrix}$

a = 6 or −6, b = −3, c = 8

6. $\begin{bmatrix} 2x + y \\ x - 3y \end{bmatrix} = \begin{bmatrix} 23 \\ 15 \end{bmatrix}$

x = 12, y = −1

Perform the indicated operations.

7. $3\begin{bmatrix} 2 & 5 & -1 & 9 \\ 4 & 0 & 8 & -6 \end{bmatrix}$

$\begin{bmatrix} 6 & 15 & -3 & 27 \\ 12 & 0 & 24 & -18 \end{bmatrix}$

8. $\begin{bmatrix} 2 & -1 \\ 3 & 7 \\ 14 & -9 \end{bmatrix} + \begin{bmatrix} -6 & 9 \\ 7 & -11 \\ -8 & 17 \end{bmatrix}$

$\begin{bmatrix} -4 & 8 \\ 10 & -4 \\ 6 & 8 \end{bmatrix}$

9. $6\begin{bmatrix} 1 \\ -3 \\ 0 \end{bmatrix} + 5\begin{bmatrix} 2 \\ 7 \\ -8 \end{bmatrix} - 3\begin{bmatrix} -1 \\ 4 \\ 12 \end{bmatrix}$

$\begin{bmatrix} 19 \\ 5 \\ -76 \end{bmatrix}$

10. $6\begin{bmatrix} 2 & 3 \\ -1 & 4 \\ 8 & -6 \end{bmatrix} + 5\begin{bmatrix} 7 & -4 \\ 3 & 2 \\ 0 & -1 \end{bmatrix}$

$\begin{bmatrix} 47 & -2 \\ 9 & 34 \\ 48 & -41 \end{bmatrix}$

11. $7\begin{bmatrix} 2 & -1 & 8 \\ 4 & 7 & 9 \end{bmatrix} - 2\begin{bmatrix} -1 & 4 & -3 \\ 7 & 2 & -6 \end{bmatrix}$

$\begin{bmatrix} 16 & -15 & 62 \\ 14 & 45 & 75 \end{bmatrix}$

12. $\frac{3}{4}\begin{bmatrix} 8 & 12 \\ -16 & 20 \end{bmatrix} + \frac{2}{3}\begin{bmatrix} 27 & -9 \\ 54 & -18 \end{bmatrix}$

$\begin{bmatrix} 24 & 3 \\ 24 & 3 \end{bmatrix}$

Glencoe Division, Macmillan/McGraw-Hill

NAME ____________________ DATE ____________

4-3

Practice Worksheet

Matrices and Determinants

Determine the value of the determinant of each matrix.

1. $\begin{bmatrix} -5 & 2 \\ -8 & -7 \end{bmatrix}$

2. $\begin{bmatrix} -2 & 3 & 1 \\ 0 & 4 & -3 \\ 2 & 5 & -1 \end{bmatrix}$

3. $\begin{bmatrix} 0 & -4 & 0 \\ 2 & -1 & 1 \\ 3 & -2 & 5 \end{bmatrix}$

4. $\begin{bmatrix} 2 & -4 & 1 \\ 3 & 0 & 9 \\ -1 & 5 & 7 \end{bmatrix}$

5. $\begin{bmatrix} 3 & -4 \\ 7 & 9 \end{bmatrix}$

6. $\begin{bmatrix} 2 & 7 & -6 \\ 8 & 4 & 0 \\ 1 & -1 & 3 \end{bmatrix}$

Solve for the variable.

7. $\begin{vmatrix} 3 & -4 \\ 2x & 5 \end{vmatrix} = 30$

8. $\begin{vmatrix} 2 & -1 \\ 3 & 4m \end{vmatrix} = -16$

9. $\begin{vmatrix} x & 3 & -1 \\ 2 & 1 & -2 \\ 4 & 1 & x \end{vmatrix} = 10$

10. $\begin{vmatrix} 2x & 0 & 3 \\ 7 & 5 & -1 \\ 4 & 2 & x \end{vmatrix} = 8x^2 - 3x + 12$

11. Find the area of a triangle whose vertices have coordinates (3, 5), (6, −5), and (−4, 10).

12. Find the area of a triangle whose vertices have coordinates (−8, 10), (6, 17), and (2, −4).

NAME ______________________ DATE ______________

4-3 Practice Worksheet

Matrices and Determinants

Determine the value of the determinant of each matrix.

1. $\begin{bmatrix} -5 & 2 \\ -8 & -7 \end{bmatrix}$ 51

2. $\begin{bmatrix} -2 & 3 & 1 \\ 0 & 4 & -3 \\ 2 & 5 & -1 \end{bmatrix}$ −48

3. $\begin{bmatrix} 0 & -4 & 0 \\ 2 & -1 & 1 \\ 3 & -2 & 5 \end{bmatrix}$ 28

4. $\begin{bmatrix} 2 & -4 & 1 \\ 3 & 0 & 9 \\ -1 & 5 & 7 \end{bmatrix}$ 45

5. $\begin{bmatrix} 3 & -4 \\ 7 & 9 \end{bmatrix}$ 55

6. $\begin{bmatrix} 2 & 7 & -6 \\ 8 & 4 & 0 \\ 1 & -1 & 3 \end{bmatrix}$ −72

Solve for the variable.

7. $\begin{vmatrix} 3 & -4 \\ 2x & 5 \end{vmatrix} = 30$

   $x = \frac{15}{8}$

8. $\begin{vmatrix} 2 & -1 \\ 3 & 4m \end{vmatrix} = -16$

   $m = -\frac{19}{8}$

9. $\begin{vmatrix} x & 3 & -1 \\ 2 & 1 & -2 \\ 4 & 1 & x \end{vmatrix} = 10$

   $x = 8$ or $x = -4$

10. $\begin{vmatrix} 2x & 0 & 3 \\ 7 & 5 & -1 \\ 4 & 2 & x \end{vmatrix} = 8x^2 - 3x + 12$

    $x = \frac{5}{2}$ or $x = -6$

11. Find the area of a triangle whose vertices have coordinates (3, 5), (6, −5), and (−4, 10).

    27 units^2

12. Find the area of a triangle whose vertices have coordinates (−8, 10), (6, 17), and (2, −4).

    133 units^2

NAME ____________________ DATE __________

4-4 Practice Worksheet

Multiplication of Matrices

Determine the dimensions of each matrix M.

1. $A_{7\times 4} \cdot B_{4\times 3} = M$

2. $A_{3\times 5} \cdot M = B_{3\times 8}$

3. $M \cdot A_{1\times 6} = B_{2\times 6}$

Perform the indicated operations.

4. $2\begin{bmatrix} 2 & 4 \\ 3 & -1 \end{bmatrix} + 3\begin{bmatrix} -3 & 0 \\ 2 & 5 \end{bmatrix}$

5. $\begin{bmatrix} 2 & 4 \\ 3 & -1 \end{bmatrix} \cdot \begin{bmatrix} 3 & -2 & 7 \\ 6 & 0 & -5 \end{bmatrix}$

6. $\begin{bmatrix} 2 & 4 \\ 3 & -1 \end{bmatrix} \cdot \begin{bmatrix} -3 & 0 \\ 2 & 5 \end{bmatrix} + 2\begin{bmatrix} -3 & 0 \\ 2 & 5 \end{bmatrix}$

7. $\begin{bmatrix} 3 & -2 & 7 \\ 6 & 0 & -5 \end{bmatrix} \cdot \begin{bmatrix} 3 & -2 & 7 \\ 6 & 0 & -5 \end{bmatrix}$

8. $\begin{bmatrix} 2 & 4 \\ 7 & -1 \end{bmatrix} \cdot \begin{bmatrix} -3 & 0 \\ 2 & 5 \end{bmatrix}$

9. $\begin{bmatrix} -3 & 0 \\ 2 & 5 \end{bmatrix} \cdot \begin{bmatrix} 2 & 4 \\ 7 & -1 \end{bmatrix}$

Find the new coordinates of the vertices of each polygon after the polygon is rotated 90° counterclockwise about the origin.

10. triangle *ABC* with vertices *A*(2, 5), *B*(5, 8), *C*(3, 15)

11. square *DEFG* with vertices *D*(−1, 2), *E*(−1, −2), *F*(3, −2), *G*(3, 2)

12. rectangle *HIJK* with vertices *H*(−1, 1), *I*(1, −1), *J*(7, 5), *K*(5, 7)

Glencoe Division, Macmillan/McGraw-Hill

NAME ____________________ DATE ________

4-4 Practice Worksheet

Multiplication of Matrices

Determine the dimensions of each matrix M.

1. $A_{7\times4} \cdot B_{4\times3} = M$
   7×3

2. $A_{3\times5} \cdot M = B_{3\times8}$
   5×8

3. $M \cdot A_{1\times6} = B_{2\times6}$
   2×1

Perform the indicated operations.

4. $2\begin{bmatrix} 2 & 4 \\ 3 & -1 \end{bmatrix} + 3\begin{bmatrix} -3 & 0 \\ 2 & 5 \end{bmatrix}$
   $\begin{bmatrix} -5 & 8 \\ 12 & 13 \end{bmatrix}$

5. $\begin{bmatrix} 2 & 4 \\ 3 & -1 \end{bmatrix} \cdot \begin{bmatrix} 3 & -2 & 7 \\ 6 & 0 & -5 \end{bmatrix}$
   $\begin{bmatrix} 30 & -4 & -6 \\ 3 & -6 & 26 \end{bmatrix}$

6. $\begin{bmatrix} 2 & 4 \\ 3 & -1 \end{bmatrix} \cdot \begin{bmatrix} -3 & 0 \\ 2 & 5 \end{bmatrix} + 2\begin{bmatrix} -3 & 0 \\ 2 & 5 \end{bmatrix}$
   $\begin{bmatrix} -4 & 20 \\ -7 & 5 \end{bmatrix}$

7. $\begin{bmatrix} 3 & -2 & 7 \\ 6 & 0 & -5 \end{bmatrix} \cdot \begin{bmatrix} 3 & -2 & 7 \\ 6 & 0 & -5 \end{bmatrix}$
   not possible to evaluate

8. $\begin{bmatrix} 2 & 4 \\ 7 & -1 \end{bmatrix} \cdot \begin{bmatrix} -3 & 0 \\ 2 & 5 \end{bmatrix}$
   $\begin{bmatrix} 2 & 20 \\ -23 & -5 \end{bmatrix}$

9. $\begin{bmatrix} -3 & 0 \\ 2 & 5 \end{bmatrix} \cdot \begin{bmatrix} 2 & 4 \\ 7 & -1 \end{bmatrix}$
   $\begin{bmatrix} -6 & -12 \\ 39 & 3 \end{bmatrix}$

Find the new coordinates of the vertices of each polygon after the polygon is rotated 90° counterclockwise about the origin.

10. triangle ABC with vertices $A(2, 5)$, $B(5, 8)$, $C(3, 15)$
    (−5, 2), (−8, 5), (−15, 3)

11. square $DEFG$ with vertices $D(-1, 2)$, $E(-1, -2)$, $F(3, -2)$, $G(3, 2)$
    (−2, −1), (2, −1), (2, 3), (−2, 3)

12. rectangle $HIJK$ with vertices $H(-1, 1)$, $I(1, -1)$, $J(7, 5)$, $K(5, 7)$
    (−1, −1), (1, 1), (−5, 7), (−7, 5)

Glencoe Division, Macmillan/McGraw-Hill

NAME ____________________ DATE ____________

4-5

Practice Worksheet

Identity and Inverse Matrices

Find the inverse of each matrix, if it exists.

1. $\begin{bmatrix} 3 & 1 \\ -4 & 2 \end{bmatrix}$

2. $\begin{bmatrix} 4 & 5 \\ -4 & -3 \end{bmatrix}$

3. $\begin{bmatrix} 4 & 6 \\ 6 & 9 \end{bmatrix}$

4. $\begin{bmatrix} 2 & 5 \\ -1 & 3 \end{bmatrix}$

5. $\begin{bmatrix} -4 & 7 \\ 8 & 1 \end{bmatrix}$

6. $\begin{bmatrix} 2 & 0 \\ 3 & 5 \end{bmatrix}$

7. $\begin{bmatrix} 2 & -5 \\ 3 & 1 \end{bmatrix}$

8. $\begin{bmatrix} -1 & 3 \\ 4 & -7 \end{bmatrix}$

Glencoe Division, Macmillan/McGraw-Hill

NAME ______________________ DATE ______________

4-5

Practice Worksheet

Identity and Inverse Matrices

Find the inverse of each matrix, if it exists.

1. $\begin{bmatrix} 3 & 1 \\ -4 & 2 \end{bmatrix}$

$\begin{bmatrix} \frac{1}{5} & -\frac{1}{10} \\ \frac{2}{5} & \frac{3}{10} \end{bmatrix}$

2. $\begin{bmatrix} 4 & 5 \\ -4 & -3 \end{bmatrix}$

$\begin{bmatrix} -\frac{3}{8} & -\frac{5}{8} \\ \frac{1}{2} & \frac{1}{2} \end{bmatrix}$

3. $\begin{bmatrix} 4 & 6 \\ 6 & 9 \end{bmatrix}$

does not exist

4. $\begin{bmatrix} 2 & 5 \\ -1 & 3 \end{bmatrix}$

$\begin{bmatrix} \frac{3}{11} & -\frac{5}{11} \\ \frac{1}{11} & \frac{2}{11} \end{bmatrix}$

5. $\begin{bmatrix} -4 & 7 \\ 8 & 1 \end{bmatrix}$

$\begin{bmatrix} -\frac{1}{60} & \frac{7}{60} \\ \frac{2}{15} & \frac{1}{15} \end{bmatrix}$

6. $\begin{bmatrix} 2 & 0 \\ 3 & 5 \end{bmatrix}$

$\begin{bmatrix} \frac{1}{2} & 0 \\ -\frac{3}{10} & \frac{1}{5} \end{bmatrix}$

7. $\begin{bmatrix} 2 & -5 \\ 3 & 1 \end{bmatrix}$

$\begin{bmatrix} \frac{1}{17} & \frac{5}{17} \\ -\frac{3}{17} & \frac{2}{17} \end{bmatrix}$

8. $\begin{bmatrix} -1 & 3 \\ 4 & -7 \end{bmatrix}$

$\begin{bmatrix} \frac{7}{5} & \frac{3}{5} \\ \frac{4}{5} & \frac{1}{5} \end{bmatrix}$

Glencoe Division, Macmillan/McGraw-Hill

NAME ______________________ DATE ______________

4-6 Practice Worksheet

Using Inverse Matrices

Write the system of linear equations represented by each matrix equation.

1. $\begin{bmatrix} 3 & -2 & 5 \\ 1 & 1 & -4 \\ -2 & 2 & 7 \end{bmatrix} \cdot \begin{bmatrix} x \\ y \\ z \end{bmatrix} = \begin{bmatrix} 3 \\ 2 \\ -5 \end{bmatrix}$

2. $\begin{bmatrix} 2 & 1 & -3 \\ 5 & 2 & -2 \\ 3 & -3 & 5 \end{bmatrix} \cdot \begin{bmatrix} x \\ y \\ z \end{bmatrix} = \begin{bmatrix} -5 \\ 8 \\ 17 \end{bmatrix}$

Write a matrix equation for each system of linear equations.

3. $-3x + 2y = 9$
$5x - 3y = -13$

4. $6x - 2y = -2$
$3x + 3y = 10$

Use the given inverse matrix $\mathbf{M}^{-1}$ to solve each matrix equation.

5. $\begin{bmatrix} 2 & 1 \\ 3 & 2 \end{bmatrix} \cdot \begin{bmatrix} x \\ y \end{bmatrix} = \begin{bmatrix} 0 \\ -2 \end{bmatrix}$

6. $\begin{bmatrix} 1 & 5 \\ 2 & -3 \end{bmatrix} \cdot \begin{bmatrix} x \\ y \end{bmatrix} = \begin{bmatrix} 10 \\ 7 \end{bmatrix}$

7. $\begin{bmatrix} 1 & 3 & 2 \\ -1 & 2 & 1 \\ 4 & 1 & -2 \end{bmatrix} \cdot \begin{bmatrix} x \\ y \\ z \end{bmatrix} = \begin{bmatrix} 2 \\ -1 \\ -1 \end{bmatrix}$

8. $\begin{bmatrix} 2 & 3 & -1 \\ 4 & 1 & 5 \\ 1 & 2 & -1 \end{bmatrix} \cdot \begin{bmatrix} x \\ y \\ z \end{bmatrix} = \begin{bmatrix} 17 \\ -9 \\ 12 \end{bmatrix}$

Glencoe Division, Macmillan/McGraw-Hill

NAME ______________________ DATE ____________

4-6

Practice Worksheet

Using Inverse Matrices

Write the system of linear equations represented by each matrix equation.

1. $\begin{bmatrix} 3 & -2 & 5 \\ 1 & 1 & -4 \\ -2 & 2 & 7 \end{bmatrix} \cdot \begin{bmatrix} x \\ y \\ z \end{bmatrix} = \begin{bmatrix} 3 \\ 2 \\ -5 \end{bmatrix}$

$3x - 2y + 5z = 3$
$x + y - 4z = 2$
$-2x + 2y + 7z = -5$

2. $\begin{bmatrix} 2 & 1 & -3 \\ 5 & 2 & -2 \\ 3 & -3 & 5 \end{bmatrix} \cdot \begin{bmatrix} x \\ y \\ z \end{bmatrix} = \begin{bmatrix} -5 \\ 8 \\ 17 \end{bmatrix}$

$2x + y - 3z = -5$
$5x + 2y - 2z = 8$
$3x - 3y + 5z = 17$

Write a matrix equation for each system of linear equations.

3. $-3x + 2y = 9$
$5x - 3y = -13$

$\begin{bmatrix} -3 & 2 \\ 5 & -3 \end{bmatrix} \cdot \begin{bmatrix} x \\ y \end{bmatrix} = \begin{bmatrix} 9 \\ -13 \end{bmatrix}$

4. $6x - 2y = -2$
$3x + 3y = 10$

$\begin{bmatrix} 6 & -2 \\ 3 & 3 \end{bmatrix} \cdot \begin{bmatrix} x \\ y \end{bmatrix} = \begin{bmatrix} -2 \\ 10 \end{bmatrix}$

Use the given inverse matrix M^{-1} to solve each matrix equation.

5. $\begin{bmatrix} 2 & 1 \\ 3 & 2 \end{bmatrix} \cdot \begin{bmatrix} x \\ y \end{bmatrix} = \begin{bmatrix} 0 \\ -2 \end{bmatrix}$ $M^{-1} = \begin{bmatrix} 2 & -1 \\ -3 & 2 \end{bmatrix}$; (2, −4)

6. $\begin{bmatrix} 1 & 5 \\ 2 & -3 \end{bmatrix} \cdot \begin{bmatrix} x \\ y \end{bmatrix} = \begin{bmatrix} 10 \\ 7 \end{bmatrix}$ $M^{-1} = -\frac{1}{13}\begin{bmatrix} -3 & -5 \\ -2 & 1 \end{bmatrix}$; (5, 1)

7. $\begin{bmatrix} 1 & 3 & 2 \\ -1 & 2 & 1 \\ 4 & 1 & -2 \end{bmatrix} \cdot \begin{bmatrix} x \\ y \\ z \end{bmatrix} = \begin{bmatrix} 2 \\ -1 \\ -1 \end{bmatrix}$ $M^{-1} = -\frac{1}{17}\begin{bmatrix} -5 & 8 & -1 \\ 2 & -10 & -3 \\ -9 & 11 & 5 \end{bmatrix}$; (1, −1, 2)

8. $\begin{bmatrix} 2 & 3 & -1 \\ 4 & 1 & 5 \\ 1 & 2 & -1 \end{bmatrix} \cdot \begin{bmatrix} x \\ y \\ z \end{bmatrix} = \begin{bmatrix} 17 \\ -9 \\ 12 \end{bmatrix}$ $M^{-1} = \frac{1}{2}\begin{bmatrix} 11 & -1 & -16 \\ -9 & 1 & 14 \\ -7 & 1 & 10 \end{bmatrix}$ (2, 3, −4)

NAME ______________________ DATE ______________

4-7 Practice Worksheet

Using Cramer's Rule

Determine whether each system of equations has a unique solution.

1. $x - 3y + 2z = 5$
$3x - 2y - 3z = 4$
$2x + 5y - z = 11$

2. $4x + y + 3z = 8$
$3x + 4y - z = 5$
$-x + 3y - 4z = 2$

Solve each system of equations using Cramer's Rule.

3. $2x - y + z = 6$
$-x + 2y + z = 0$
$x + y - z = -3$

4. $4x - 3y + z = 5$
$2x + y - z = 7$
$3x + 2y + 2z = 0$

5. $5x - y + z = -12$
$2x + y - 3z = -4$
$-x + 4y + z = 15$

6. $3x - 4y + 2z = 28$
$2x + 3y + 5z = -6$
$4x - 2y + 3z = 21$

7. $5x + 4y - 3z = 2$
$2x - 3y + 2z = -3$
$4x - y - 6z = 1$

8. $2x + 6y - z = 4$
$4x + 5z = 7$
$3y - 2z = 0$

Glencoe Division, Macmillan/McGraw-Hill

NAME ________________________ DATE ____________

4-7

Practice Worksheet

Using Cramer's Rule

Determine whether each system of equations has a unique solution.

1. $x - 3y + 2z = 5$
$3x - 2y - 3z = 4$
$2x + 5y - z = 11$ **yes**

2. $4x + y + 3z = 8$
$3x + 4y - z = 5$
$-x + 3y - 4z = 2$ **no**

Solve each system of equations using Cramer's Rule.

3. $2x - y + z = 6$
$-x + 2y + z = 0$
$x + y - z = -3$
(1, −1, 3)

4. $4x - 3y + z = 5$
$2x + y - z = 7$
$3x + 2y + 2z = 0$
(2, 0, −3)

5. $5x - y + z = -12$
$2x + y - 3z = -4$
$-x + 4y + z = 15$
(−2, 3, 1)

6. $3x - 4y + 2z = 28$
$2x + 3y + 5z = -6$
$4x - 2y + 3z = 21$
(2, −5, 1)

7. $5x + 4y - 3z = 2$
$2x - 3y + 2z = -3$
$4x - y - 6z = 1$ $\left(-\frac{7}{25}, \frac{13}{25}, \frac{-11}{25}\right)$

8. $2x + 6y - z = 4$
$4x + 5z = 7$
$3y - 2z = 0$ $\left(\frac{1}{2}, \frac{2}{3}, 1\right)$

NAME ______________________ DATE ______________

4-8 Practice Worksheet

Using Augmented Matrices

Solve each system of equations using augmented matrices.

1. $5x + 9y = 19$
   $2x - y = -20$

2. $2x + y - 3z = -3$
   $3x + 2y + 4z = 5$
   $-4x - y + 2z = 4$

3. $4x - 3y - z = -3$
   $5x + 2y + 2z = 7$
   $3x + 3y + z = 10$

4. $x + 2z = 11$
   $2x + y = 4$
   $x + 3y + z = 1$

5. $2x + y + z = 2$
   $-x - y + 2z = 7$
   $-3x + 2y + 3z = 7$

6. $3x - 2y + 5z = -14$
   $x + 5y - 3z = 18$
   $-2x - 3y + 8z = -8$

7. $2x - y + z = 4$
   $x + y - z = 11$
   $4x - 2y + 2z = 5$

8. $3x - 2y + 4z = 8$
   $x + y - 3z = 1$
   $6x - 4y + 8z = 16$

Glencoe Division, Macmillan/McGraw-Hill

NAME ______________________ DATE ____________

4-8

Practice Worksheet

Using Augmented Matrices

Solve each system of equations using augmented matrices.

1. $5x + 9y = 19$
$2x - y = -20$
(−7, 6)

2. $2x + y - 3z = -3$
$3x + 2y + 4z = 5$
$-4x - y + 2z = 4$
(−1, 2, 1)

3. $4x - 3y - z = -3$
$5x + 2y + 2z = 7$
$3x + 3y + z = 10$
(1, 3, −2)

4. $x + 2z = 11$
$2x + y = 4$
$x + 3y + z = 1$
(3, −2, 4)

5. $2x + y + z = 2$
$-x - y + 2z = 7$
$-3x + 2y + 3z = 7$
(0, −1, 3)

6. $3x - 2y + 5z = -14$
$x + 5y - 3z = 18$
$-2x - 3y + 8z = -8$
(−2, 4, 0)

7. $2x - y + z = 4$
$x + y - z = 11$
$4x - 2y + 2z = 5$
∅

8. $3x - 2y + 4z = 8$
$x + y - 3z = 1$
$6x - 4y + 8z = 16$
$\left(\frac{2}{5}z + 2, \frac{13}{5}z - 1, z\right)$

NAME ____________________ DATE ____________

5-1 Practice Worksheet

Monomials

Simplify.

1. $3n^2v^3 - n^2v^3 + 8v^3n^2$

2. $4r^6w^2 + 9r^2w^6 - r^6w^2$

3. $y^7 \cdot y^3 \cdot y^2$

4. $(n^6)^3$

5. $(2n)^4 + 2n^4$

6. $(3r^7t^2)(-5rt^9)$

7. $(4a^3c^2)^3(-3ac^4)^2$

8. $\left(\frac{3}{2}e^2f^4\right)^4\left(-\frac{4}{3}e^5f\right)^3\left(-\frac{1}{6}ef^5\right)$

9. $-5v^2(2r^3v^2)(rv^3) - (-r^2)(16r^2v^7)$

10. $(-n)^4(2xy^2n)^3 + (4xy^3n^2)^2(-3xn^3)$

11. $(3b^2)^4(-2b^3)^8$

12. $(m^4n^6)^4(m^3n^2p^5)^6$

13. $(3x^2y)(2xy^4) + (4xy^2)(3x^2y^3)$

14. $(7v^3w^4)(2v^2w^6) + (3vw^5)(2v^4w^5)$

Evaluate. Express each answer in both scientific and decimal notation.

15. $(2.3 \times 10^4)^2$

16. $(8.7 \times 10^3)^2$

17. $(4.8 \times 10^2)(6.9 \times 10^4)$

18. $(3.7 \times 10^9)(8.7 \times 10^2)$

19. $(46{,}000)(0.025)$

20. $(54{,}000)(0.00073)$

Glencoe Division, Macmillan/McGraw-Hill

NAME ____________________ DATE ____________

5-1 Practice Worksheet

Monomials

Simplify.

1. $3n^2v^3 - n^2v^3 + 8v^3n^2$ **$10n^2v^3$**

2. $4r^6w^2 + 9r^2w^6 - r^6w^2$ **$3r^6w^2 + 9r^2w^6$**

3. $y^7 \cdot y^3 \cdot y^2$ **y^{12}**

4. $(n^6)^3$ **n^{18}**

5. $(2n)^4 + 2n^4$ **$18n^4$**

6. $(3r^7t^2)(-5rt^9)$ **$-15r^8t^{11}$**

7. $(4a^3c^2)^3(-3ac^4)^2$ **$576a^{11}c^{14}$**

8. $\left(\frac{3}{2}e^2f^4\right)^4\left(-\frac{4}{3}e^5f\right)^3\left(-\frac{1}{6}ef^5\right)$ **$2e^{24}f^{24}$**

9. $-5v^2(2r^3v^2)(rv^3) - (-r^2)(16r^2v^7)$
$6r^4v^7$

10. $(-n)^4(2xy^2n)^3 + (4xy^3n^2)^2(-3xn^3)$
$-40x^3y^6n^7$

11. $(3b^2)^4(-2b^3)^8$
$20{,}736b^{32}$

12. $(m^4n^6)^4(m^3n^2p^5)^6$
$m^{34}n^{36}p^{30}$

13. $(3x^2y)(2xy^4) + (4xy^2)(3x^2y^3)$
$18x^3y^5$

14. $(7v^3w^4)(2v^2w^6) + (3vw^5)(2v^4w^5)$
$20v^5w^{10}$

Evaluate. Express each answer in both scientific and decimal notation.

15. $(2.3 \times 10^4)^2$
5.29×10^8; 529,000,000

16. $(8.7 \times 10^3)^2$
7.569×10^7; 75,690,000

17. $(4.8 \times 10^2)(6.9 \times 10^4)$
3.312×10^7; 33,120,000

18. $(3.7 \times 10^9)(8.7 \times 10^2)$
**3.219×10^{12};
3,219,000,000,000**

19. $(46{,}000)(0.025)$
1.15×10^3; 1150

20. $(54{,}000)(0.00073)$
3.942×10^1; 39.42

NAME ____________________ DATE ____________

5-2

Practice Worksheet

Dividing Monomials

Simplify. Assume no variable equals zero.

1. $p^{-7}p^3$

2. $\frac{21y^9}{35y^3}$

3. $\frac{12m^8y^6}{-9my^4}$

4. $\frac{14(x^{-3})^4}{(2x^2)^3}$

5. $\frac{5x^4}{(6x^7)^0}$

6. $\frac{-6n^9t^3}{-18n^9t^5}$

7. $\frac{-20(m^2v)(-v)^3}{5(-v)^2(-m^4)}$

8. $\frac{x^{7y+1}}{x^{7y-5}}$

9. $\frac{(3m)^{-4}}{2m^{-4}}$

10. $(x^7y^3)^{-3}$

11. $\left(\frac{3}{8}\right)^{-2}x^8y^{-3}z$

12. $\frac{5m^3}{t^{-6}}$

13. $\frac{6^{-2}x^4}{2^{-3}x^{-3}}$

14. $\frac{(3x^{-2}y^3)(5xy^{-8})}{(x^{-3})^4y^{-2}}$

15. $t^{-5}(t^2 - t^4 + 5t)$

16. $\frac{(8c^2)^{-2}}{c^4}$

17. $\left(\frac{5}{n}\right)^{-4}$

18. $\left(\frac{x}{r^{-2}}\right)^{-3}$

19. $\left(\frac{12x^{-2}}{4x^6}\right)^{-1}$

20. $\left(\frac{4}{9}\right)^{-3}\left(\frac{4}{9}\right)^5$

21. $\left(\frac{1}{2ay^{-3}}\right)^{-2}$

22. $\left(\frac{6}{2ay^2}\right)^3$

23. $\left(\frac{1}{8}\right)^{-2} - \left(\frac{1}{2}\right)^{-4}$

24. $\left(\frac{n^3}{(n^2)^{-2}}\right)^{-1}$

Evaluate. Express each answer in both scientific and decimal notation.

25. $\frac{4 \times 10^8}{1.6 \times 10^4}$

26. $\frac{2.7 \times 10^6}{9 \times 10^{10}}$

NAME ______________________ DATE ____________

5-2 Practice Worksheet

Dividing Monomials

Simplify. Assume no variable equals zero.

1. $p^{-7}p^3$ $\frac{1}{p^4}$

2. $\frac{21y^9}{35y^3}$ $\frac{3y^6}{5}$

3. $\frac{12m^8y^6}{-9my^4}$ $\frac{4m^7y^2}{-3}$

4. $\frac{14(x^{-3})^4}{(2x^2)^3}$ $\frac{7}{4x^{18}}$

5. $\frac{5x^4}{(6x^7)^0}$ $5x^4$

6. $\frac{-6n^9t^3}{-18n^9t^5}$ $\frac{1}{3t^2}$

7. $\frac{-20(m^2v)(-v)^3}{5(-v)^2(-m^4)}$ $-\frac{4v^2}{m^2}$

8. $\frac{x^{7y+1}}{x^{7y-5}}$ x^6

9. $\frac{(3m)^{-4}}{2m^{-4}}$ $\frac{1}{162}$

10. $(x^7y^3)^{-3}$ $\frac{1}{x^{21}y^9}$

11. $\left(\frac{3}{8}\right)^{-2}x^8y^{-3}z$ $\frac{64x^8z}{9y^3}$

12. $\frac{5m^3}{t^{-6}}$ $5m^3t^6$

13. $\frac{6^{-2}x^4}{2^{-3}x^{-3}}$ $\frac{2x^7}{9}$

14. $\frac{(3x^{-2}y^3)(5xy^{-8})}{(x^{-3})^4y^{-2}}$ $\frac{15x^{11}}{y^3}$

15. $t^{-5}(t^2 - t^4 + 5t)$ $\frac{1}{t^3} - \frac{1}{t} + \frac{5}{t^4}$

16. $\frac{(8c^2)^{-2}}{c^4}$ $\frac{1}{64c^8}$

17. $\left(\frac{5}{n}\right)^{-4}$ $\frac{n^4}{625}$

18. $\left(\frac{x}{r^{-2}}\right)^{-3}$ $\frac{1}{x^3r^6}$

19. $\left(\frac{12x^{-2}}{4x^6}\right)^{-1}$ $\frac{x^8}{3}$

20. $\left(\frac{4}{9}\right)^{-3}\left(\frac{4}{9}\right)^5$ $\frac{16}{81}$

21. $\left(\frac{1}{2ay^{-3}}\right)^{-2}$ $\frac{4a^2}{y^6}$

22. $\left(\frac{6}{2ay^2}\right)^3$ $\frac{27}{a^3y^6}$

23. $\left(\frac{1}{8}\right)^{-2} - \left(\frac{1}{2}\right)^{-4}$ 48

24. $\left(\frac{n^3}{(n^2)^{-2}}\right)^{-1}$ $\frac{1}{n^7}$

Evaluate. Express each answer in both scientific and decimal notation.

25. $\frac{4 \times 10^8}{1.6 \times 10^4}$
2.5×10^4; 25,000

26. $\frac{2.7 \times 10^6}{9 \times 10^{10}}$
3×10^{-5}; 0.00003

NAME ________________ DATE ________

5-3

Practice Worksheet

Problem Solving Strategy: Draw a Diagram

Solve. Use any strategy.

16. How many different squares can be traced using the figure at the right?

2. Find the digit represented by each different letter in problem at the right.

$$\begin{array}{r} AB \\ AB \\ +AB \\ \hline CCC \end{array}$$

3. A farmer wants to build a pen for her cow. She will use the barn as one side of the pen. She has 12 meters of fencing she can use for the other three sides. If the length of each side must be an integer, what is the greatest area that the pen can have?

4. Express 72 as the difference of two squares. There are three different possibilities.

Glencoe Division, Macmillan/McGraw-Hill

5-3

NAME ____________ DATE ____________

Practice Worksheet

Problem Solving Strategy: Draw a Diagram

Solve. Use any strategy.

16. How many different squares can be traced using the figure at the right?
55

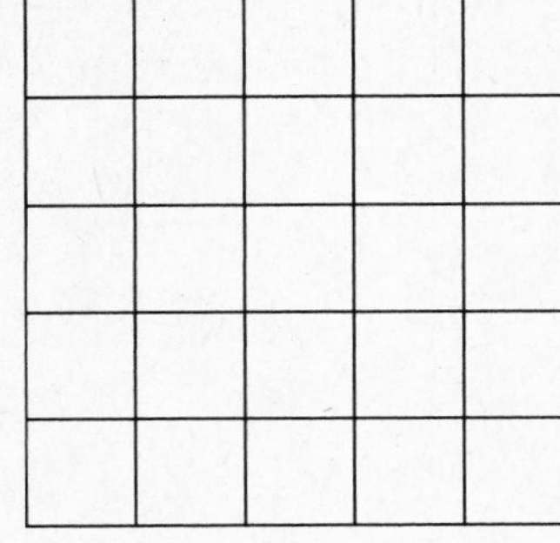

2. Find the digit represented by each different letter in problem at the right.
***A* = 7, *B* = 4, *C* = 2; or**
***A* = 3, *B* = 7, *C* = 1**

$$\begin{array}{r} AB \\ AB \\ +AB \\ \hline CCC \end{array}$$

3. A farmer wants to build a pen for her cow. She will use the barn as one side of the pen. She has 12 meters of fencing she can use for the other three sides. If the length of each side must be an integer, what is the greatest area that the pen can have? **18 m^2**

4. Express 72 as the difference of two squares. There are three different possibilities. **$19^2 - 17^2$, $11^2 - 7^2$, $9^2 - 3^2$**

NAME ______________________ DATE ____________

5-4 Practice Worksheet

Polynomials

Simplify.

1. $(-6n - 13n^2) + (-3n + 9n^2)$

2. $(8x^2 - 3x) - (4x^2 + 5x - 3)$

3. $(5m^2 - 2mp - 6p^2) - (-3m^2 + 5mp + p^2)$

4. $-9(y - 7w) + 4(2y + w)$

Find each product.

5. $-6a^2w(a^3w - aw^4)$

6. $-9r^4y^2(-3ry^7 + 2r^3y^4 - 8r^{10})$

7. $5a^2w^3(a^2w^6 - 3a^4w^2 + 9aw^6)$

8. $2x^2(x - 1) + (x + 1)^2$

9. $(v^2 - 6)(v^2 + 4)$

10. $(7a + 9y)(2a - y)$

11. $(y - 8)^2$

12. $(x^2 + 5y)^2$

13. $(5x + 4w)(5x - 4w)$

14. $(2n^4 - 3)(2n^4 + 3)$

15. $(x + y)(x^2 - 3xy + 2y^2)$

16. $u(u - 6)(u - 3)$

17. $(n - 3)(n + 4)(n - 1)$

18. $(a - r)^2(2a - 3r)$

19. $(2x + 3y)(4x - 6y + 7z)$

20. $(3a + 4b)^2$

Glencoe Division, Macmillan/McGraw-Hill

NAME ____________________ DATE ____________

5-4 Practice Worksheet

Polynomials

Simplify.

1. $(-6n - 13n^2) + (-3n + 9n^2)$
$-9n - 4n^2$

2. $(8x^2 - 3x) - (4x^2 + 5x - 3)$
$4x^2 - 8x + 3$

3. $(5m^2 - 2mp - 6p^2) - (-3m^2 + 5mp + p^2)$
$8m^2 - 7mp - 7p^2$

4. $-9(y - 7w) + 4(2y + w)$
$-y + 67w$

Find each product.

5. $-6a^2w(a^3w - aw^4)$
$-6a^5w^2 + 6a^3w^5$

6. $-9r^4y^2(-3ry^7 + 2r^3y^4 - 8r^{10})$
$27r^5y^9 - 18r^7y^6 + 72r^{14}y^2$

7. $5a^2w^3(a^2w^6 - 3a^4w^2 + 9aw^6)$
$5a^4w^9 - 15a^6w^5 + 45a^3w^9$

8. $2x^2(x - 1) + (x + 1)^2$
$2x^3 - x^2 + 2x + 1$

9. $(v^2 - 6)(v^2 + 4)$
$v^4 - 2v^2 - 24$

10. $(7a + 9y)(2a - y)$
$14a^2 + 11ay - 9y^2$

11. $(y - 8)^2$
$y^2 - 16y + 64$

12. $(x^2 + 5y)^2$
$x^4 + 10x^2y + 25y^2$

13. $(5x + 4w)(5x - 4w)$
$25x^2 - 16w^2$

14. $(2n^4 - 3)(2n^4 + 3)$
$4n^8 - 9$

15. $(x + y)(x^2 - 3xy + 2y^2)$
$x^3 - 2x^2y - xy^2 + 2y^3$

16. $u(u - 6)(u - 3)$
$u^3 - 9u^2 + 18u$

17. $(n - 3)(n + 4)(n - 1)$
$n^3 - 13n + 12$

18. $(a - r)^2(2a - 3r)$
$2a^3 - 7a^2r + 8ar^2 - 3r^3$

19. $(2x + 3y)(4x - 6y + 7z)$
$8x^2 - 14xz - 18y^2 + 21yz$

20. $(3a + 4b)^2$
$9a^2 + 24ab + 16b^2$

Glencoe Division, Macmillan/McGraw-Hill

NAME ______________________ DATE ____________

5-5 Practice Worksheet

Factoring

Factor.

1. $15a^2b - 10ab^2$

2. $2x^3y - x^2y + 5xy^2 + xy^3$

3. $16r^2 - 169$

4. $c^2 - 49$

5. $2y^2 - 242$

6. $x^3 + 8$

7. $8m^3 - 1$

8. $b^4 - 81$

9. $x^2 - 3x - 10$

10. $r^3 + 3r^2 - 54r$

11. $4a^2 + a - 3$

12. $2t^3 + 32t^2 + 128t$

13. $y^2 + 20y + 96$

14. $6n^2 - 11n - 2$

15. $x^2 - 8x + 16$

16. $21 - 7t + 3r - rt$

17. $x^2 + 2x - xy - 2y$

18. $x^2 + 2xy + 2x + y^2 + 2y - 8$

19. $4x^6 - 4x^2$

20. $k^3 - 2k^2r - 3kr^2$

21. $45x^2 - 80y^2$

22. $36a^3b^2 + 66a^2b^3 - 210ab^4$

23. $4a^2 + 12ab + 9b^2 - 25c^2$

24. $81x^4 - 16$

25. $5y^5 + 135y^2$

26. $18p^3 - 51p^2 - 135p$

NAME ______________________ DATE ____________

5-5 Practice Worksheet

Factoring

Factor.

1. $15a^2b - 10ab^2$
$5ab(3a - 2b)$

2. $2x^3y - x^2y + 5xy^2 + xy^3$
$xy(2x^2 - x + 5y + y^2)$

3. $16r^2 - 169$
$(4r + 13)(4r - 13)$

4. $c^2 - 49$
$(c + 7)(c - 7)$

5. $2y^2 - 242$
$2(y + 11)(y - 11)$

6. $x^3 + 8$
$(x + 2)(x^2 - 2x + 4)$

7. $8m^3 - 1$
$(2m - 1)(4m^2 + 2m + 1)$

8. $b^4 - 81$
$(b^2 + 9)(b + 3)(b - 3)$

9. $x^2 - 3x - 10$
$(x - 5)(x + 2)$

10. $r^3 + 3r^2 - 54r$
$r(r + 9)(r - 6)$

11. $4a^2 + a - 3$
$(4a - 3)(a + 1)$

12. $2t^3 + 32t^2 + 128t$
$2t(t + 8)^2$

13. $y^2 + 20y + 96$
$(y + 8)(y + 12)$

14. $6n^2 - 11n - 2$
$(6n + 1)(n - 2)$

15. $x^2 - 8x + 16$
$(x - 4)^2$

16. $21 - 7t + 3r - rt$
$(r + 7)(3 - t)$

17. $x^2 + 2x - xy - 2y$
$(x + 2)(x - y)$

18. $x^2 + 2xy + 2x + y^2 + 2y - 8$
$(x + y + 4)(x + y - 2)$

19. $4x^6 - 4x^2$
$4x^2(x^2 + 1)(x + 1)(x - 1)$

20. $k^3 - 2k^2r - 3kr^2$
$k(k - 3r)(k + r)$

21. $45x^2 - 80y^2$
$5(3x + 4y)(3x - 4y)$

22. $36a^3b^2 + 66a^2b^3 - 210ab^4$
$6ab^2(3a - 5b)(2a + 7b)$

23. $4a^2 + 12ab + 9b^2 - 25c^2$
$(2a + 3b + 5c)(2a + 3b - 5c)$

24. $81x^4 - 16$
$(9x^2 + 4)(3x + 2)(3x - 2)$

25. $5y^5 + 135y^2$
$5y^2(y + 3)(y^2 - 3y + 9)$

26. $18p^3 - 51p^2 - 135p$
$3p(2p - 9)(3p + 5)$

Glencoe Division, Macmillan/McGraw-Hill

NAME ______________________ DATE ____________

5-6

Practice Worksheet

Dividing Polynomials

Simplify.

1. $(-30x^3y + 12x^2y^2 - 18x^2y) \div (-6x^2y)$

2. $(2x^2 + 3x - 4) \div (x - 2)$

3. $(4x^2 - 2x + 6)(2x - 3)^{-1}$

4. $(x^4 - 3x^3 + 5x - 6) \div (x + 2)$

5. $(6x^2 - x - 7) \div (3x + 1)$

6. $(2x^3 + 4x - 6) \div (x + 3)$

7. $(4x^3 - 8x^2 + 3x - 8) \div (2x - 1)$

8. $(x^4 - 2x^3 + 6x^2 - 8x + 10) \div (x + 2)$

NAME ______________________________ DATE ______________

5-6 Practice Worksheet

Dividing Polynomials

Simplify.

1. $(-30x^3y + 12x^2y^2 - 18x^2y) \div (-6x^2y)$

$5x - 2y + 3$

2. $(2x^2 + 3x - 4) \div (x - 2)$

$2x + 7 + \frac{10}{x - 2}$

3. $(4x^2 - 2x + 6)(2x - 3)^{-1}$

$2x + 2 + \frac{12}{2x - 3}$

4. $(x^4 - 3x^3 + 5x - 6) \div (x + 2)$

$x^3 - 5x^2 + 10x - 15 + \frac{24}{x + 2}$

5. $(6x^2 - x - 7) \div (3x + 1)$

$2x - 1 - \frac{6}{3x + 1}$

6. $(2x^3 + 4x - 6) \div (x + 3)$

$2x^2 - 6x + 22 - \frac{72}{x + 3}$

7. $(4x^3 - 8x^2 + 3x - 8) \div (2x - 1)$

$2x^2 - 3x - \frac{8}{2x - 1}$

8. $(x^4 - 2x^3 + 6x^2 - 8x + 10) \div (x + 2)$

$x^3 - 4x^2 + 14x - 36 + \frac{82}{x + 2}$

Glencoe Division, Macmillan/McGraw-Hill

NAME ______________________ DATE ____________

5-7

Practice Worksheet

Synthetic Division

Divide using synthetic division.

1. $(x^2 - 5x + 4) \div (x - 4)$

2. $(2y^3 + 5y + 1) \div (y + 1)$

3. $(2r^3 + 5r^2 - 2r - 15) \div (2r - 3)$

4. $(x^4 - 20) \div (x + 2)$

5. $(2x^3 - 5x^2 + 5x + 4) \div (2x + 1)$

6. $(x^4 - x^3 + x^2 - x + 1) \div (x - 1)$

7. $(x^4 - 2x^3 + 4x^2 + 6x - 8) \div (x - 2)$

8. $(2x^3 - 5x^2 + 6x - 10) \div (2x - 1)$

Glencoe Division, Macmillan/McGraw-Hill

NAME ______________________ DATE ______________

5-7 Practice Worksheet

Synthetic Division

Divide using synthetic division.

1. $(x^2 - 5x + 4) \div (x - 4)$

   $x - 1$

2. $(2y^3 + 5y + 1) \div (y + 1)$

   $2y^2 - 2y + 7 - \frac{6}{y + 1}$

3. $(2r^3 + 5r^2 - 2r - 15) \div (2r - 3)$

   $r^2 + 4r + 5$

4. $(x^4 - 20) \div (x + 2)$

   $x^3 - 2x^2 + 4x - 8 - \frac{4}{x + 2}$

5. $(2x^3 - 5x^2 + 5x + 4) \div (2x + 1)$

   $x^2 - 3x + 4$

6. $(x^4 - x^3 + x^2 - x + 1) \div (x - 1)$

   $x^3 + x + \frac{1}{x - 1}$

7. $(x^4 - 2x^3 + 4x^2 + 6x - 8) \div (x - 2)$

   $x^3 + 4x + 14 + \frac{20}{x - 2}$

8. $(2x^3 - 5x^2 + 6x - 10) \div (2x - 1)$

   $x^2 - 2x + 2 - \frac{8}{2x - 1}$

Glencoe Division, Macmillan/McGraw-Hill

NAME ____________________ DATE ____________

6-1 Practice Worksheet

Roots of Real Numbers

Simplify.

1. $\sqrt[5]{32}$

2. $-\sqrt[4]{256}$

3. $\sqrt{x^2 + 10x + 25}$

4. $\sqrt[6]{(m + 4)^6}$

5. $\sqrt[3]{-64r^6w^{15}}$

6. $\sqrt{49m^2t^8}$

7. $\sqrt[4]{81}$

8. $\sqrt[3]{-64}$

9. $\sqrt{(2x)^8}$

10. $-\sqrt[4]{625}$

11. $\sqrt[3]{216}$

12. $\sqrt{676x^4y^6}$

13. $\sqrt[3]{(2x + 1)^3}$

14. $\sqrt[5]{-32x^5y^{10}}$

15. $-\sqrt{144m^8n^6}$

16. $\sqrt[3]{-27x^9y^{12}}$

17. $\sqrt[5]{243x^{10}}$

18. $-\sqrt{49a^{10}b^{16}}$

19. $\sqrt[4]{(x - 5)^8}$

20. $\sqrt[3]{343d^6}$

21. $\sqrt{0.81}$

22. $-\sqrt{0.0016}$

23. $\sqrt[3]{0.512}$

24. $-\sqrt[4]{0.6561}$

Use a calculator to find each value to three places. Check your approximation by using the power key.

25. $\sqrt{7.8}$

26. $-\sqrt{89}$

27. $\sqrt[3]{25}$

28. $\sqrt[3]{-4}$

Glencoe Division, Macmillan/McGraw-Hill

NAME ______________________ DATE ____________

6-1

Practice Worksheet

Roots of Real Numbers

Simplify.

1. $\sqrt[5]{32}$ 2

2. $-\sqrt[4]{256}$ -4

3. $\sqrt{x^2 + 10x + 25}$ $|x + 5|$

4. $\sqrt[6]{(m + 4)^6}$ $|m + 4|$

5. $\sqrt[3]{-64r^6w^{15}}$ $-4r^2w^5$

6. $\sqrt{49m^2t^8}$ $7|m|t^4$

7. $\sqrt[4]{81}$ -3

8. $\sqrt[3]{-64}$ -4

9. $\sqrt{(2x)^8}$ $16x^4$

10. $-\sqrt[4]{625}$ -5

11. $\sqrt[3]{216}$ 6

12. $\sqrt{676x^4y^6}$ $26x^2|y^3|$

13. $\sqrt[3]{(2x + 1)^3}$ $2x + 1$

14. $\sqrt[5]{-32x^5y^{10}}$ $-2xy^2$

15. $-\sqrt{144m^8n^6}$ $-12m^4|n^3|$

16. $\sqrt[3]{-27x^9y^{12}}$ $-3x^3y^4$

17. $\sqrt[5]{243x^{10}}$ $3x^2$

18. $-\sqrt{49a^{10}b^{16}}$ $-7|a^5|b^8$

19. $\sqrt[4]{(x - 5)^8}$ $(x - 5)^2$

20. $\sqrt[3]{343d^6}$ $7d^2$

21. $\sqrt{0.81}$ 0.9

22. $-\sqrt{0.0016}$ -0.04

23. $\sqrt[3]{0.512}$ 0.8

24. $-\sqrt[4]{0.6561}$ -0.9

Use a calculator to find each value to three places. Check your approximation by using the power key.

25. $\sqrt{7.8}$ 2.793

26. $-\sqrt{89}$ -9.434

27. $\sqrt[3]{25}$ 2.924

28. $\sqrt[3]{-4}$ -1.587

NAME ______________________ DATE ______________

6-2

Practice Worksheet

Products and Quotients of Radicals

Simplify.

1. $\sqrt[3]{-432}$

2. $\sqrt{540}$

3. $\sqrt{5}(\sqrt{10} - \sqrt{45})$

4. $\sqrt[3]{6}(4\sqrt[3]{12} + 5\sqrt[3]{9})$

5. $(2\sqrt[3]{24})(7\sqrt[3]{18})$

6. $\sqrt[4]{32x^4y^5n^{10}}$

7. $\sqrt{1792}$

8. $\sqrt[3]{-6750}$

9. $\sqrt{3x^2y^3} \cdot \sqrt{75xy^5}$

10. $\sqrt[3]{9t^5v^8} \cdot \sqrt[3]{6tv^4}$

11. $\sqrt{60} \cdot \sqrt{105}$

12. $\sqrt[3]{3600} \cdot \sqrt[3]{165}$

13. $\frac{\sqrt{35}}{\sqrt{7}}$

14. $\frac{\sqrt[4]{42}}{\sqrt[4]{7}}$

15. $\sqrt{\frac{3}{5}}$

16. $\sqrt{\frac{6}{w}}$

17. $\sqrt[4]{\frac{5}{27}}$

18. $\sqrt[4]{\frac{8}{9a^3}}$

19. $\frac{\sqrt{20}}{\sqrt{5}}$

20. $\sqrt{\frac{11}{9}}$

21. $\sqrt[3]{\frac{2}{9}}$

22. $\sqrt[3]{\frac{9}{25}}$

23. $\frac{\sqrt[3]{16}}{\sqrt[3]{4}}$

24. $\frac{\sqrt[3]{9}}{\sqrt[3]{4}}$

NAME ______________________ DATE ____________

6-2

Practice Worksheet

Products and Quotients of Radicals

Simplify.

1. $\sqrt[3]{-432}$ $-6\sqrt[3]{2}$

2. $\sqrt{540}$ $6\sqrt{15}$

3. $\sqrt{5}(\sqrt{10} - \sqrt{45})$ $5\sqrt{2} - 15$

4. $\sqrt[3]{6}(4\sqrt[3]{12} + 5\sqrt[3]{9})$ $8\sqrt[3]{9} + 15\sqrt[3]{2}$

5. $(2\sqrt[3]{24})(7\sqrt[3]{18})$ $84\sqrt[3]{2}$

6. $\sqrt[4]{32x^4y^5n^{10}}$ $2|x|yn^2\sqrt[4]{2yn^2}$

7. $\sqrt{1792}$ $16\sqrt{7}$

8. $\sqrt[3]{-6750}$ $-15\sqrt[3]{2}$

9. $\sqrt{3x^2y^3} \cdot \sqrt{75xy^5}$ $15|x|y^4\sqrt{x}$

10. $\sqrt[3]{9t^5v^8} \cdot \sqrt[3]{6tv^4}$ $3t^2v^4\sqrt[3]{2}$

11. $\sqrt{60} \cdot \sqrt{105}$ $30\sqrt{7}$

12. $\sqrt[3]{3600} \cdot \sqrt[3]{165}$ $30\sqrt[3]{22}$

13. $\frac{\sqrt{35}}{\sqrt{7}}$ $\sqrt{5}$

14. $\frac{\sqrt[4]{42}}{\sqrt[4]{7}}$ $\sqrt[4]{6}$

15. $\sqrt{\frac{3}{5}}$ $\frac{\sqrt{15}}{5}$

16. $\sqrt{\frac{6}{w}}$ $\frac{\sqrt{6w}}{w}$

17. $\sqrt[4]{\frac{5}{27}}$ $\frac{\sqrt[4]{15}}{3}$

18. $\sqrt[4]{\frac{8}{9a^3}}$ $\frac{\sqrt[4]{72a}}{3a}$

19. $\frac{\sqrt{20}}{\sqrt{5}}$ 2

20. $\sqrt{\frac{11}{9}}$ $\frac{\sqrt{11}}{3}$

21. $\sqrt[3]{\frac{2}{9}}$ $\frac{\sqrt[3]{6}}{3}$

22. $\sqrt[3]{\frac{9}{25}}$ $\frac{\sqrt[3]{45}}{5}$

23. $\frac{\sqrt[3]{16}}{\sqrt[3]{4}}$ $\sqrt[3]{4}$

24. $\frac{\sqrt[3]{9}}{\sqrt[3]{4}}$ $\frac{\sqrt[3]{18}}{2}$

NAME ______________________ DATE ____________

6-3

Practice Worksheet

Computing with Radicals

Simplify.

1. $4\sqrt{24} + \sqrt{18} - 5\sqrt{54} - 4\sqrt{450}$

2. $\sqrt{45} - (\sqrt{5})^2 + \sqrt{180}$

3. $\sqrt[3]{56} + \sqrt[3]{24} - \sqrt{28}$

4. $9\sqrt[4]{5} - \sqrt[4]{5} + 11\sqrt[4]{5}$

5. $\sqrt[4]{x^8} + 2\sqrt[3]{x^6} - \sqrt{x^2} + \sqrt[3]{x^3}$

6. $\sqrt{75v^5t^3} - \sqrt{48v^3t^7}$

7. $(6 - \sqrt{3})^2$

8. $(4\sqrt{7} + 5\sqrt{2})(2\sqrt{7} - 3\sqrt{2})$

9. $(x^2 + \sqrt[3]{a^2})(x^4 - \sqrt[3]{a^2}\, x^2 + \sqrt[3]{a^4})$

10. $(6 - \sqrt[3]{4})(\sqrt[3]{32} + \sqrt[3]{16})$

11. $2\sqrt{48} - \sqrt{12} - 3\sqrt{63} + \sqrt{112}$

12. $\sqrt[3]{108} + 2\sqrt[3]{32} + 2\sqrt[3]{500} - 2\sqrt[3]{4}$

13. $\sqrt{810} + \sqrt{240} + \sqrt{135} - \sqrt{250}$

14. $\sqrt[3]{216} - \sqrt[3]{48} + \sqrt[3]{432}$

15. $(\sqrt{12} - 2\sqrt{3})^2$

16. $(\sqrt{18} + 2\sqrt{3})^2$

17. $(\sqrt{5} - \sqrt{6})(\sqrt{5} + \sqrt{2})$

18. $(\sqrt{50} + \sqrt{27})(\sqrt{2} - \sqrt{6})$

19. $\frac{3}{2 - \sqrt{5}}$

20. $\frac{6}{\sqrt{2} - 1}$

21. $\frac{5 + \sqrt{3}}{4 + \sqrt{3}}$

22. $\frac{6}{2 - \sqrt{7}}$

23. $\sqrt[3]{144} + \sqrt[3]{\frac{2}{3}} - 5\sqrt[3]{18}$

24. $\sqrt{\frac{3}{8}} + \sqrt{54} - \sqrt{6}$

Glencoe Division, Macmillan/McGraw-Hill

NAME ______________________ DATE ____________

6-3 Practice Worksheet

Computing with Radicals

Simplify.

1. $4\sqrt{24} + \sqrt{18} - 5\sqrt{54} - 4\sqrt{450}$
   $-7\sqrt{6} - 57\sqrt{2}$

2. $\sqrt{45} - (\sqrt{5})^2 + \sqrt{180}$
   $9\sqrt{5} - 5$

3. $\sqrt[3]{56} + \sqrt[3]{24} - \sqrt{28}$
   $2\sqrt[3]{7} + 2\sqrt[3]{3} - 2\sqrt{7}$

4. $9\sqrt[4]{5} - \sqrt[4]{5} + 11\sqrt[4]{5}$
   $19\sqrt[4]{5}$

5. $\sqrt[4]{x^8} + 2\sqrt[3]{x^6} - \sqrt{x^2} + \sqrt[3]{x^3}$
   $3x^2 - |x| + x$

6. $\sqrt{75v^5t^3} - \sqrt{48v^3t^7}$
   $(5v^2t - 4vt^3)\sqrt{3vt}$

7. $(6 - \sqrt{3})^2$
   $39 - 12\sqrt{3}$

8. $(4\sqrt{7} + 5\sqrt{2})(2\sqrt{7} - 3\sqrt{2})$
   $26 - 2\sqrt{14}$

9. $(x^2 + \sqrt[3]{a^2})(x^4 - \sqrt[3]{a^2}\, x^2 + \sqrt[3]{a^4})$
   $x^6 + a^2$

10. $(6 - \sqrt[3]{4})(\sqrt[3]{32} + \sqrt[3]{16})$
    $8\sqrt[3]{2} + 12\sqrt[3]{4} - 4$

11. $2\sqrt{48} - \sqrt{12} - 3\sqrt{63} + \sqrt{112}$
    $6\sqrt{3} - 5\sqrt{7}$

12. $\sqrt[3]{108} + 2\sqrt[3]{32} + 2\sqrt[3]{500} - 2\sqrt[3]{4}$
    $15\sqrt[3]{4}$

13. $\sqrt{810} + \sqrt{240} + \sqrt{135} - \sqrt{250}$
    $4\sqrt{10} + 7\sqrt{15}$

14. $\sqrt[3]{216} - \sqrt[3]{48} + \sqrt[3]{432}$
    $6 - 2\sqrt[3]{6} + 6\sqrt[3]{2}$

15. $(\sqrt{12} - 2\sqrt{3})^2$ 0

16. $(\sqrt{18} + 2\sqrt{3})^2$ $30 + 12\sqrt{6}$

17. $(\sqrt{5} - \sqrt{6})(\sqrt{5} + \sqrt{2})$
    $5 + \sqrt{10} - \sqrt{30} - 2\sqrt{3}$

18. $(\sqrt{50} + \sqrt{27})(\sqrt{2} - \sqrt{6})$
    $10 - 10\sqrt{3} + 3\sqrt{6} - 9\sqrt{2}$

19. $\frac{3}{2 - \sqrt{5}}$ $-6 - 3\sqrt{5}$

20. $\frac{6}{\sqrt{2} - 1}$ $6\sqrt{2} + 6$

21. $\frac{5 + \sqrt{3}}{4 + \sqrt{3}}$ $\frac{17 - \sqrt{3}}{13}$

22. $\frac{6}{2 - \sqrt{7}}$ $-4 - 2\sqrt{7}$

23. $\sqrt[3]{144} + \sqrt[3]{\frac{2}{3}} - 5\sqrt[3]{18}$ $-\frac{8}{3}\sqrt[3]{18}$

24. $\sqrt{\frac{3}{8}} + \sqrt{54} - \sqrt{6}$ $\frac{9}{4}\sqrt{6}$

Glencoe Division, Macmillan/McGraw-Hill

NAME ____________________ DATE ____________

6-4 Practice Worksheet

Rational Exponents

Express using rational exponents.

1. $\sqrt[3]{26}$

2. $\sqrt[5]{8}$

3. $\sqrt{36x^5y^6}$

4. $\sqrt[7]{y^3}$

5. $\sqrt[10]{x^6}$

6. $\sqrt[3]{28x^2y^3t^{11}}$

7. $3\sqrt[4]{27n^{10}w}$

8. $2\sqrt[4]{2z^{\frac{1}{2}}n^{1.2}}$

9. $4\sqrt{2a^{10}b^3}$

10. $\sqrt[3]{27m^6n^4}$

Express in simplest radical form.

11. $x^{\frac{3}{5}}$

12. $27^{\frac{1}{6}}$

13. $2^{\frac{5}{7}}a^{\frac{3}{7}}y^{\frac{9}{7}}$

14. $(3w)^{\frac{2}{3}}m^{\frac{7}{3}}$

15. $a^{\frac{2}{3}}g^{\frac{1}{4}}e^{\frac{1}{2}}$

16. $w^{\frac{3}{7}}n^{\frac{5}{3}}$

17. $\sqrt[6]{36}$

18. $\sqrt[10]{81}$

19. $m^{\frac{1}{3}}v^{\frac{3}{4}}z^{\frac{5}{6}}$

20. $27^{\frac{1}{2}}b^{\frac{2}{3}}c^{\frac{7}{6}}$

Evaluate each expression using a calculator.

21. $32^{\frac{2}{5}}$

22. $(25^{\frac{2}{3}})^{\frac{3}{4}}$

23. $(0.216)^{\frac{1}{3}}$

24. $\left(\frac{27}{125}\right)^{\frac{2}{3}}$

25. $\sqrt[4]{2401}$

26. $36^{2.5}$

Glencoe Division, Macmillan/McGraw-Hill

NAME ______________________ DATE ____________

6-4 Practice Worksheet

Rational Exponents

Express using rational exponents.

1. $\sqrt[3]{26}$ $26^{\frac{1}{2}}$

2. $\sqrt[5]{8}$ $8^{\frac{1}{5}}$ or $2^{\frac{3}{5}}$

3. $\sqrt{36x^5y^6}$ $6x^{\frac{5}{2}}y^3$ or $36^{\frac{1}{2}}x^{\frac{5}{2}}y^3$

4. $\sqrt[7]{y^3}$ $y^{\frac{3}{7}}$

5. $\sqrt[10]{x^6}$ $x^{\frac{3}{5}}$

6. $\sqrt[3]{28x^2y^3t^{11}}$ $28^{\frac{1}{3}}x^{\frac{2}{3}}yt^{\frac{11}{3}}$

7. $3\sqrt[4]{27n^{10}w}$ $3^{\frac{7}{4}}n^{\frac{5}{2}}w^{\frac{1}{4}}$ or $3 \cdot 27^{\frac{1}{4}}n^{\frac{5}{2}}w^{\frac{1}{4}}$

8. $2\sqrt[4]{2z^{\frac{1}{2}}n^{1.2}}$ $2^{\frac{5}{4}}z^{\frac{1}{8}}n^{0.3}$

9. $4\sqrt{2a^{10}b^3}$ $2^{\frac{5}{2}}a^5b^{\frac{3}{2}}$ or $4 \cdot 2^{\frac{1}{2}}a^5b^{\frac{3}{10}}$

10. $\sqrt[3]{27m^6n^4}$ $3m^2n^{\frac{4}{3}}$

Express in simplest radical form.

11. $x^{\frac{3}{5}}$ $\sqrt[5]{x^3}$

12. $27^{\frac{1}{6}}$ $\sqrt{3}$

13. $2^{\frac{5}{7}}a^{\frac{3}{7}}y^{\frac{9}{7}}$ $y\sqrt[7]{32a^3y^2}$

14. $(3w)^{\frac{2}{3}}m^{\frac{7}{3}}$ $m^2\sqrt[3]{9w^2m}$

15. $a^{\frac{2}{3}}g^{\frac{1}{4}}e^{\frac{1}{2}}$ $\sqrt[12]{a^8g^3e^6}$

16. $w^{\frac{3}{7}}n^{\frac{5}{3}}$ $n\sqrt[21]{w^9n^{14}}$

17. $\sqrt[6]{36}$ $\sqrt[3]{6}$

18. $\sqrt[10]{81}$ $\sqrt[5]{9}$

19. $m^{\frac{1}{3}}v^{\frac{3}{4}}z^{\frac{5}{6}}$ $\sqrt[12]{m^4v^9z^{10}}$

20. $27^{\frac{1}{2}}b^{\frac{2}{3}}c^{\frac{7}{6}}$ $3c\sqrt[6]{27b^4c}$

Evaluate each expression using a calculator.

21. $32^{\frac{2}{5}}$ 4

22. $(25^{\frac{2}{3}})^{\frac{3}{4}}$ 5

23. $(0.216)^{\frac{1}{3}}$ 0.6

24. $\left(\frac{27}{125}\right)^{\frac{2}{3}}$ 0.36

25. $\sqrt[4]{2401}$ 7

26. $36^{2.5}$ 7776

Glencoe Division, Macmillan/McGraw-Hill

6-5 NAME ____________________ DATE ____________

Practice Worksheet

Problem Solving Strategy: Identify Subgoals

Solve. Use any strategy.

1. How many factors of 10,000 are perfect squares?

2. Find the sum of $\frac{2}{3^1} + \frac{2}{3^2} + \frac{2}{3^3} + \ldots + \frac{2}{3^{10}}$.

3. Recall that the proper divisors of a number are the factors of the number that are less than the number. What is the least natural number that has eight proper factors?

4. Find the sum of the whole numbers from 1 through 300 that are not multiples of 5 or 6.

5. If the area of a 5 cm by 5 cm square is increased by 144 cm^2, what are the dimensions of the new square?

Glencoe Division, Macmillan/McGraw-Hill

NAME ____________________ DATE __________

6-5 Practice Worksheet

Problem Solving Strategy: Identify Subgoals

Solve. Use any strategy.

1. How many factors of 10,000 are perfect squares? **9**

2. Find the sum of $\frac{2}{3^1} + \frac{2}{3^2} + \frac{2}{3^3} + \ldots + \frac{2}{3^{10}}$. $\frac{59{,}048}{59{,}049}$

3. Recall that the proper divisors of a number are the factors of the number that are less than the number. What is the least natural number that has eight proper factors? **36**

4. Find the sum of the whole numbers from 1 through 300 that are not multiples of 5 or 6. **30,000**

5. If the area of a 5 cm by 5 cm square is increased by 144 cm^2, what are the dimensions of the new square? **13 cm by 13 cm**

Glencoe Division, Macmillan/McGraw-Hill

NAME ______________________ DATE ____________

6-6 Practice Worksheet

Simplifying Expressions with Rational Exponents

Simplify.

1. $y^{-\frac{1}{2}}$

2. $b^{-\frac{3}{5}}$

3. $v^{-\frac{4}{9}}$

4. $t^{-\frac{3}{2}}$

5. $\frac{1}{w^{\frac{4}{5}}}$

6. $\frac{1}{b^{\frac{4}{7}}}$

7. $\frac{2}{4^{\frac{2}{3}}}$

8. $\frac{3}{6^{\frac{1}{2}}}$

9. $\frac{14}{7^{\frac{2}{3}}}$

10. $\frac{12}{3^{\frac{5}{2}}}$

11. $x^{-\frac{3}{5}}$

12. $\frac{r^2t^3}{\sqrt[4]{a^3}}$

13. $\frac{m^{\frac{7}{4}} + 3m^{-\frac{1}{4}}}{m^{\frac{3}{4}}}$

14. $\frac{7y^{\frac{4}{5}} + y^{\frac{6}{5}}}{y^{-\frac{1}{5}}}$

15. $(w^{-\frac{3}{8}})^{-\frac{4}{9}}$

16. $(\sqrt[8]{11}\, x^{\frac{3}{4}}y^{-\frac{1}{2}})^4$

17. $\frac{x^{\frac{3}{2}}}{x^{\frac{1}{2}} + y^{\frac{1}{2}}}$

18. $\frac{2 - n^{\frac{1}{2}}}{6 - n^{\frac{1}{2}}}$

19. $\frac{r^{-\frac{3}{4}}y^{-\frac{3}{2}}}{\sqrt{y}\, r^{-\frac{1}{2}}}$

20. $\left(\frac{n^{-\frac{4}{5}}}{x^{-10}n^{\frac{2}{5}}}\right)^{-5}$

NAME ______ DATE ______

6-6

Practice Worksheet

Simplifying Expressions with Rational Exponents

Simplify.

1. $y^{-\frac{1}{2}}$ $\frac{y^{\frac{1}{2}}}{y}$

2. $b^{-\frac{3}{5}}$ $\frac{b^{\frac{2}{5}}}{b}$

3. $v^{-\frac{4}{9}}$ $\frac{v^{\frac{5}{9}}}{v}$

4. $t^{-\frac{3}{2}}$ $\frac{t^{\frac{1}{2}}}{t^2}$

5. $\frac{1}{w^{\frac{4}{5}}}$ $\frac{w^{\frac{1}{5}}}{w}$

6. $\frac{1}{b^{\frac{4}{7}}}$ $\frac{b^{\frac{3}{7}}}{b}$

7. $\frac{2}{4^{\frac{2}{3}}}$ $\frac{4^{\frac{1}{3}}}{2}$ or $\frac{2^{\frac{2}{3}}}{2}$

8. $\frac{3}{6^{\frac{1}{2}}}$ $\frac{6^{\frac{1}{2}}}{2}$

9. $\frac{14}{7^{\frac{2}{3}}}$ $2 \cdot 7^{\frac{1}{3}}$

10. $\frac{12}{3^{\frac{5}{2}}}$ $\frac{4 \cdot 3^{\frac{1}{2}}}{9}$

11. $x^{-\frac{3}{5}}$ $\frac{x^{\frac{2}{5}}}{x}$

12. $\frac{r^2t^3}{\sqrt[4]{a^3}}$ $\frac{r^2t^3a^{\frac{1}{4}}}{a}$

13. $\frac{m^{\frac{7}{4}} + 3m^{-\frac{1}{4}}}{m^{\frac{3}{4}}}$ $\frac{m^2 + 3}{m}$

14. $\frac{7y^{\frac{4}{5}} + y^{\frac{6}{5}}}{y^{-\frac{1}{5}}}$ $7y + y^{\frac{7}{5}}$

15. $(w^{-\frac{3}{8}})^{-\frac{4}{9}}$ $w^{\frac{1}{6}}$

16. $(\sqrt[8]{11}\, x^{\frac{3}{4}}y^{-\frac{1}{2}})^4$ $\frac{\sqrt{11}\, x^3}{y^2}$

17. $\frac{x^{\frac{3}{2}}}{x^{\frac{1}{2}} + y^{\frac{1}{2}}}$ $\frac{x^2 - x^{\frac{3}{2}}y^{\frac{1}{2}}}{x - y}$

18. $\frac{2 - n^{\frac{1}{2}}}{6 - n^{\frac{1}{2}}}$ $\frac{12 - 4n^{\frac{1}{2}} - n}{36 - n}$

19. $\frac{r^{-\frac{3}{4}}y^{-\frac{3}{2}}}{\sqrt{y}\, r^{-\frac{1}{2}}}$ $\frac{r^{\frac{3}{4}}}{y^2 r}$

20. $\left(\frac{n^{-\frac{4}{5}}}{x^{-10}n^{\frac{2}{5}}}\right)^{-5}$ $\frac{n^6}{x^{50}}$

6-7

NAME ________________ DATE ________

Practice Worksheet

Solving Equations Containing Radicals

Solve each equation.

1. $7x\sqrt{3} - 5 = 0$

2. $4x - x\sqrt{3} = 6$

3. $18 - 3x = x\sqrt{2}$

4. $\sqrt{x + 8} - 5 = 0$

5. $\sqrt[3]{y - 7} = 4$

6. $\sqrt[4]{3x} - 2 = 0$

7. $\sqrt{8n - 5} - 1 = 2$

8. $\sqrt{1 - 4t} - 8 = -6$

9. $\sqrt[4]{7v - 2} + 12 = 7$

10. $\sqrt[3]{6u - 5} + 2 = -3$

11. $\sqrt{6x - 4} = \sqrt{2x + 10}$

12. $\sqrt{9u - 4} = \sqrt{7u - 20}$

13. $\sqrt{k + 9} - \sqrt{k} = \sqrt{3}$

14. $\sqrt{x + 10} + \sqrt{x - 6} = 8$

15. $\sqrt{x + 2} - 7 = \sqrt{x + 9}$

16. $\sqrt{4x^2 - 3x + 2} - 2x - 5 = 0$

Glencoe Division, Macmillan/McGraw-Hill

NAME ______________________ DATE ____________

6-7

Practice Worksheet

Solving Equations Containing Radicals

Solve each equation.

1. $7x\sqrt{3} - 5 = 0$

$\frac{5\sqrt{3}}{21}$

2. $4x - x\sqrt{3} = 6$

$\frac{24 + 6\sqrt{3}}{13}$

3. $18 - 3x = x\sqrt{2}$

$\frac{54 - 18\sqrt{2}}{7}$

4. $\sqrt{x + 8} - 5 = 0$

17

5. $\sqrt[3]{y - 7} = 4$

71

6. $\sqrt[4]{3x} - 2 = 0$

$\frac{16}{3}$

7. $\sqrt{8n - 5} - 1 = 2$

$\frac{7}{4}$

8. $\sqrt{1 - 4t} - 8 = -6$

$-\frac{3}{4}$

9. $\sqrt[4]{7v - 2} + 12 = 7$

no real solution

10. $\sqrt[3]{6u - 5} + 2 = -3$

-20

11. $\sqrt{6x - 4} = \sqrt{2x + 10}$

$\frac{7}{2}$

12. $\sqrt{9u - 4} = \sqrt{7u - 20}$

no real solution

13. $\sqrt{k + 9} - \sqrt{k} = \sqrt{3}$

3

14. $\sqrt{x + 10} + \sqrt{x - 6} = 8$

15

15. $\sqrt{x + 2} - 7 = \sqrt{x + 9}$

no real solution

16. $\sqrt{4x^2 - 3x + 2} - 2x - 5 = 0$

-1

NAME ______________________ DATE ____________

6-8

Practice Worksheet

Imaginary Numbers

Simplify.

1. $\sqrt{-49}$
2. $\sqrt{-48}$
3. $6\sqrt{-12}$
4. $\sqrt{\frac{-16}{25}}$
5. $\sqrt{\frac{-2}{7}}$
6. $\sqrt{\frac{-8}{3}}$
7. i^{42}
8. i^{91}
9. i^{101}
10. i^{76}
11. $\sqrt{-8} \cdot \sqrt{-18}$
12. $\sqrt{-42} \cdot \sqrt{-6}$
13. $(5\sqrt{-6})(3\sqrt{-10})$
14. $(2\sqrt{-3})(-5\sqrt{-27})$
15. $(\sqrt{-7})^4$
16. $(\sqrt{-5})^3$
17. $3i(4i)^2$
18. $(-5i)^2(6i)$

Solve each equation.

19. $n^2 + 25 = 0$
20. $m^2 + 10 = 0$
21. $6y^2 + 42 = 0$
22. $4r^2 + 64 = 0$
23. $v^2 = -81$
24. $5x^2 = -125$

NAME ____________________ DATE __________

6-8

Practice Worksheet

Imaginary Numbers

Simplify.

1. $\sqrt{-49}$ $7i$
2. $\sqrt{-48}$ $4\sqrt{3}i$
3. $6\sqrt{-12}$ $12\sqrt{3}i$
4. $\sqrt{\frac{-16}{25}}$ $\frac{4}{5}i$
5. $\sqrt{\frac{-2}{7}}$ $\frac{\sqrt{14}}{7}i$
6. $\sqrt{\frac{-8}{3}}$ $\frac{2\sqrt{6}}{3}i$
7. i^{42} -1
8. i^{91} $-i$
9. i^{101} i
10. i^{76} 1
11. $\sqrt{-8} \cdot \sqrt{-18}$ -12
12. $\sqrt{-42} \cdot \sqrt{-6}$ $-6\sqrt{7}$
13. $(5\sqrt{-6})(3\sqrt{-10})$ $-30\sqrt{15}$
14. $(2\sqrt{-3})(-5\sqrt{-27})$ 90
15. $(\sqrt{-7})^4$ 49
16. $(\sqrt{-5})^3$ $-5\sqrt{5}i$
17. $3i(4i)^2$ $-48i$
18. $(-5i)^2(6i)$ $-150i$

Solve each equation.

19. $n^2 + 25 = 0$ $\pm 5i$
20. $m^2 + 10 = 0$ $\pm\sqrt{10}i$
21. $6y^2 + 42 = 0$ $\pm\sqrt{7}i$
22. $4r^2 + 64 = 0$ $\pm 4i$
23. $v^2 = -81$ $\pm 9i$
24. $5x^2 = -125$ $\pm 5i$

Glencoe Division, Macmillan/McGraw-Hill

6-9 NAME ______________________ DATE __________

Practice Worksheet

Complex Numbers

Simplify.

1. $(7 - 6i) + (9 + 11i)$

2. $(5 + \sqrt{-8}) + (-13 + 4\sqrt{-2})$

3. $(-5 + 2i\sqrt{7}) - (2 - 7i\sqrt{7})$

4. $(-3 - 10i) - (-5 - 4i)$

5. $-6(2 - 8i) + 3(5 + 7i)$

6. $4(7 - i) - 5(2 - 6i)$

7. $(3 + 5i)(4 - i)$

8. $(4 - 2i\sqrt{3})(1 + 5i\sqrt{3})$

9. $(3 - 4i)^2$

10. $(\sqrt{5} + 2i)^2$

11. $(6 - 4i)(6 + 4i)$

12. $(8 - \sqrt{-11})(8 + \sqrt{-11})$

13. $5(2 + 3i) + 6(8 - 5i)$

14. $7(2 + 6i) - 9(-3 + 4i)$

15. $(3 - i)(1 + 2i)(2 + 3i)$

16. $(4 + 3i)(2 - 5i)(4 - 3i)$

Find the values of x and y for which each equation is true.

17. $3x - 5yi = 15 - 20i$

18. $\sqrt{3}\,x + 7yi = 6 - 2i$

19. $(x - y) + (2x + y)i = -3 + 9i$

20. $(2x - y) + (x + y)i = -4 - 5i$

NAME ____________________ DATE ____________

6-9 Practice Worksheet

Complex Numbers

Simplify.

1. $(7 - 6i) + (9 + 11i)$
   $16 + 5i$

2. $(5 + \sqrt{-8}) + (-13 + 4\sqrt{-2})$
   $-8 + 6\sqrt{2}\, i$

3. $(-5 + 2i\sqrt{7}) - (2 - 7i\sqrt{7})$
   $-7 + 9i\sqrt{7}$

4. $(-3 - 10i) - (-5 - 4i)$
   $2 - 6i$

5. $-6(2 - 8i) + 3(5 + 7i)$
   $3 + 69i$

6. $4(7 - i) - 5(2 - 6i)$
   $18 + 26i$

7. $(3 + 5i)(4 - i)$
   $17 + 17i$

8. $(4 - 2i\sqrt{3})(1 + 5i\sqrt{3})$
   $34 + 18i\sqrt{3}$

9. $(3 - 4i)^2$
   $-7 - 24i$

10. $(\sqrt{5} + 2i)^2$
    $1 + 4i\sqrt{5}$

11. $(6 - 4i)(6 + 4i)$
    52

12. $(8 - \sqrt{-11})(8 + \sqrt{-11})$
    75

13. $5(2 + 3i) + 6(8 - 5i)$
    $58 - 15i$

14. $7(2 + 6i) - 9(-3 + 4i)$
    $41 + 6i$

15. $(3 - i)(1 + 2i)(2 + 3i)$
    $-5 + 25i$

16. $(4 + 3i)(2 - 5i)(4 - 3i)$
    $50 - 150i$

Find the values of x and y for which each equation is true.

17. $3x - 5yi = 15 - 20i$
    $x = 5$
    $y = 4$

18. $\sqrt{3}\, x + 7yi = 6 - 2i$
    $x = 2\sqrt{3}$
    $y = -\frac{2}{7}$

19. $(x - y) + (2x + y)i = -3 + 9i$
    $x = 2$ $y = 5$

20. $(2x - y) + (x + y)i = -4 - 5i$
    $x = -3$ $y = -2$

Glencoe Division, Macmillan/McGraw-Hill

NAME ________________________ DATE ____________

6-10 Practice Worksheet

Simplifying Expressions Containing Complex Numbers

Simplify.

1. $\frac{2 - 4i}{1 + 3i}$

2. $\frac{3 - i}{2 - i}$

3. $\frac{6 + 5i}{-2i}$

4. $\frac{1 + 6i}{5i}$

5. $\frac{3 - 6i}{-4i}$

6. $\frac{2 + 7i}{-5i}$

7. $\frac{3}{6 + 4i}$

8. $\frac{2}{7 - 8i}$

9. $\frac{3}{\sqrt{2} - 5i}$

10. $\frac{2 + i\sqrt{3}}{1 + i\sqrt{3}}$

11. $\frac{(1 - 2i)^2}{(2 - i)^2}$

12. $\frac{2 + i}{(1 - i)^2}$

13. $\frac{3}{\sqrt{5} + 2i}$

14. $\frac{2 - i}{\sqrt{2} + 2i}$

15. $\frac{(1 + 3i)^2}{(4 - i)^2}$

16. $\frac{2 - i\sqrt{3}}{1 + i\sqrt{3}}$

Find the multiplicative inverse of each complex number.

17. $5 + 2i$

18. $3 - i$

19. $\frac{i}{7 + 4i}$

20. $\frac{-6i}{4 - 5i}$

NAME ____________________ DATE ____________

6-10 Practice Worksheet

Simplifying Expressions Containing Complex Numbers

Simplify.

1. $\frac{2 - 4i}{1 + 3i}$ $-1 - i$

2. $\frac{3 - i}{2 - i}$ $\frac{7 + i}{5}$

3. $\frac{6 + 5i}{-2i}$ $\frac{-5 + 6i}{2}$

4. $\frac{1 + 6i}{5i}$ $\frac{6 - i}{5}$

5. $\frac{3 - 6i}{-4i}$ $\frac{6 + 3i}{4}$

6. $\frac{2 + 7i}{-5i}$ $\frac{-7 + 2i}{5}$

7. $\frac{3}{6 + 4i}$ $\frac{9 - 6i}{26}$

8. $\frac{2}{7 - 8i}$ $\frac{14 + 16i}{113}$

9. $\frac{3}{\sqrt{2} - 5i}$ $\frac{\sqrt{2} + 5i}{9}$

10. $\frac{2 + i\sqrt{3}}{1 + i\sqrt{3}}$ $\frac{5 - i\sqrt{3}}{4}$

11. $\frac{(1 - 2i)^2}{(2 - i)^2}$ $\frac{7 - 24i}{25}$

12. $\frac{2 + i}{(1 - i)^2}$ $\frac{-1 + 2i}{2}$

13. $\frac{3}{\sqrt{5} + 2i}$ $\frac{\sqrt{5} - 2i}{3}$

14. $\frac{2 - i}{\sqrt{2} + 2i}$ $\frac{-2 + 2\sqrt{2} - (4 + \sqrt{2})i}{6}$

15. $\frac{(1 + 3i)^2}{(4 - i)^2}$ $\frac{-168 + 26i}{289}$

16. $\frac{2 - i\sqrt{3}}{1 + i\sqrt{3}}$ $\frac{-1 - 3i\sqrt{3}}{4}$

Find the multiplicative inverse of each complex number.

17. $5 + 2i$ $\frac{5 - 2i}{29}$

18. $3 - i$ $\frac{3 + i}{10}$

19. $\frac{i}{7 + 4i}$ $4 - 7i$

20. $\frac{-6i}{4 - 5i}$ $\frac{5 + 4i}{6}$

NAME ______________________ DATE ______________

7-1

Practice Worksheet

Problem Solving Strategy: Guess and Check

Solve. Use any strategy.

1. At a cattle pen at the county fair, Jody counted 65 heads and 236 legs. How many cattle and how many workers were there in the pen at that time?

2. Replace each letter with a whole number so that the addition problem at the right is correct. Each letter represents a different number. (There are four possible answers.)

$$\begin{array}{cccc} A & B & C & D \\ D & C & B & A \\ \hline 5 & 5 & 5 & 5 \end{array}$$

3. In a tennis tournament, each player had to play each other player exactly once. If 253 matches were scheduled, how many players were in the tournament?

4. Find the least prime number greater than 840.

Glencoe Division, Macmillan/McGraw-Hill

NAME ______________________ DATE ____________

7-1

Practice Worksheet

Problem Solving Strategy: Guess and Check

Solve. Use any strategy.

1. At a cattle pen at the county fair, Jody counted 65 heads and 236 legs. How many cattle and how many workers were there in the pen at that time?
   53 cattle, 12 workers

2. Replace each letter with a whole number so that the addition problem at the right is correct. Each letter represents a different number. (There are four possible answers.)

$$\begin{array}{cccc} A & B & C & D \\ D & C & B & A \\ \hline 5 & 5 & 5 & 5 \end{array}$$

   A = 1, B = 2, C = 3, D = 4; A = 1, B = 3, C = 2, D = 4;
   A = 2, B = 4, C = 1, D = 3; A = 2, B = 1, C = 4, D = 3

3. In a tennis tournament, each player had to play each other player exactly once. If 253 matches were scheduled, how many players were in the tournament?
   23

4. Find the least prime number greater than 840.
   853

NAME ______________________ DATE ____________

7-2 Practice Worksheet

Solving Quadratic Equations

Solve each equation by factoring.

1. $x^2 - 4x - 12 = 0$

2. $y^2 - 16y + 64 = 0$

3. $n^2 + 25 = 10n$

4. $9z = 10z^2$

5. $7y^2 = 4y$

6. $c^2 = 2c + 99$

7. $5w^2 - 35w + 60 = 0$

8. $3d^2 + 24d + 45 = 0$

9. $15v^2 + 19v + 6 = 0$

10. $4j^2 + 6 = 11j$

11. $36k^2 = 25$

12. $12m^3 - 8m^2 = 15m$

13. $6e^3 = 5e^2 + 6e$

14. $9 = 64p^2$

Solve each equation by graphing.

15. $x^2 + 2x = 0$

16. $x^2 + x = 6$

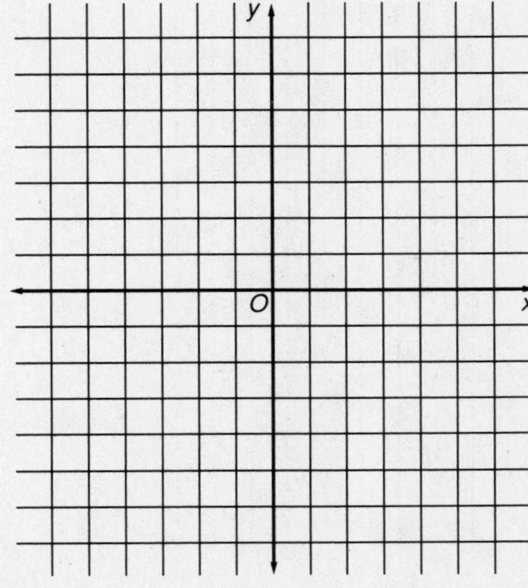

NAME ______________________ DATE ______________

7-2

Practice Worksheet

Solving Quadratic Equations

Solve each equation by factoring.

1. $x^2 - 4x - 12 = 0$ **6, −2**

2. $y^2 - 16y + 64 = 0$ **8**

3. $n^2 + 25 = 10n$ **5**

4. $9z = 10z^2$ **$0, \frac{9}{10}$**

5. $7y^2 = 4y$ **$0, \frac{4}{7}$**

6. $c^2 = 2c + 99$ **−9, 11**

7. $5w^2 - 35w + 60 = 0$ **3, 4**

8. $3d^2 + 24d + 45 = 0$ **−5, −3**

9. $15v^2 + 19v + 6 = 0$ **$-\frac{3}{5}, -\frac{2}{3}$**

10. $4j^2 + 6 = 11j$ **$\frac{3}{4}, 2$**

11. $36k^2 = 25$ **$\frac{5}{6}, -\frac{5}{6}$**

12. $12m^3 - 8m^2 = 15m$ **$0, -\frac{5}{6}, \frac{3}{2}$**

13. $6e^3 = 5e^2 + 6e$ **$0, \frac{3}{2}, -\frac{2}{3}$**

14. $9 = 64p^2$ **$\frac{3}{8}, -\frac{3}{8}$**

Solve each equation by graphing.

15. $x^2 + 2x = 0$ **−2, 0**

16. $x^2 + x = 6$ **−3, 2**

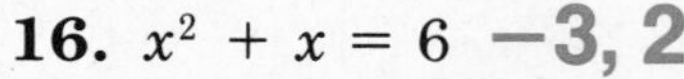

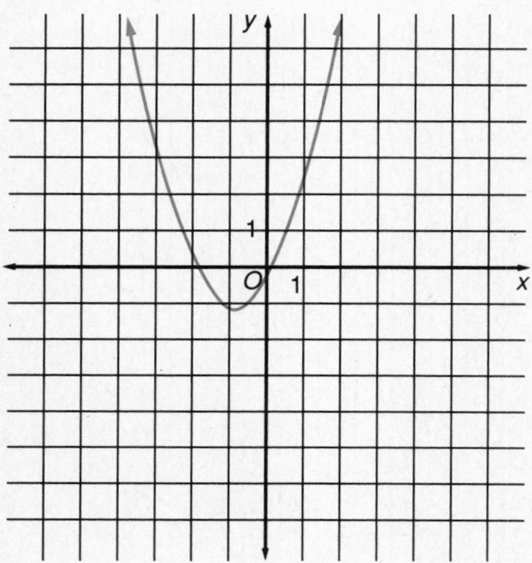

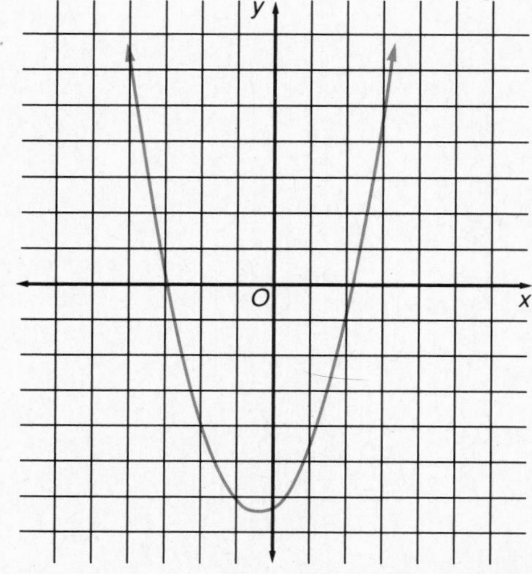

NAME ______________________ DATE ______________

7-3

Practice Worksheet

Completing the Square

Find the value of c that makes each trinomial a perfect square.

1. $a^2 + 12a + c$

2. $h^2 - 20h + c$

3. $p^2 - p + c$

4. $m^2 + 11m + c$

5. $t^2 + \frac{5}{6}t + c$

6. $u^2 - \frac{u}{4} + c$

7. $b^2 - \frac{5}{3}b + c$

8. $x^2 + 17x + c$

Solve each equation by completing the square.

9. $x^2 - 14x + 19 = 0$

10. $n^2 + 16n - 7 = 0$

11. $d^2 + d - 5 = 0$

12. $v^2 + 18 = 9v$

13. $3x^2 - 5x + 2 = 0$

14. $2x^2 + 8x - 3 = 0$

15. $2b^2 - 5b - 6 = 0$

16. $p^2 + 8p + 10 = 0$

17. $q^2 - 9q + 11 = 0$

18. $3a^2 + a - 2 = 0$

19. $c^2 + 6c + 8 = 0$

20. $2d^2 - 10d + 5 = 0$

NAME ______________________ DATE __________

7-3 Practice Worksheet

Completing the Square

Find the value of c that makes each trinomial a perfect square.

1. $a^2 + 12a + c$ 36

2. $h^2 - 20h + c$ 100

3. $p^2 - p + c$ $\frac{1}{4}$

4. $m^2 + 11m + c$ $\frac{121}{4}$

5. $t^2 + \frac{5}{6}t + c$ $\frac{25}{144}$

6. $u^2 - \frac{u}{4} + c$ $\frac{1}{64}$

7. $b^2 - \frac{5}{3}b + c$ $\frac{25}{36}$

8. $x^2 + 17x + c$ $\frac{289}{4}$

Solve each equation by completing the square.

9. $x^2 - 14x + 19 = 0$ $7 \pm \sqrt{30}$

10. $n^2 + 16n - 7 = 0$ $-8 \pm \sqrt{71}$

11. $d^2 + d - 5 = 0$ $\frac{-1 \pm \sqrt{21}}{2}$

12. $v^2 + 18 = 9v$ 6, 3

13. $3x^2 - 5x + 2 = 0$ $1, \frac{2}{3}$

14. $2x^2 + 8x - 3 = 0$ $\frac{-4 \pm \sqrt{22}}{2}$

15. $2b^2 - 5b - 6 = 0$ $\frac{5 \pm \sqrt{73}}{4}$

16. $p^2 + 8p + 10 = 0$ $-4 \pm \sqrt{6}$

17. $q^2 - 9q + 11 = 0$ $\frac{9 \pm \sqrt{37}}{2}$

18. $3a^2 + a - 2 = 0$ $\frac{2}{3}, -1$

19. $c^2 + 6c + 8 = 0$ $-4, -2$

20. $2d^2 - 10d + 5 = 0$ $\frac{5 \pm \sqrt{15}}{2}$

Glencoe Division, Macmillan/McGraw-Hill

NAME ____________________ DATE ____________

7-4

Practice Worksheet

The Quadratic Formula

Find the value of the discriminant for each quadratic equation. Fully describe the nature of its roots. Then solve the equation. Express irrational roots as exact and then use your calculator to give an approximation.

1. $x^2 - 9x + 14 = 0$

2. $r^2 = 3r$

3. $9u^2 - 24u + 16 = 0$

4. $n^2 - 3n = 40$

5. $3t^2 + 9t - 2 = 0$

6. $7u^2 + 6u + 2 = 0$

7. $5w^2 - 2w + 4 = 0$

8. $12x^2 - x - 6 = 0$

9. $2m^2 + 7m = 0$

10. $x^2 - \frac{1}{2}x + \frac{1}{16} = 0$

11. $12x^2 + 2x - 4 = 0$

12. $6w^2 - 2w - 1 = 0$

Glencoe Division, Macmillan/McGraw-Hill

NAME ____________________ DATE ____________

7-4 Practice Worksheet

The Quadratic Formula

Find the value of the discriminant for each quadratic equation. Fully describe the nature of its roots. Then solve the equation. Express irrational roots as exact and then use your calculator to give an approximation.

1. $x^2 - 9x + 14 = 0$

25; 2 real, rational; 7, 2

2. $r^2 = 3r$

9; 2 real, rational; 0, 3

3. $9u^2 - 24u + 16 = 0$

0; 1 real, rational; $\frac{4}{3}$

4. $n^2 - 3n = 40$

169; 2 real, rational; −5, 8

5. $3t^2 + 9t - 2 = 0$

105; 2 real, irrational; $\frac{-9 \pm \sqrt{105}}{6}$**; 0.21, −3.21**

6. $7u^2 + 6u + 2 = 0$

−20; 2 imaginary; $\frac{-3 \pm \sqrt{5}i}{7}$

7. $5w^2 - 2w + 4 = 0$

−76; 2 imaginary; $\frac{1 \pm \sqrt{19}i}{5}$

8. $12x^2 - x - 6 = 0$

289; 2 real, rational; $\frac{3}{4}, -\frac{2}{3}$

9. $2m^2 + 7m = 0$

49; 2 real, rational; $0, -\frac{7}{2}$

10. $x^2 - \frac{1}{2}x + \frac{1}{16} = 0$

0; 1 real, rational; $\frac{1}{4}$

11. $12x^2 + 2x - 4 = 0$

196; 2 real, rational; $\frac{1}{2}, -\frac{2}{3}$

12. $6w^2 - 2w - 1 = 0$

28; 2 real, irrational; $\frac{1 \pm \sqrt{7}}{6}$**; 0.61, −0.27**

Glencoe Division, Macmillan/McGraw-Hill

NAME ______________________ DATE ______________

7-5 Practice Worksheet

Sum and Product of Roots

Solve each equation. Then find the sum and the product of the roots to check your solutions.

1. $x^2 - 7x + 4 = 0$

2. $x^2 + 3x + 6 = 0$

3. $2n^2 + 5n + 6 = 0$

4. $7x^2 - 5x = 0$

5. $4r^2 - 9 = 0$

6. $-5x^2 - x + 4 = 0$

7. $3x^2 + 8x = 3$

8. $\frac{2}{3}x^2 - \frac{1}{2}x - 1 = 0$

Write a quadratic equation that has the given roots.

9. $7, -3$

10. $4, \frac{1}{3}$

11. $-\frac{2}{3}, -\frac{4}{5}$

12. $-2\sqrt{5}, 4\sqrt{5}$

13. $3 - \sqrt{6}, 3 + \sqrt{6}$

14. $7 - 2i, 7 + 2i$

15. $7i, -7i$

16. $\frac{2 + \sqrt{10}}{5}, \frac{2 - \sqrt{10}}{5}$

17. $2 + i\sqrt{11}, 2 - i\sqrt{11}$

18. $\frac{1 + 6i}{4}, \frac{1 - 6i}{4}$

Find k such that the number given is a root of the equation.

19. $7;\ 2x^2 + kx - 21 = 0$

20. $-2;\ x^2 - 13x + k = 0$

NAME ________ DATE ________

7-5

Practice Worksheet

Sum and Product of Roots

Solve each equation. Then find the sum and the product of the roots to check your solutions.

1. $x^2 - 7x + 4 = 0$ $\frac{7 \pm \sqrt{33}}{2}$; 7; 4

2. $x^2 + 3x + 6 = 0$ $\frac{-3 \pm \sqrt{15}i}{2}$; −3, 6

3. $2n^2 + 5n + 6 = 0$ $\frac{-5 \pm \sqrt{23}i}{4}$; $-\frac{5}{3}$; 3

4. $7x^2 - 5x = 0$ 0, $\frac{5}{7}$; $\frac{5}{7}$; 0

5. $4r^2 - 9 = 0$ $\frac{3}{2}$, $-\frac{3}{2}$; 0; $-\frac{9}{4}$

6. $-5x^2 - x + 4 = 0$ −1, $\frac{4}{5}$; $-\frac{1}{5}$; $-\frac{4}{5}$

7. $3x^2 + 8x = 3$ $\frac{1}{3}$, −3; $-\frac{8}{3}$; −1

8. $\frac{2}{3}x^2 - \frac{1}{2}x - 1 = 0$ $\frac{3 \pm \sqrt{105}}{8}$; $\frac{3}{4}$; $-\frac{3}{2}$

Write a quadratic equation that has the given roots.

9. 7, −3 $x^2 - 4x - 21 = 0$

10. 4, $\frac{1}{3}$ $3x^2 - 13x + 4 = 0$

11. $-\frac{2}{3}$, $-\frac{4}{5}$ $15x^2 + 22x + 8 = 0$

12. $-2\sqrt{5}$, $4\sqrt{5}$ $x^2 - 2\sqrt{5}x - 40 = 0$

13. $3 - \sqrt{6}$, $3 + \sqrt{6}$ $x^2 - 6x + 3 = 0$

14. $7 - 2i$, $7 + 2i$ $x^2 - 14x + 53 = 0$

15. $7i$, $-7i$ $x^2 + 49 = 0$

16. $\frac{2 + \sqrt{10}}{5}$, $\frac{2 - \sqrt{10}}{5}$ $25x^2 - 20x - 6 = 0$

17. $2 + i\sqrt{11}$, $2 - i\sqrt{11}$ $x^2 - 4x + 15 = 0$

18. $\frac{1 + 6i}{4}$, $\frac{1 - 6i}{4}$ $16x^2 - 8x + 37 = 0$

Find k such that the number given is a root of the equation.

19. 7; $2x^2 + kx - 21 = 0$ −11

20. −2; $x^2 - 13x + k = 0$ −30

Glencoe Division, Macmillan/McGraw-Hill

NAME ______________________ DATE __________

7-6

Practice Worksheet

Using Quadratic Techniques to Solve Polynomial Equations

Solve each equation.

1. $x^4 - 50x^2 + 49 = 0$

2. $t^4 - 21t^2 + 80 = 0$

3. $m^4 - 625 = 0$

4. $n^4 - 49n^2 = 0$

5. $w - 12\sqrt{w} + 27 = 0$

6. $n - 10\sqrt{n} + 25 = 0$

7. $y^6 - 8y^3 = 0$

8. $n^6 - 1 = 0$

9. $x^{\frac{1}{2}} - 5x^{\frac{1}{4}} + 6 = 0$

10. $r^{\frac{2}{3}} - r^{\frac{1}{3}} - 20 = 0$

11. $x^{\frac{4}{3}} - 29x^{\frac{2}{3}} + 100 = 0$

12. $y^3 - 28y^{\frac{3}{2}} + 27 = 0$

13. $y^{-1} - 8y^{-\frac{1}{2}} + 12 = 0$

14. $y^{-\frac{2}{3}} - 7y^{-\frac{1}{3}} + 12 = 0$

Glencoe Division, Macmillan/McGraw-Hill

NAME ______________________ DATE ____________

7-6 Practice Worksheet

Using Quadratic Techniques to Solve Polynomial Equations

Solve each equation.

1. $x^4 - 50x^2 + 49 = 0$
   $\pm 7, \pm 1$

2. $t^4 - 21t^2 + 80 = 0$
   $\pm\sqrt{5}, \pm 4$

3. $m^4 - 625 = 0$
   $\pm 5, \pm 5i$

4. $n^4 - 49n^2 = 0$
   $0, \pm 7$

5. $w - 12\sqrt{w} + 27 = 0$
   9, 81

6. $n - 10\sqrt{n} + 25 = 0$
   25

7. $y^6 - 8y^3 = 0$
   $0, 2, -1 \pm i\sqrt{3}$

8. $n^6 - 1 = 0$
   $\pm 1, \frac{-1 \pm i\sqrt{3}}{2}, \frac{1 \pm i\sqrt{3}}{2}$

9. $x^{\frac{1}{2}} - 5x^{\frac{1}{4}} + 6 = 0$
   16, 81

10. $r^{\frac{2}{3}} - r^{\frac{1}{3}} - 20 = 0$
    125, −64

11. $x^{\frac{4}{3}} - 29x^{\frac{2}{3}} + 100 = 0$
    8, 125

12. $y^3 - 28y^{\frac{3}{2}} + 27 = 0$
    1, 9

13. $y^{-1} - 8y^{-\frac{1}{2}} + 12 = 0$
    $\frac{1}{36}, \frac{1}{4}$

14. $y^{-\frac{2}{3}} - 7y^{-\frac{1}{3}} + 12 = 0$
    $\frac{1}{27}, \frac{1}{64}$

NAME ______________________ DATE ____________

8-1

Practice Worksheet

Quadratic Functions

Write each function in quadratic form.

1. $f(x) = (x + 7)^2$

2. $f(x) = (4x - 3)^2$

3. $f(x) = -3(2x + 1)^2$

4. $f(x) = 6(3x + 1)^2 + 4$

5. $f(x) = \frac{1}{2}(4x - 5)^2 - 3$

6. $f(x) = -\frac{2}{3}(x - 6)^2 + 4$

7. $f(x) = 2(3x - 1)^2 + 6$

8. $f(x) = -3(x + 7)^2 - 8$

9. $f(x) = \frac{1}{2}(2x - 6)^2 + 4$

10. $f(x) = -\frac{3}{4}(2x + 8)^2 - 1$

Define a variable and write a quadratic function to describe each situation.

11. the product of two numbers whose difference is 6

12. the area of a rectangle whose perimeter is 20 feet

13. A movie theatre averages 160 customers per show. The charge is \$6.00 per person. The owner estimates that for each \$0.50 decrease in price, 20 more people will attend each show. Write a quadratic function to describe the owner's ticket income after the price is decreased.

14. Wanda wants to put fencing around a rectangular garden. One side of the garden is her house. She has 70 feet of fencing for the other 3 sides. Write a quadratic function to describe the area of the garden.

Glencoe Division, Macmillan/McGraw-Hill

NAME ______________________ DATE ______________

8-1 Practice Worksheet

Quadratic Functions

Write each function in quadratic form.

1. $f(x) = (x + 7)^2$
   $f(x) = x^2 + 14x + 49$

2. $f(x) = (4x - 3)^2$
   $f(x) = 16x^2 - 24x + 9$

3. $f(x) = -3(2x + 1)^2$
   $f(x) = -12x^2 - 12x - 3$

4. $f(x) = 6(3x + 1)^2 + 4$
   $f(x) = 54x^2 + 36x + 10$

5. $f(x) = \frac{1}{2}(4x - 5)^2 - 3$
   $f(x) = 8x^2 - 20x + \frac{19}{2}$

6. $f(x) = -\frac{2}{3}(x - 6)^2 + 4$
   $f(x) = -\frac{2}{3}x^2 + 8x - 20$

7. $f(x) = 2(3x - 1)^2 + 6$
   $f(x) = 18x^2 - 12x + 8$

8. $f(x) = -3(x + 7)^2 - 8$
   $f(x) = -3x^2 - 42x - 155$

9. $f(x) = \frac{1}{2}(2x - 6)^2 + 4$
   $f(x) = 2x^2 - 12x + 22$

10. $f(x) = -\frac{3}{4}(2x + 8)^2 - 1$
    $f(x) = -3x^2 - 24x - 49$

Define a variable and write a quadratic function to describe each situation.

11. the product of two numbers whose difference is 6
    Let x = the larger number; $f(x) = x^2 - 6x$

12. the area of a rectangle whose perimeter is 20 feet
    Let x = the length; $f(x) = -x^2 + 10x$

13. A movie theatre averages 160 customers per show. The charge is \$6.00 per person. The owner estimates that for each \$0.50 decrease in price, 20 more people will attend each show. Write a quadratic function to describe the owner's ticket income after the price is decreased.
    Let x = the number of \$0.50 decreases; $f(x) = -10x^2 + 40x + 960$

14. Wanda wants to put fencing around a rectangular garden. One side of the garden is her house. She has 70 feet of fencing for the other 3 sides. Write a quadratic function to describe the area of the garden.
    Let x = the length of the two sides that are the same; $f(x) = -2x^2 + 70x$

Glencoe Division, Macmillan/McGraw-Hill

8-2

NAME ______________________ DATE ______________

Practice Worksheet

Problem Solving Strategy: Make a Table

Use any strategy.

1. A toll on a tollroad is 40¢. The automatic lane takes exact change only. If the automatic gate will take pennies, how many combinations of coins must the gate be programmed to accept?

2. What is the ones' digit of 8^{90}?

3. The difference of the squares of two consecutive integers is 853. What is the sum of the two integers?

4. Find the least positive integer that is divisible by 2, 5, 7, 15, 21, 24, 25, and 30.

8-2

NAME ____________________ DATE ____________

Practice Worksheet

Problem Solving Strategy: Make a Table

Use any strategy.

1. A toll on a tollroad is 40¢. The automatic lane takes exact change only. If the automatic gate will take pennies, how many combinations of coins must the gate be programmed to accept? **31 combinations**

2. What is the ones' digit of 8^{90}? **4**

3. The difference of the squares of two consecutive integers is 853. What is the sum of the two integers? **853**

4. Find the least positive integer that is divisible by 2, 5, 7, 15, 21, 24, 25, and 30. **4200**

NAME ______________________ DATE ____________

8-3 Practice Worksheet

Graphing Quadratic Functions

Write each equation in the form f(x) = (x − h)² + k. Then name the vertex and the axis of symmetry for the graph of each function.

1. $f(x) = x^2 - 10x + 25$

2. $f(x) = x^2 + 12x + 36$

3. $f(x) = x^2 + 2$

4. $f(x) = x^2 - 6x$

5. $f(x) = x^2 - 3x + 1$

6. $f(x) = x^2 - 2x - 1$

Graph each equation.

7. $f(x) = (x - 3)^2 + 2$

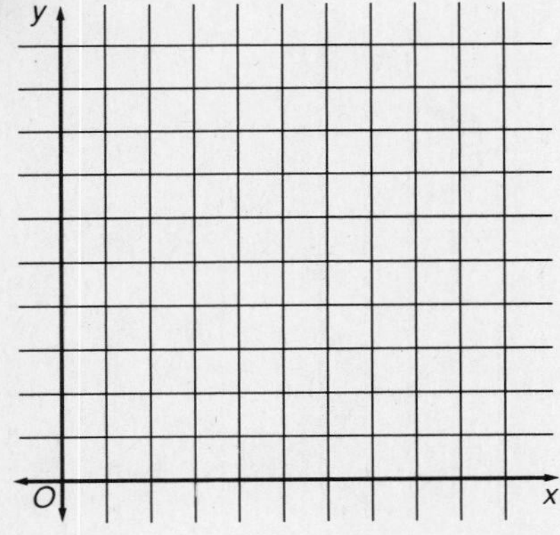

8. $y = (x + 5)^2 - 1$

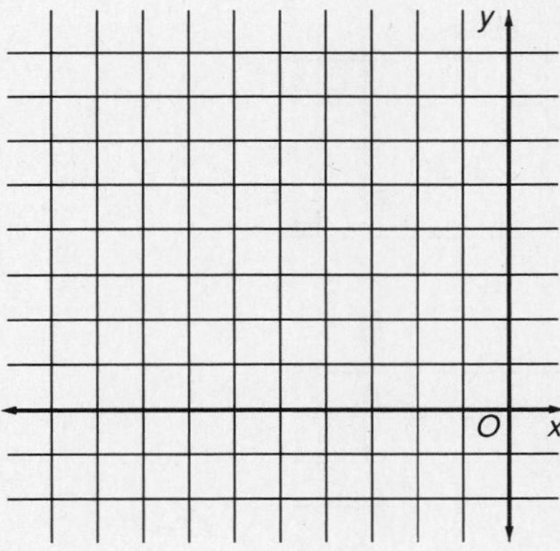

9. $y = x^2 + 2x + 6$

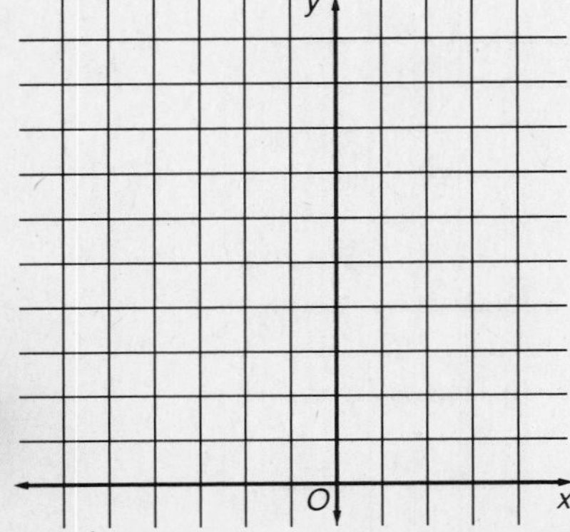

10. $f(x) = x^2 - 4x + 7$

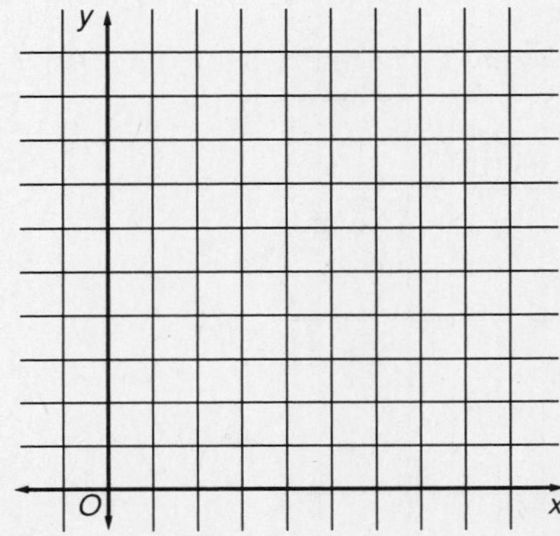

Glencoe Division, Macmillan/McGraw-Hill

8-3

NAME ____________________ DATE ____________

Practice Worksheet

Graphing Quadratic Functions

Write each equation in the form $f(x) = (x - h)^2 + k$. Then name the vertex and the axis of symmetry for the graph of each function.

1. $f(x) = x^2 - 10x + 25$

$f(x) = (x - 5)^2$;
$(5, 0)$; $x = 5$

2. $f(x) = x^2 + 12x + 36$

$f(x) = (x + 6)^2$;
$(-6, 0)$; $x = -6$

3. $f(x) = x^2 + 2$

$f(x) = (x - 0)^2 + 2$;
$(0, 2)$; $x = 0$

4. $f(x) = x^2 - 6x$

$f(x) = (x - 3)^2 - 9$;
$(3, -9)$; $x = 3$

5. $f(x) = x^2 - 3x + 1$

$f(x) = \left(x - \frac{3}{2}\right)^2 - \frac{5}{4}$;
$\left(\frac{3}{2}, -\frac{5}{4}\right)$; $x = \frac{3}{2}$

6. $f(x) = x^2 - 2x - 1$

$f(x) = (x - 1)^2 - 2$;
$(1, -2)$; $x = 1$

Graph each equation.

7. $f(x) = (x - 3)^2 + 2$

8. $y = (x + 5)^2 - 1$

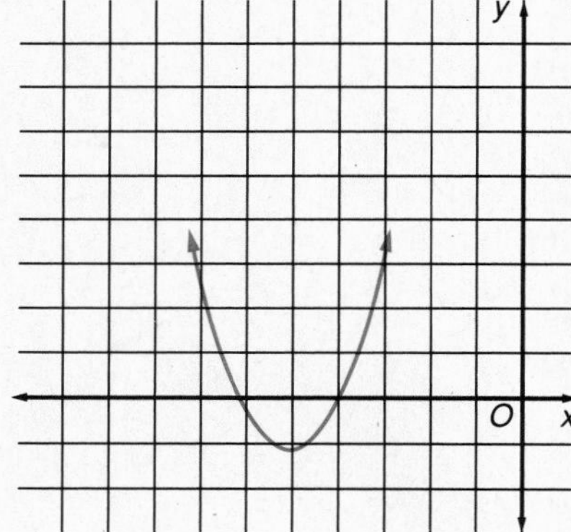

9. $y = x^2 + 2x + 6$

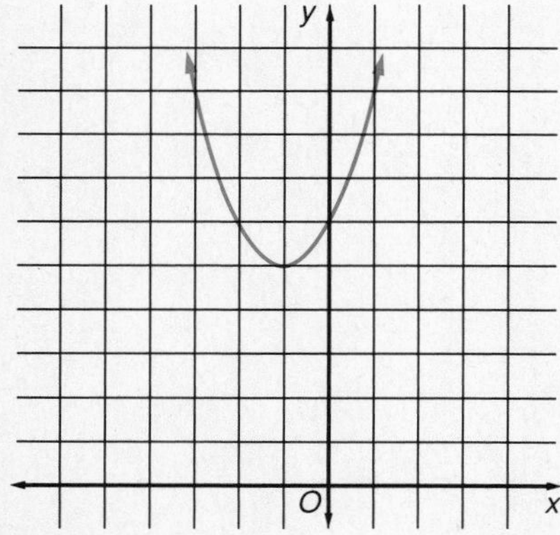

10. $f(x) = x^2 - 4x + 7$

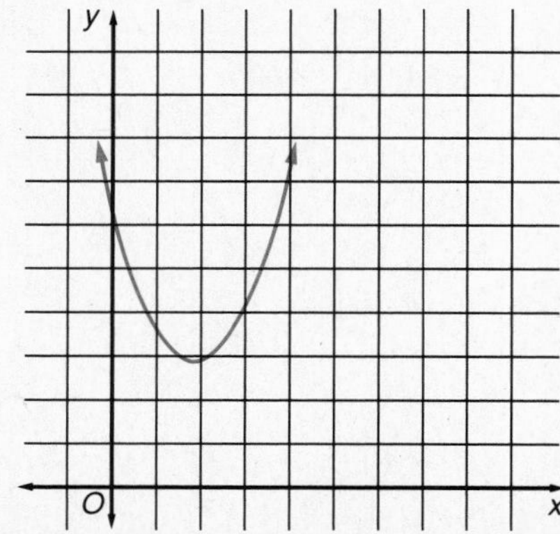

Glencoe Division, Macmillan/McGraw-Hill

8-4

NAME ______________________ DATE ______________

Practice Worksheet

Analyzing Graphs of Quadratic Functions

Write each equation in the form f(x) = a(x − h)² + k. Then name the vertex, axis of symmetry, and direction of opening for the graph of each equation.

1. $f(x) = -6x^2$

2. $y = -2x^2 - 16x - 32$

3. $h(x) = \frac{2}{3}x^2 + 4x + 6$

4. $y = 2x^2 + 16x + 29$

5. $g(x) = -9x^2 + 12x - 4$

6. $y = -3x^2 + 6x - 5$

Write the equation of a parabola that passes through the given points.

7. (0, 1), (2, −1), (1, 3)

8. (0, 0), (2, 3), (−1, 4)

Graph each equation.

9. $y = -2x^2 + 1$

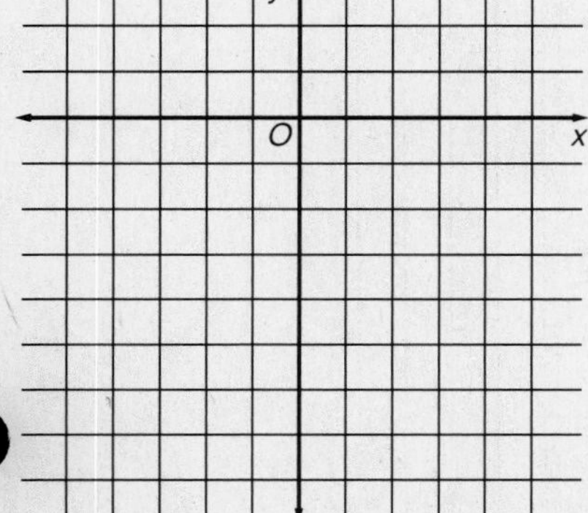

10. $f(x) = -3x^2 + 6x - 5$

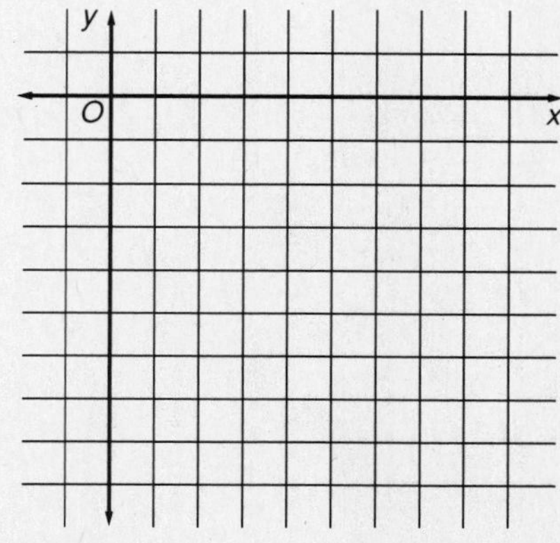

NAME ______________________ DATE ______________

8-4 Practice Worksheet

Analyzing Graphs of Quadratic Functions

Write each equation in the form f(x) = a(x − h)² + k. Then name the vertex, axis of symmetry, and direction of opening for the graph of each equation.

1. $f(x) = -6x^2$
$f(x) = -6x^2$;
(0, 0); $x = 0$; down

2. $y = -2x^2 - 16x - 32$
$f(x) = -2(x + 4)^2$;
(−4, 0); $x = -4$; down

3. $h(x) = \frac{2}{3}x^2 + 4x + 6$
$f(x) = \frac{2}{3}(x + 3)^2$;
(−3, 0); $x = -3$; up

4. $y = 2x^2 + 16x + 29$
$f(x) = 2(x + 4)^2 - 3$;
(−4, −3);
$x = -4$; up

5. $g(x) = -9x^2 + 12x - 4$
$g(x) = -9\left(x - \frac{2}{3}\right)^2$;
$\left(\frac{2}{3}, 0\right)$;
$x = \frac{2}{3}$; down

6. $y = -3x^2 + 6x - 5$
$f(x) = -3(x - 1)^2 - 2$;
(1, −2);
$x = 1$; down

Write the equation of a parabola that passes through the given points.

7. (0, 1), (2, −1), (1, 3)
$f(x) = -3x^2 + 5x + 1$

8. (0, 0), (2, 3), (−1, 4)
$f(x) = \frac{11}{6}x^2 - \frac{13}{6}x$

Graph each equation.

9. $y = -2x^2 + 1$

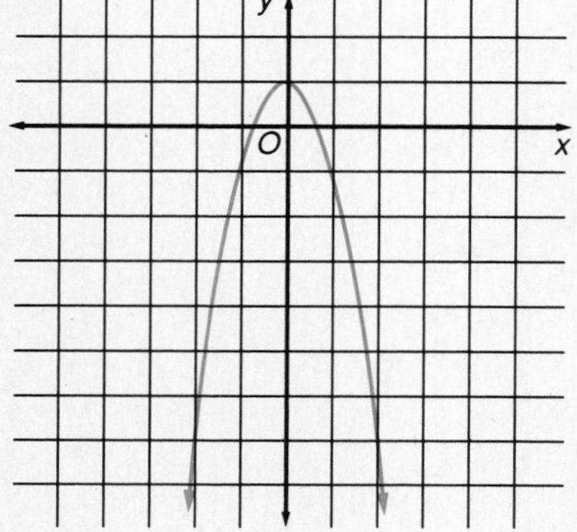

10. $f(x) = -3x^2 + 6x - 5$

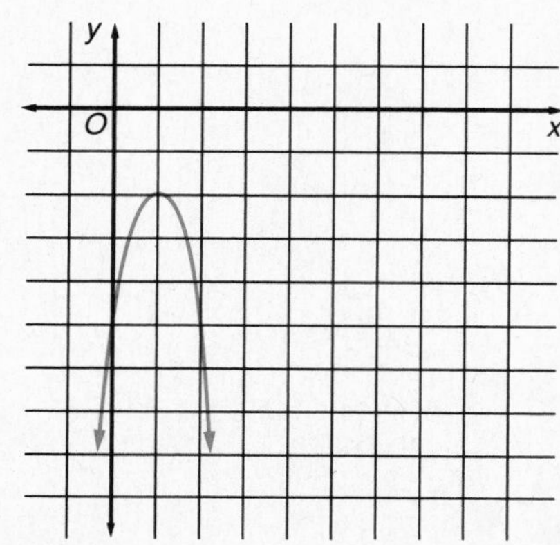

NAME ____________________ DATE ____________

8-5

Practice Worksheet

Applications of Quadratic Equations

Solve each problem.

1. Find two numbers whose difference is 8 and whose product is a minimum.

2. Find the dimensions and maximum area of a rectangle if its perimeter is 48 inches.

3. Lorenzo has 48 feet of fencing to make a rectangular dog pen. If a house is used for one side of the pen, what would be the length and width for maximum area?

4. A clothing store sells 40 pairs of jeans daily at $30 each. The owner figures that for each $3 increase in price, 2 fewer pairs will be sold each day. What price should be charged to maximize profit?

5. An object is thrown upward into the air with an initial velocity of 128 feet per second. The formula $h(t) = 128t - 16t^2$ gives its height above the ground after t seconds. What is the height after 2 seconds? What is the maximum height reached? For how many seconds will the object be in the air?

6. A square, which is 2 inches by 2 inches, is cut from each corner of a rectangular piece of metal. The sides are folded up to make a box. If the bottom must have a perimeter of 32 inches, what would be the length and width for maximum volume?

Glencoe Division, Macmillan/McGraw-Hill

NAME ______________________ DATE ______________

8-5 Practice Worksheet

Applications of Quadratic Equations

Solve each problem.

1. Find two numbers whose difference is 8 and whose product is a minimum. **4, −4**

2. Find the dimensions and maximum area of a rectangle if its perimeter is 48 inches.
12 in. by 12 in.; max area = 144 sq in.

3. Lorenzo has 48 feet of fencing to make a rectangular dog pen. If a house is used for one side of the pen, what would be the length and width for maximum area?
12 ft by 24 ft

4. A clothing store sells 40 pairs of jeans daily at \$30 each. The owner figures that for each \$3 increase in price, 2 fewer pairs will be sold each day. What price should be charged to maximize profit? **\$45**

5. An object is thrown upward into the air with an initial velocity of 128 feet per second. The formula $h(t) = 128t - 16t^2$ gives its height above the ground after t seconds. What is the height after 2 seconds? What is the maximum height reached? For how many seconds will the object be in the air?
192 ft; 256 ft; 8 sec

6. A square, which is 2 inches by 2 inches, is cut from each corner of a rectangular piece of metal. The sides are folded up to make a box. If the bottom must have a perimeter of 32 inches, what would be the length and width for maximum volume? **8 in. by 8 in.**

Glencoe Division, Macmillan/McGraw-Hill

NAME ________________________ DATE ______________

8-6 Practice Worksheet

Graphing Quadratic Inequalities

Draw the graph of each inequality.

1. $y > x^2 - 2$

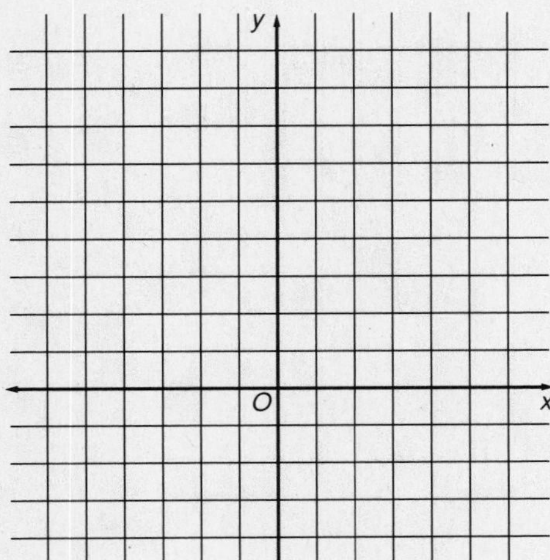

2. $y \leq x^2 + 4$

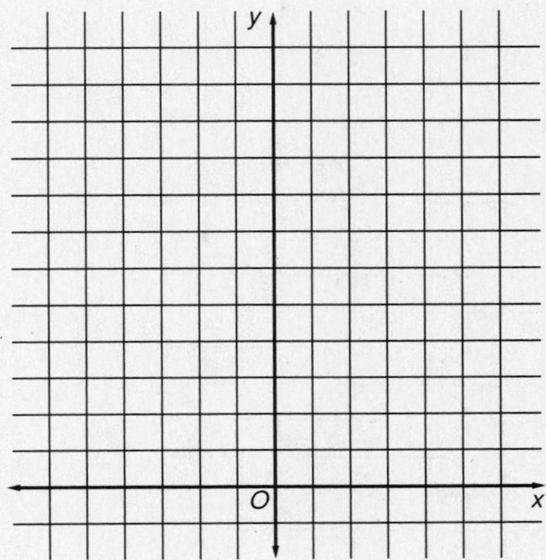

3. $y < x^2 + 8x - 5$

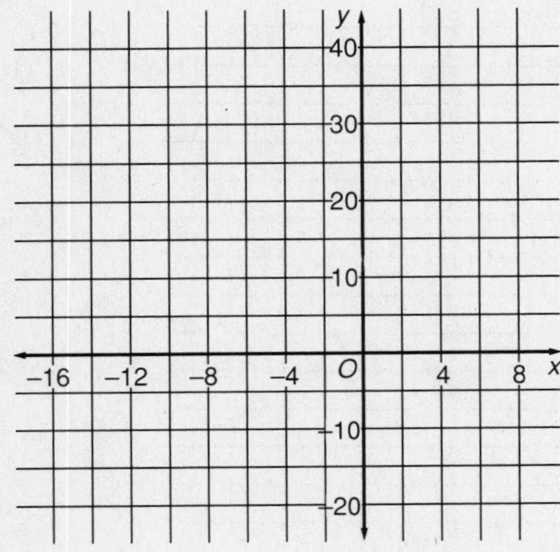

4. $y \geq 2x^2 - 12x + 17$

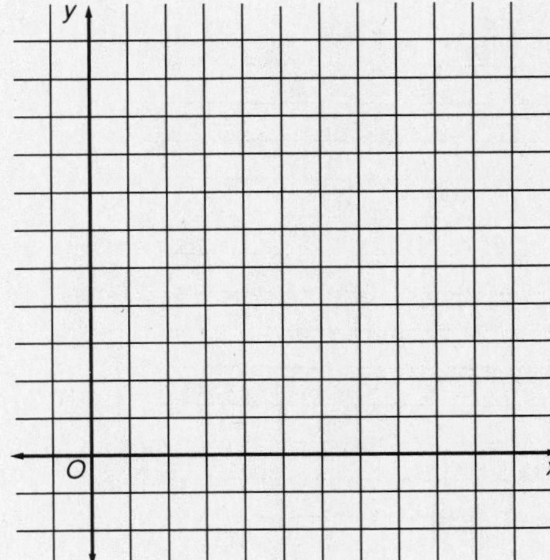

NAME ______________________ DATE ____________

8-6

Practice Worksheet

Graphing Quadratic Inequalities

Draw the graph of each inequality.

1. $y > x^2 - 2$

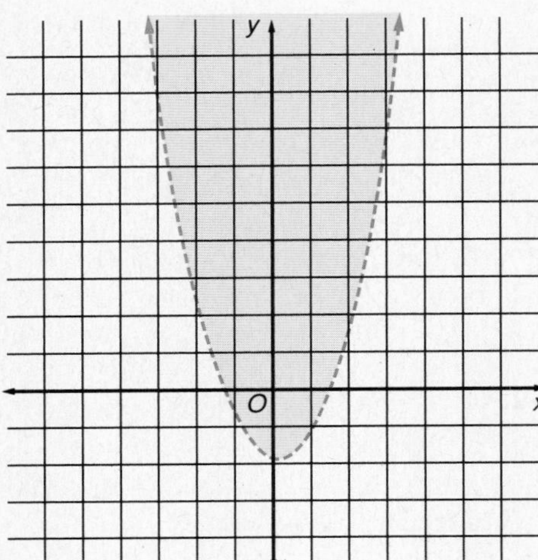

2. $y \leq x^2 + 4$

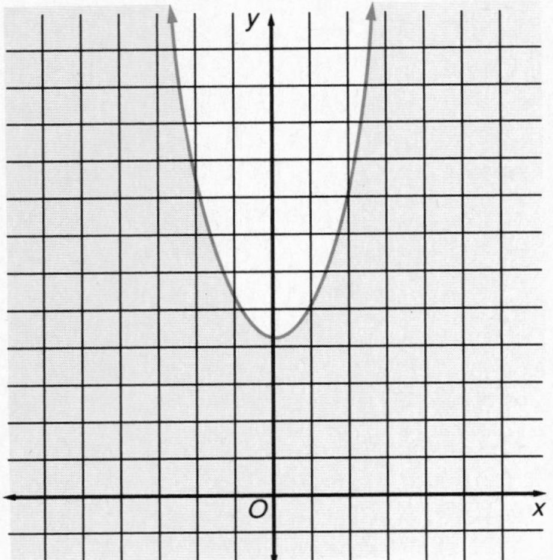

3. $y < x^2 + 8x - 5$

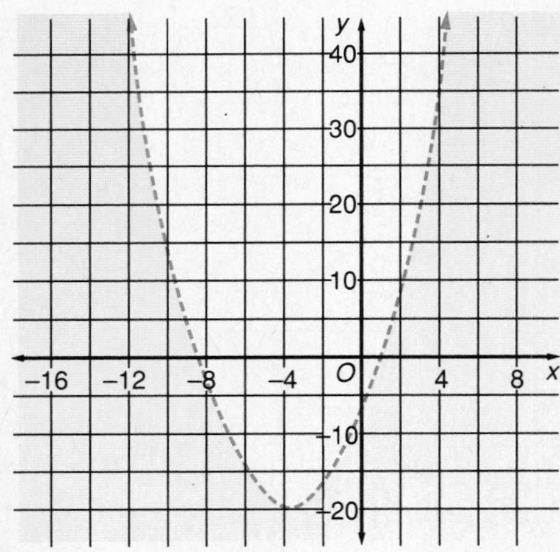

4. $y \geq 2x^2 - 12x + 17$

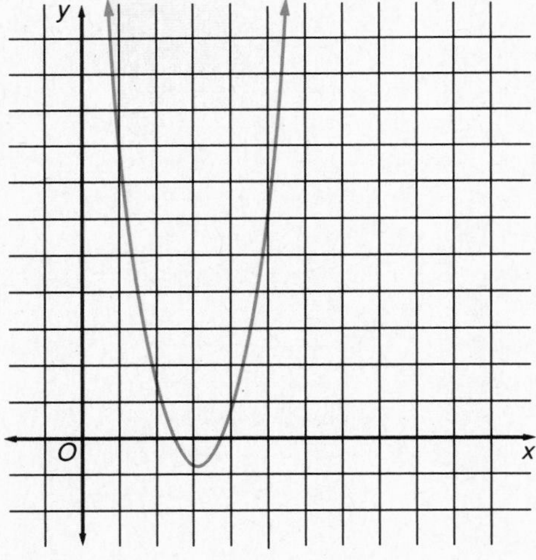

NAME ____________________ DATE ____________

8-7 Practice Worksheet

Solving Quadratic Inequalities

Solve each inequality.

1. $x^2 - x - 20 > 0$

2. $x^2 - 10x + 16 < 0$

3. $x^2 + 4x + 3 \leq 0$

4. $x^2 + 5x \geq 24$

5. $5x^2 + 10 \geq 27x$

6. $9x^2 + 31x + 12 \leq 0$

7. $9z \leq 12z^2$

8. $4t^2 < 9$

9. $x^2 + 64 \geq 16x$

10. $4x^2 + 4x + 1 > 0$

11. $9x^2 + 6x + 1 \leq 0$

12. $x^2 + \frac{4}{3}x + \frac{4}{9} < 0$

13. $x^2 + 1 > 6x$

14. $2x^2 + 3 \leq 8x$

15. $5 - 2x^2 \geq -3x$

16. $14 - 3x^2 \leq 19x$

Glencoe Division, Macmillan/McGraw-Hill

NAME ____________________ DATE ____________

8-7

Practice Worksheet

Solving Quadratic Inequalities

Solve each inequality.

1. $x^2 - x - 20 > 0$
$\{x|x > 5 \text{ or } x < -4\}$

2. $x^2 - 10x + 16 < 0$
$\{x|2 < x < 8\}$

3. $x^2 + 4x + 3 \leq 0$
$\{x|-3 \leq x \leq -1\}$

4. $x^2 + 5x \geq 24$
$\{x|x \geq 3 \text{ or } x \leq -8\}$

5. $5x^2 + 10 \geq 27x$
$\left\{x|x \geq 5 \text{ or } x \leq \frac{2}{5}\right\}$

6. $9x^2 + 31x + 12 \leq 0$
$\left\{x|-3 \leq x \leq -\frac{4}{9}\right\}$

7. $9z \leq 12z^2$
$\left\{z|z > \frac{3}{4} \text{ or } z < 0\right\}$

8. $4t^2 < 9$
$\left\{t|-\frac{3}{2} < t < \frac{3}{2}\right\}$

9. $x^2 + 64 \geq 16x$
all reals

10. $4x^2 + 4x + 1 > 0$
$\left\{x|x \neq -\frac{1}{2}\right\}$

11. $9x^2 + 6x + 1 \leq 0$
$\left\{-\frac{1}{3}\right\}$

12. $x^2 + \frac{4}{3}x + \frac{4}{9} < 0$
no solution

13. $x^2 + 1 > 6x$
$\{x|x > 3 + 2\sqrt{2} \text{ or } x < 3 - 2\sqrt{2}\}$

14. $2x^2 + 3 \leq 8x$
$\left\{x|\frac{4 - \sqrt{10}}{2} \leq x \leq \frac{4 + \sqrt{10}}{2}\right\}$

15. $5 - 2x^2 \geq -3x$
$\left\{x|-1 \leq x \leq \frac{5}{2}\right\}$

16. $14 - 3x^2 \leq 19x$
$\left\{x|x \leq -7 \text{ or } x \geq \frac{2}{3}\right\}$

Glencoe Division, Macmillan/McGraw-Hill

NAME ____________________ DATE ____________

9-1

Practice Worksheet

The Distance and Midpoint Formulas

Use the distance formula to find the distance between each pair of points.

1. $(-3, 5), (2, 8)$

2. $(6, -1), (-3, -2)$

3. $\left(\frac{2}{5}, 3\right), \left(\frac{3}{4}, \frac{5}{2}\right)$

4. $(-4\sqrt{2}, -\sqrt{8}), (-5\sqrt{2}, \sqrt{18})$

5. $(3\sqrt{5}, 4\sqrt{2}), (-2\sqrt{5}, 3\sqrt{8})$

6. $(\frac{1}{2}, \frac{2}{3}), (\frac{4}{5}, \frac{9}{10})$

Find the value of c such that each pair of points is 5 units apart.

7. $(5, 2), (c, -3)$

8. $(-2, c), (2, -1)$

9. $(0, c), (3, 1)$

10. $(c, 0), (-4, 1)$

Find the midpoint of each line segment whose endpoints are given below.

11. $(8, -3), (-6, -11)$

12. $(-14, 5), (10, 6)$

13. $\left(-\frac{1}{2}, \sqrt{27}\right), (3, 5\sqrt{3})$

14. $(1.3, -0.6), (4, -8)$

15. $(2.6, -4.7), (8.4, 2.5)$

16. $(5, 8\sqrt{6}), (9, -2\sqrt{24})$

NAME ____________________ DATE ____________

9-1 Practice Worksheet

The Distance and Midpoint Formulas

Use the distance formula to find the distance between each pair of points.

1. $(-3, 5), (2, 8)$ $\sqrt{34}$

2. $(6, -1), (-3, -2)$ $\sqrt{82}$

3. $\left(\frac{2}{5}, 3\right), \left(\frac{3}{4}, \frac{5}{2}\right)$ $\frac{\sqrt{149}}{20}$

4. $(-4\sqrt{2}, -\sqrt{8}), (-5\sqrt{2}, \sqrt{18})$ $2\sqrt{13}$

5. $(3\sqrt{5}, 4\sqrt{2}), (-2\sqrt{5}, 3\sqrt{8})$ $\sqrt{133}$

6. $(\frac{1}{2}, \frac{2}{3}), (\frac{4}{5}, \frac{9}{10})$ $\frac{\sqrt{130}}{30}$

Find the value of c such that each pair of points is 5 units apart.

7. $(5, 2), (c, -3)$ 5

8. $(-2, c), (2, -1)$ -4 or 2

9. $(0, c), (3, 1)$ -3 or 5

10. $(c, 0), (-4, 1)$
$-4 + 2\sqrt{6}$ or $-4 - 2\sqrt{6}$

Find the midpoint of each line segment whose endpoints are given below.

11. $(8, -3), (-6, -11)$
$(1, -7)$

12. $(-14, 5), (10, 6)$
$\left(-2, \frac{11}{2}\right)$

13. $\left(-\frac{1}{2}, \sqrt{27}\right), (3, 5\sqrt{3})$
$\left(\frac{5}{4}, 4\sqrt{3}\right)$

14. $(1.3, -0.6), (4, -8)$
$(2.65, -4.3)$

15. $(2.6, -4.7), (8.4, 2.5)$
$(5.5, -1.1)$

16. $(5, 8\sqrt{6}), (9, -2\sqrt{24})$
$(7, 2\sqrt{6})$

Glencoe Division, Macmillan/McGraw-Hill

NAME ______________________ DATE ____________

9-2

Practice Worksheet

Parabolas

Name the vertex, axis of symmetry, focus, directrix, and direction of opening of the parabola whose equation is given. Then find the length of the latus rectum and graph the parabola.

1. $y = 5(x - 3)^2 + 2$

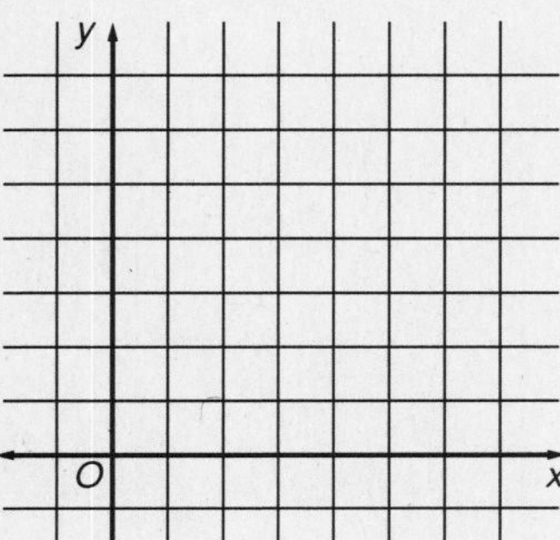

2. $y = -3(x + 1)^2 - 4$

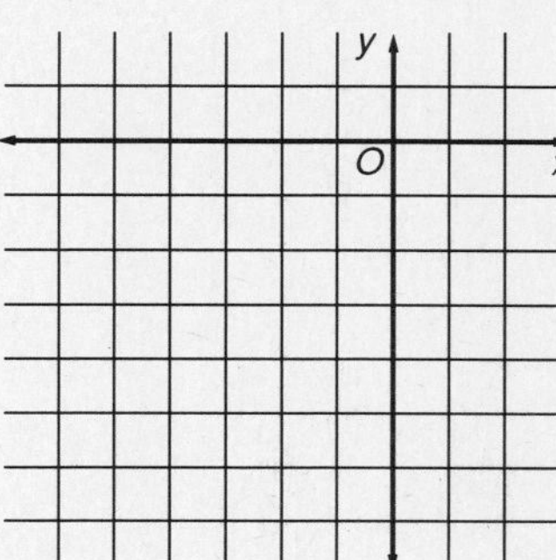

The focus and directrix of a parabola are given. Write an equation for each parabola. Then draw the graph.

3. $(3, 2)$, $x = -1$

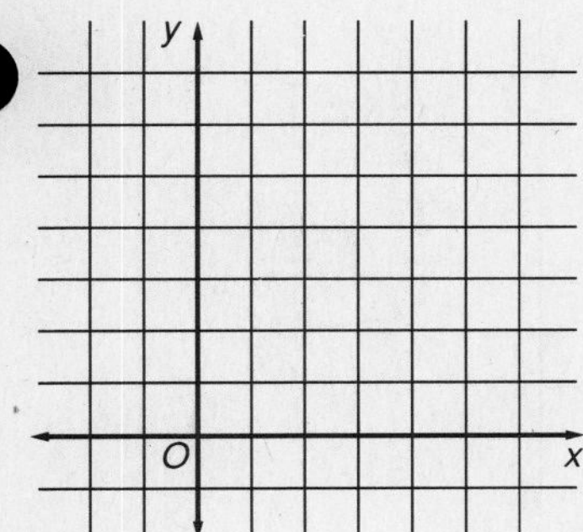

4. $(4, 1)$, $y = 3$

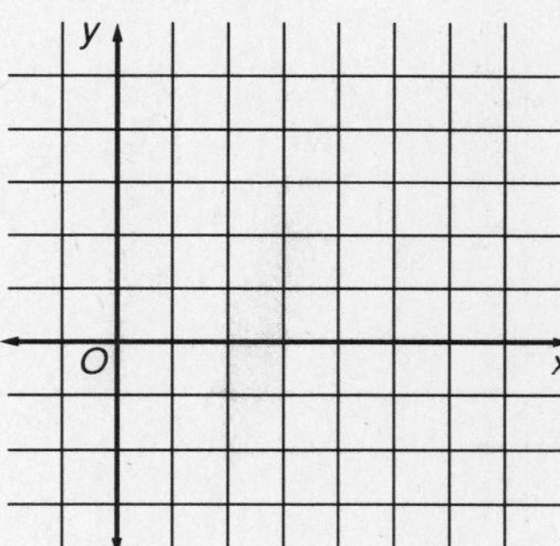

Write the equation of each parabola described below. Then draw the graph.

5. vertex $(4, 1)$, focus $(4, 3)$

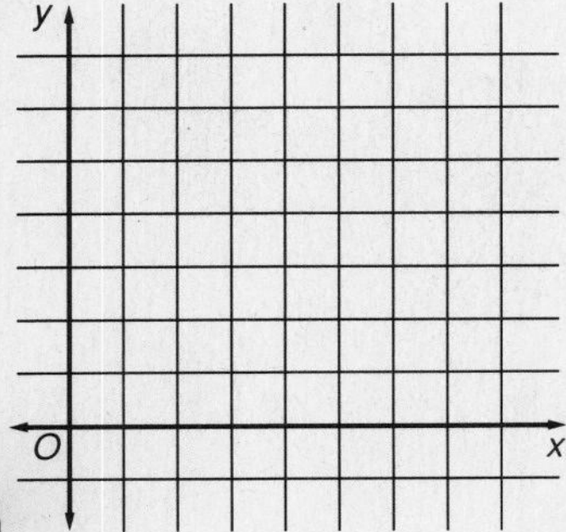

6. vertex $(1, 2)$, focus $(6, 2)$

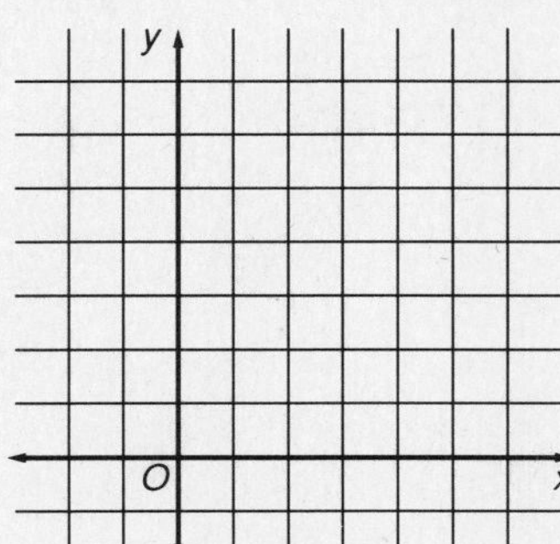

Glencoe Division, Macmillan/McGraw-Hill

NAME ______________________________ DATE ______________

9-2 Practice Worksheet

Parabolas

Name the vertex, axis of symmetry, focus, directrix, and direction of opening of the parabola whose equation is given. Then find the length of the latus rectum and graph the parabola.

1. $y = 5(x - 3)^2 + 2$ **(3, 2); x = 3; $\left(3, 2\frac{1}{20}\right)$; $y = 1\frac{19}{20}$; up; $\frac{1}{5}$**

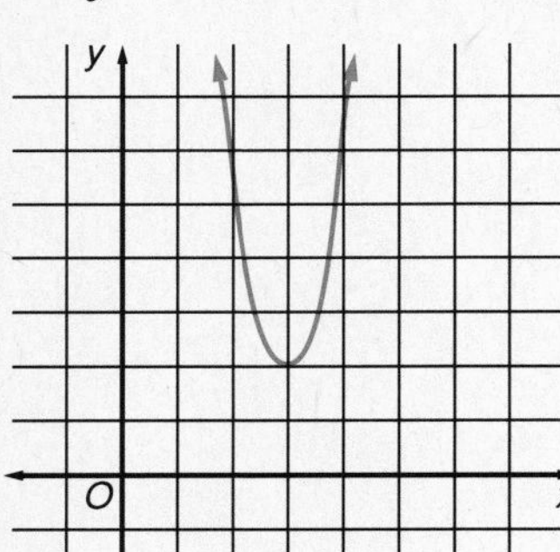

2. $y = -3(x + 1)^2 - 4$ **(−1, −4); x = −1; $\left(-1, -4\frac{1}{12}\right)$; $y = -3\frac{11}{12}$; down; $\frac{1}{3}$**

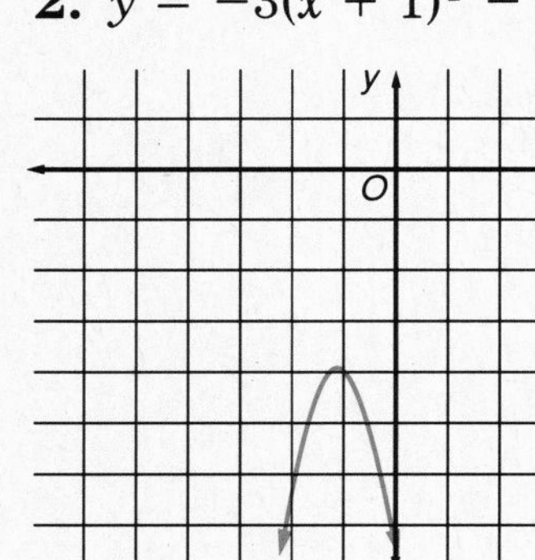

The focus and directrix of a parabola are given. Write an equation for each parabola. Then draw the graph.

3. (3, 2), $x = -1$ **$x = \frac{1}{8}(y - 2)^2 + 1$**

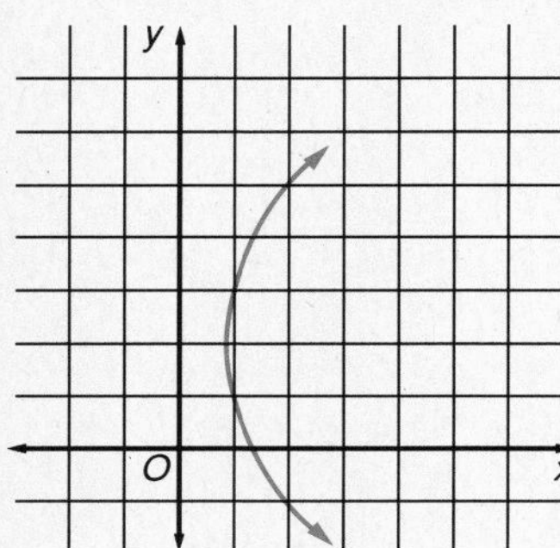

4. (4, 1), $y = 3$ **$y = -\frac{1}{4}(x - 4)^2 + 2$**

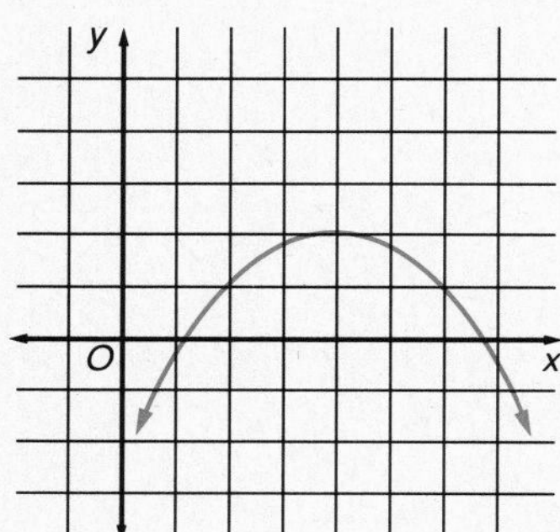

Write the equation of each parabola described below. Then draw the graph.

5. vertex (4, 1), focus (4, 3) **$y = \frac{1}{8}(x - 4)^2 + 1$**

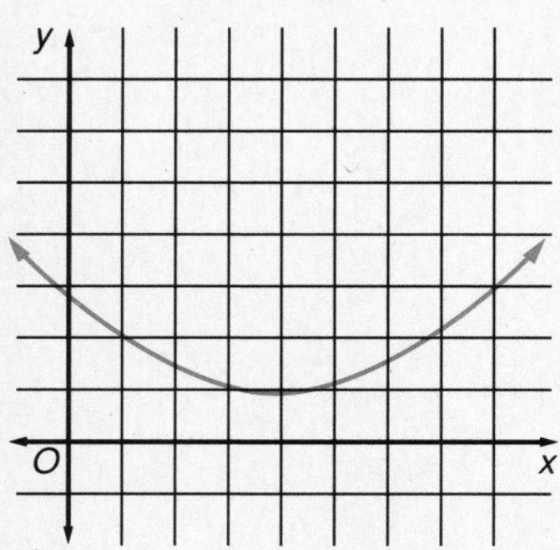

6. vertex (1, 2), focus (6, 2) **$x = \frac{1}{20}(y - 2)^2 + 1$**

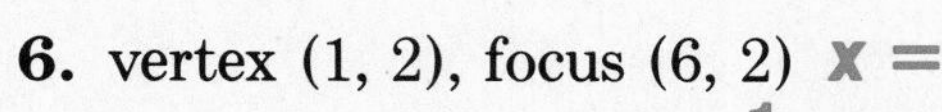

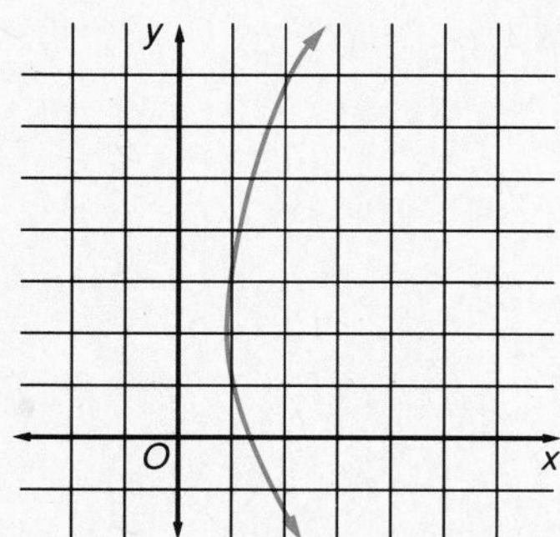

Glencoe Division, Macmillan/McGraw-Hill

NAME ______________________ DATE ____________

9-3

Practice Worksheet

Circles

Find the center and radius of each circle whose equation is given. Then draw the graph.

1. $(x + 3)^2 + y^2 = 16$

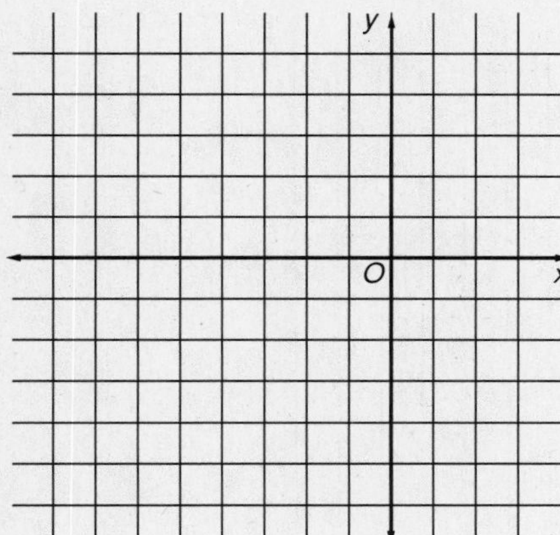

2. $3x^2 + 3y^2 = 12$

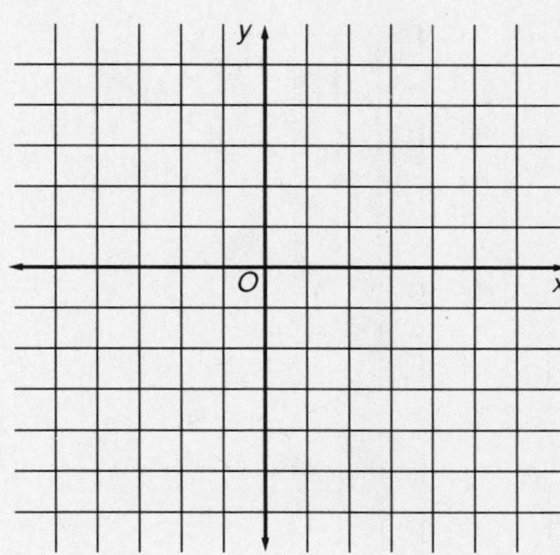

3. $x^2 + y^2 - 6x - 12y + 36 = 0$

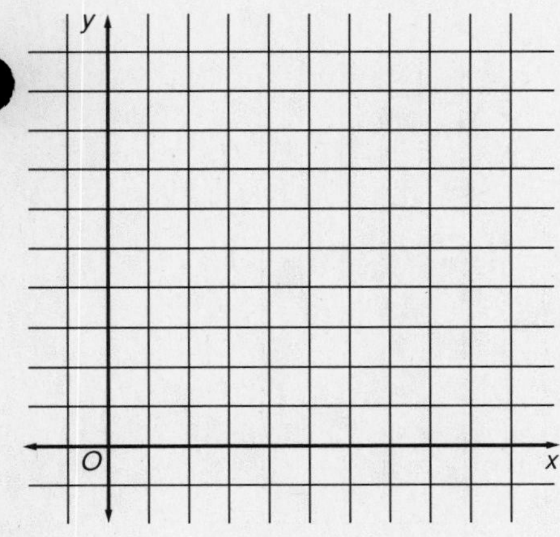

4. $x^2 + y^2 + 2x + 6y = 26$

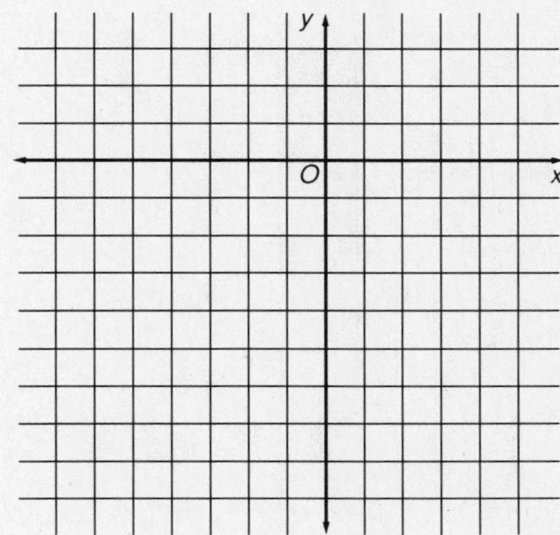

Write an equation for each circle whose center and radius are given.

5. center $(-4, 2)$; radius 8

6. center $(5, -6)$; radius 11

7. center $\left(-\frac{1}{4}, -\sqrt{3}\right)$; radius $5\sqrt{2}$

8. center $\left(3.8, 1\frac{1}{3}\right)$; radius $\frac{3}{7}$

Glencoe Division, Macmillan/McGraw-Hill

NAME ________________________ DATE ____________

9-3 Practice Worksheet

Circles

Find the center and radius of each circle whose equation is given. Then draw the graph.

1. $(x + 3)^2 + y^2 = 16$ **(−3, 0); 4**

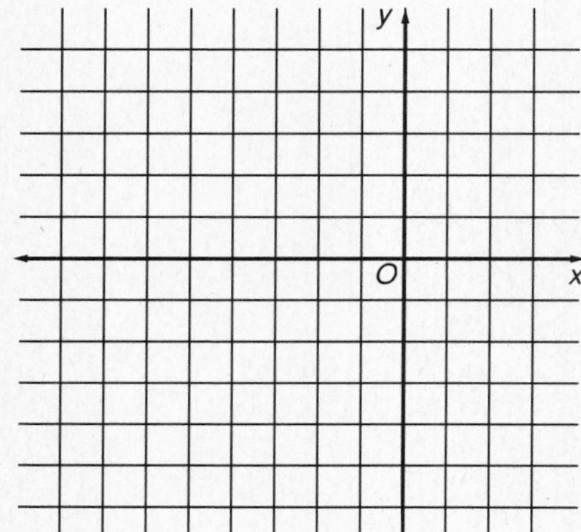

2. $3x^2 + 3y^2 = 12$ **(0, 0); 2**

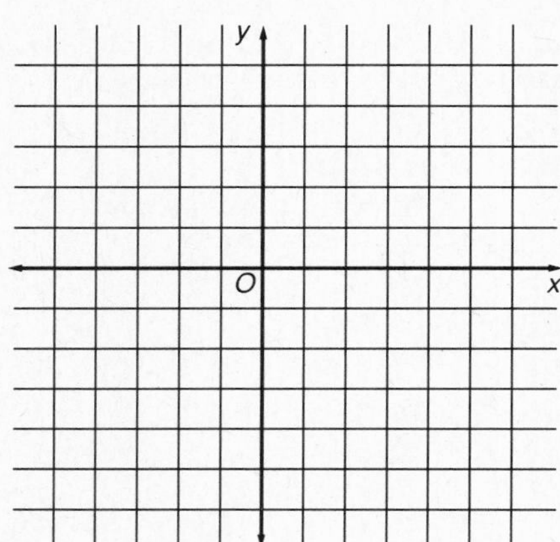

3. $x^2 + y^2 - 6x - 12y + 36 = 0$ **(3, 6); 3**

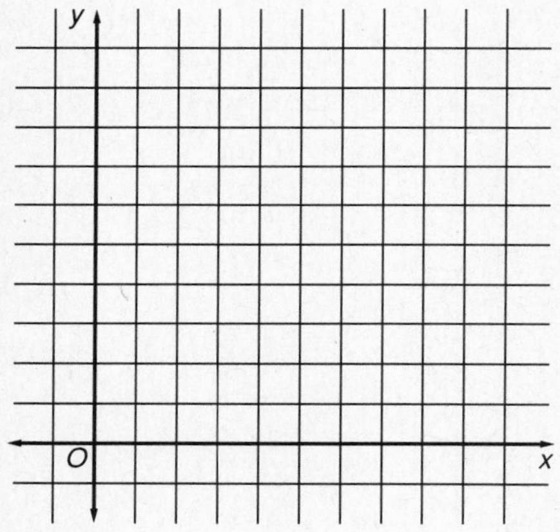

4. $x^2 + y^2 + 2x + 6y = 26$ **(−1, −3); 6**

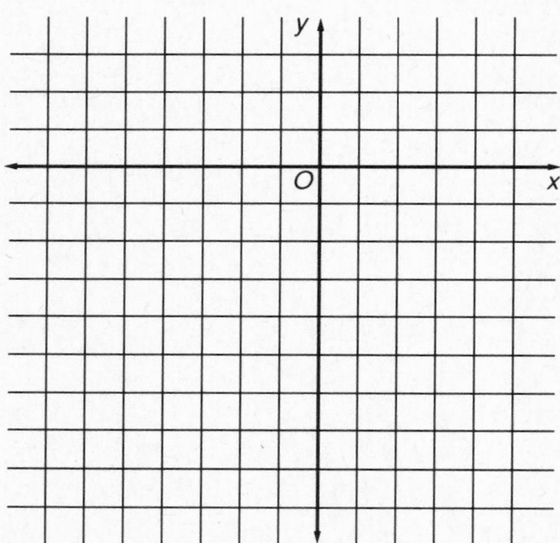

Write an equation for each circle whose center and radius are given.

5. center $(-4, 2)$; radius 8
$(x + 4)^2 + (y - 2)^2 = 64$

6. center $(5, -6)$; radius 11
$(x - 5)^2 + (y + 6)^2 = 121$

7. center $\left(-\frac{1}{4}, -\sqrt{3}\right)$; radius $5\sqrt{2}$
$\left(x + \frac{1}{4}\right)^2 + (y + \sqrt{3})^2 = 50$

8. center $\left(3.8, 1\frac{1}{3}\right)$; radius $\frac{3}{7}$
$(x - 3.8)^2 + \left(y - 1\frac{1}{3}\right)^2 = \frac{9}{49}$

Glencoe Division, Macmillan/McGraw-Hill

NAME ______________________ DATE ____________

9-4 Practice Worksheet

Ellipses

Find the center, foci, and lengths of the major and minor axes for each ellipse whose equation is given. Then draw the graph.

1. $\frac{x^2}{9} + \frac{y^2}{16} = 1$

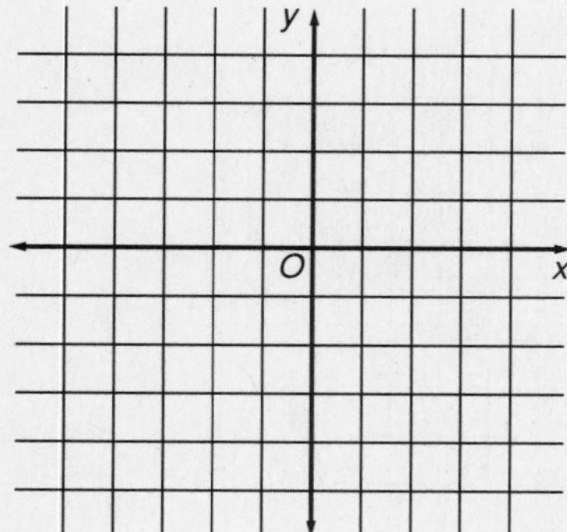

2. $16x^2 + y^2 = 64$

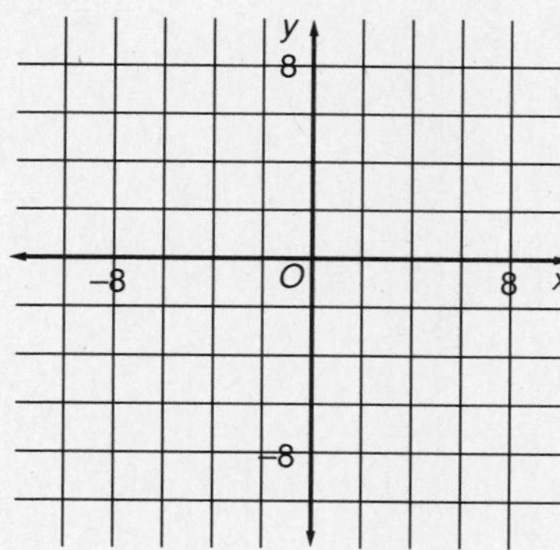

3. $\frac{(x-3)^2}{1} + \frac{(y-1)^2}{36} = 1$

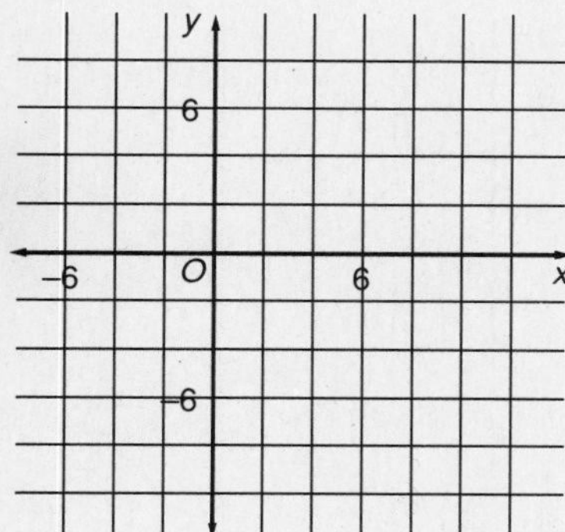

4. $\frac{(x+4)^2}{49} + \frac{(y+3)^2}{25} = 1$

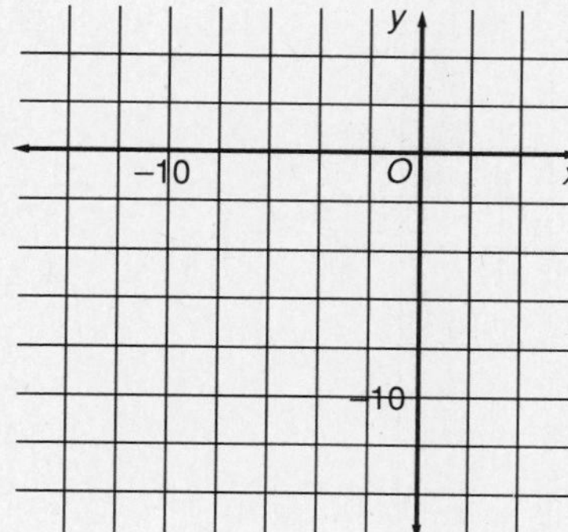

Write the equation of each ellipse described below.

5. The foci are at (4, 0) and (−4, 0). The endpoints of the minor axis are at (0, 2) and (0, −2).

6. The center has coordinates (2, −4). The minor axis is parallel to the x-axis with a length of 6. The major axis has a length of 10.

Glencoe Division, Macmillan/McGraw-Hill

NAME ____________________ DATE ____________

9-4 Practice Worksheet

Ellipses

Find the center, foci, and lengths of the major and minor axes for each ellipse whose equation is given. Then draw the graph.

1. $\frac{x^2}{9} + \frac{y^2}{16} = 1$ $(0, 0); (0, \pm\sqrt{7});$ $8; 6$

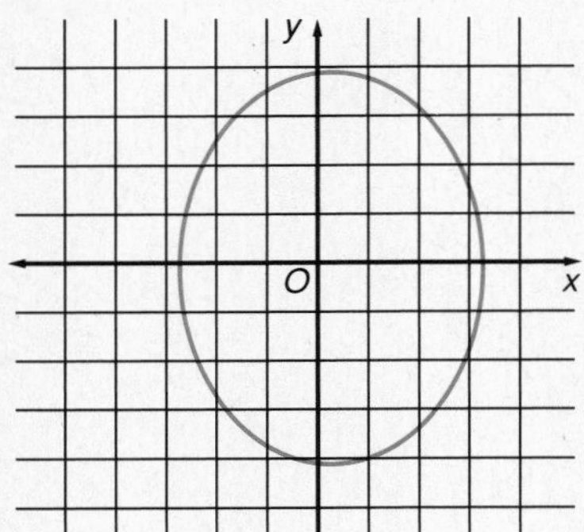

2. $16x^2 + y^2 = 64$ $(0, 0); (0, \pm2\sqrt{15});$ $16; 4$

3. $\frac{(x-3)^2}{1} + \frac{(y-1)^2}{36} = 1$ $(3, 1);$ $(3, 1 \pm \sqrt{35});$ $12; 2$

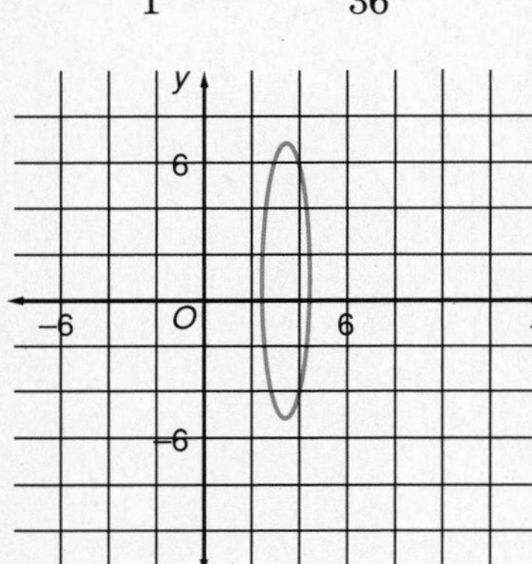

4. $\frac{(x+4)^2}{49} + \frac{(y+3)^2}{25} = 1$ $(-4, -3);$ $(-4 \pm 2\sqrt{6}, -3);$ $14; 10$

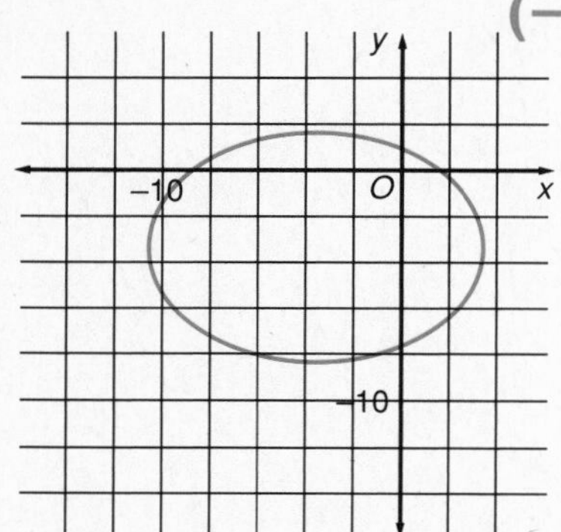

Write the equation of each ellipse described below.

5. The foci are at (4, 0) and (−4, 0). The endpoints of the minor axis are at (0, 2) and (0, −2).

$\frac{x^2}{20} + \frac{y^2}{4} = 1$

6. The center has coordinates (2, −4). The minor axis is parallel to the x-axis with a length of 6. The major axis has a length of 10.

$\frac{(x-2)^2}{9} + \frac{(y+4)^2}{25} = 1$

Glencoe Division, Macmillan/McGraw-Hill

NAME ____________________ DATE ____________

9-5 Practice Worksheet

Hyperbolas

Find the vertices, foci, and slopes of the asymptotes for each hyperbola whose equation is given. Then draw the graph.

1. $\frac{y^2}{9} - \frac{x^2}{36} = 1$

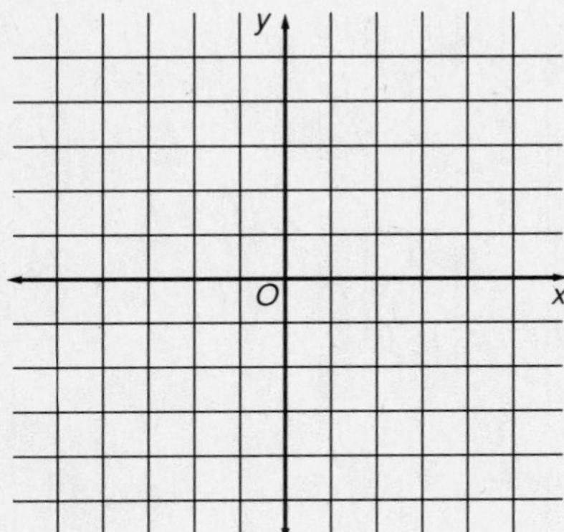

2. $y^2 - 4x^2 = 16$

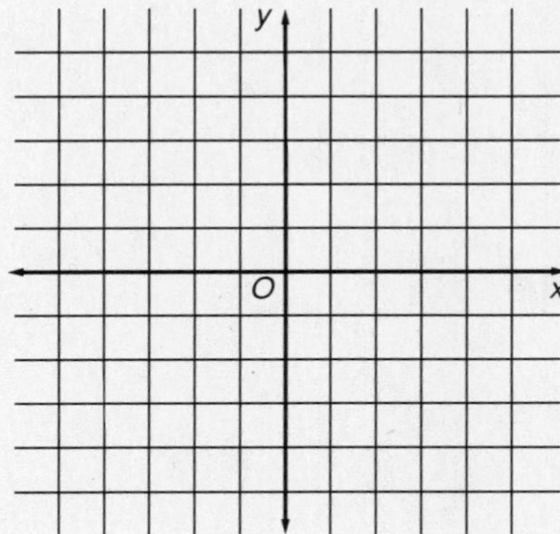

3. $\frac{(y-2)^2}{9} - \frac{(x+3)^2}{25} = 1$

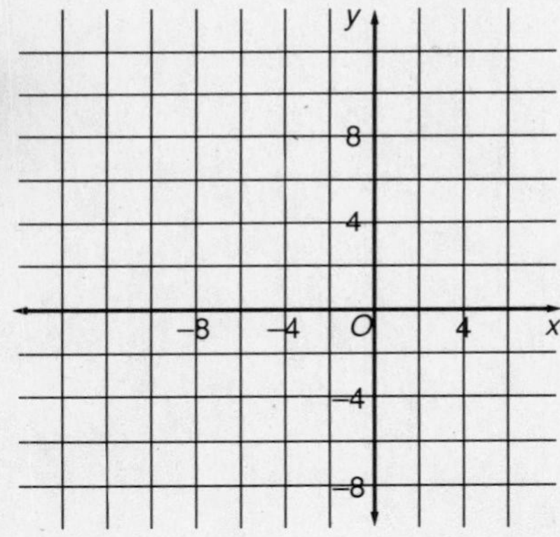

4. $\frac{(x-1)^2}{64} - \frac{(y+4)^2}{16} = 1$

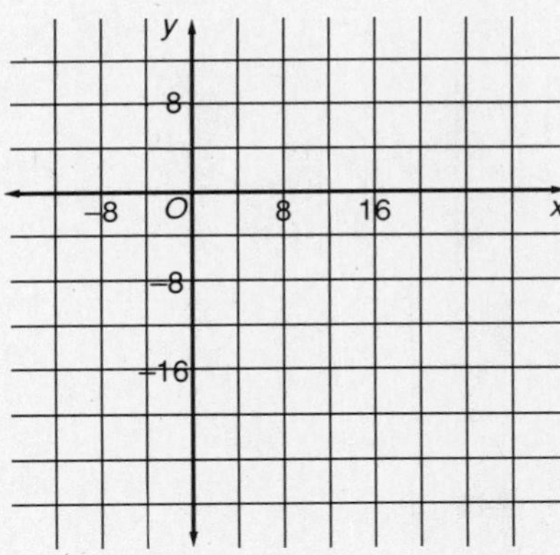

5. $4y^2 - x^2 - 16y + 2x + 11 = 0$

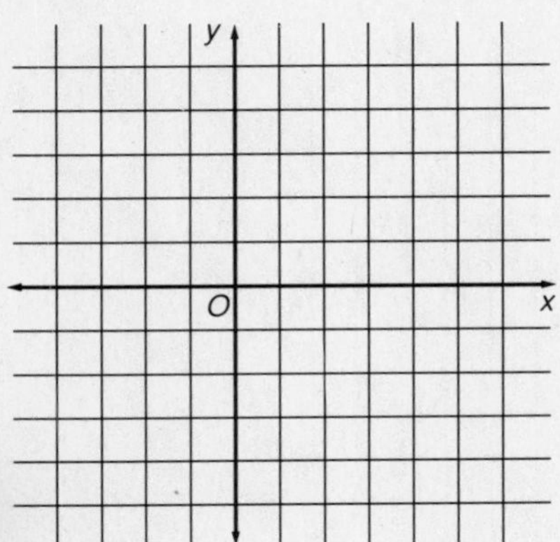

6. $3y^2 - 4x^2 + 12y + 24x = 36$

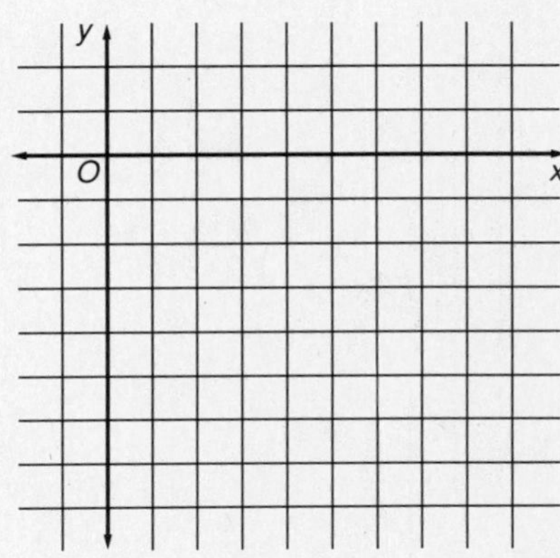

NAME ______________________ DATE ____________

9-5 Practice Worksheet

Hyperbolas

Find the vertices, foci, and slopes of the asymptotes for each hyperbola whose equation is given. Then draw the graph.

1. $\frac{y^2}{9} - \frac{x^2}{36} = 1$ **$(0, \pm 3); (0, \pm 3\sqrt{5}); \pm\frac{1}{2}$**

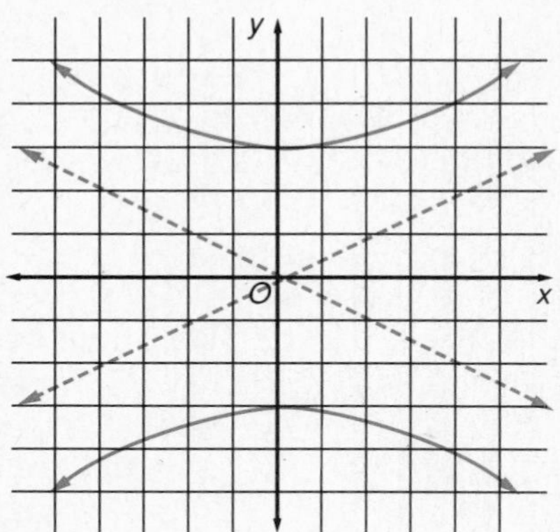

2. $y^2 - 4x^2 = 16$

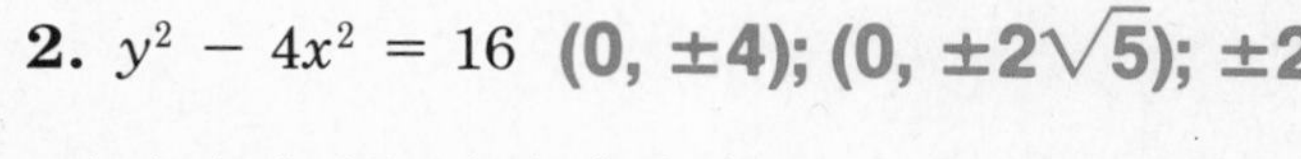
$(0, \pm 4); (0, \pm 2\sqrt{5}); \pm 2$

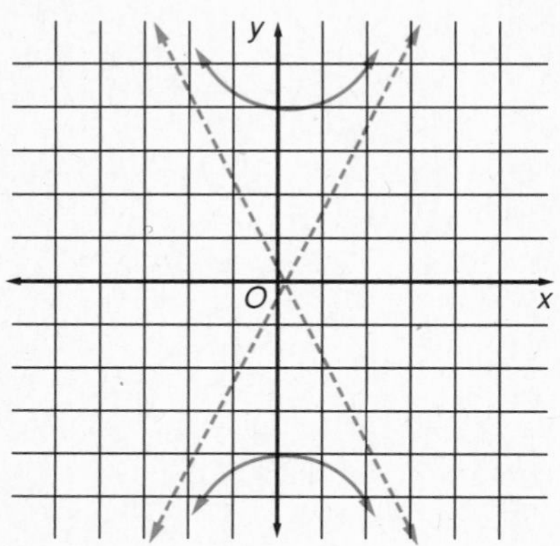

3. $\frac{(y-2)^2}{9} - \frac{(x+3)^2}{25} = 1$ **$(-3, 5), (-3, -1); (-3, 2 \pm \sqrt{34}); \pm\frac{3}{5}$**

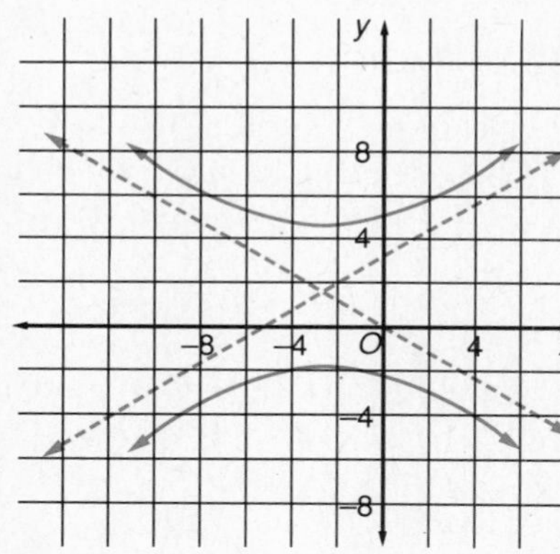

4. $\frac{(x-1)^2}{64} - \frac{(y+4)^2}{16} = 1$ **$(9, -4), (-7, -4); (1 \pm 4\sqrt{5}, -4); \pm\frac{1}{2}$**

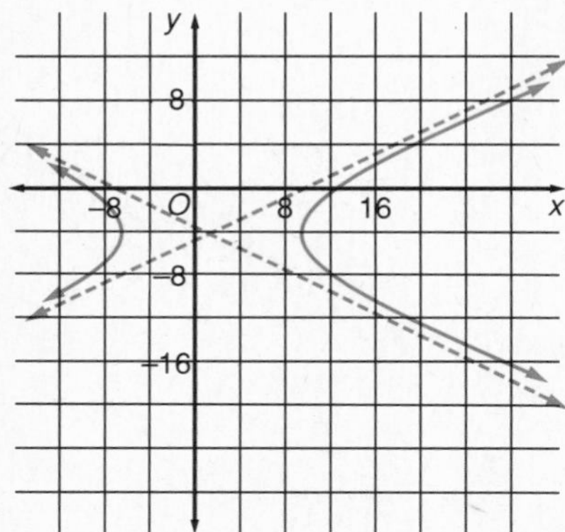

5. $4y^2 - x^2 - 16y + 2x + 11 = 0$ **$(1, 3), (1, 1); (1, 2 \pm \sqrt{5}); \pm\frac{1}{2}$**

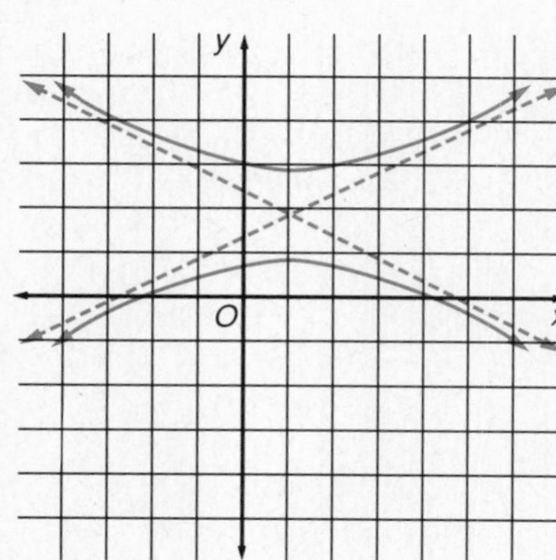

6. $3y^2 - 4x^2 + 12y + 24x = 36$ **$(3, 0), (3, -4); (3, -2 \pm \sqrt{7}); \pm\frac{2\sqrt{3}}{3}$**

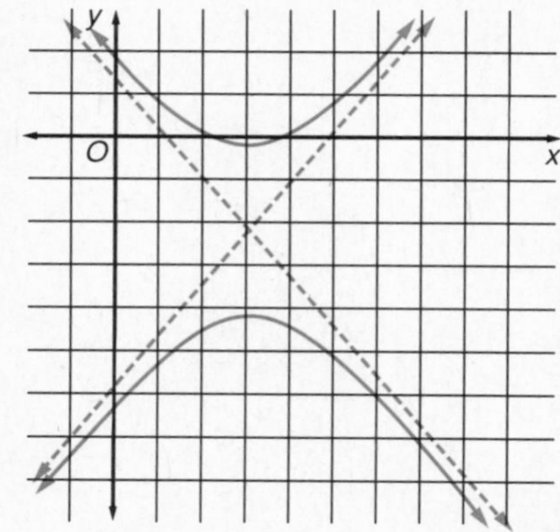

NAME ______________________ DATE ____________

9-6 Practice Worksheet

Problem Solving Strategy: Use a Simulation

Solve. Use any strategy.

1. Yummy cereal puts six different prizes in their boxes of cereal, one per box. If each prize is assigned a number 1 through 6, use the following trials to predict how many boxes of cereal you would have to buy before you get all six prizes.

Trials	Number of boxes
1: 1 2 3 6 5 2 3 5 1 4	
2: 1 1 2 5 6 2 1 4 5 6 1 3	
3: 3 2 6 1 3 5 4	
4: 5 6 5 4 5 3 1 5 6 4 6 3 2	
5: 4 3 4 5 5 6 4 3 3 3 6 5 2 2 2 1	
6: 4 2 3 4 5 3 2 4 4 1 3 2 5 4 4 3 6	

a. What device could you use to simulate this solution?

b. Would more trials permit better predictions?

2. Maria's batting average is 0.2000. Use 0 and 1 to represent hits and 2-9 to represent misses. Use the following trials to predict how many hits Maria will get if she is at bat 50 times.

Trials	Hits	Times at bat
1: 1 9 0 2 4 6 7 9 8 5 1		
2: 4 3 2 5 7 9 8 6 1 2 0		
3: 4 3 8 9 7 1 4 0 2 7 9 8 6 2		
4: 5 6 9 3 8 7 2 4 5 6 9 8 7 9 4		
5: 8 9 5 6 7 4 3 5 7 9 8 4 7 1		

Glencoe Division, Macmillan/McGraw-Hill

NAME ______________________ DATE ____________

9-6 Practice Worksheet

Problem Solving Strategy: Use a Simulation

Solve. Use any strategy.

1. Yummy cereal puts six different prizes in their boxes of cereal, one per box. If each prize is assigned a number 1 through 6, use the following trials to predict how many boxes of cereal you would have to buy before you get all six prizes.

Trials	Number of boxes
1: 1 2 3 6 5 2 3 5 1 4	10
2: 1 1 2 5 6 2 1 4 5 6 1 3	12
3: 3 2 6 1 3 5 4	7
4: 5 6 5 4 5 3 1 5 6 4 6 3 2	13
5: 4 3 4 5 5 6 4 3 3 3 6 5 2 2 2 1	16
6: 4 2 3 4 5 3 2 4 4 1 3 2 5 4 4 3 6	17

13 boxes

a. What device could you use to simulate this solution? **die**

b. Would more trials permit better predictions? **yes**

2. Maria's batting average is 0.2000. Use 0 and 1 to represent hits and 2-9 to represent misses. Use the following trials to predict how many hits Maria will get if she is at bat 50 times.

Trials	Hits	Times at bat
1: 1 9 0 2 4 6 7 9 8 5 1	3	11
2: 4 3 2 5 7 9 8 6 1 2 0	2	11
3: 4 3 8 9 7 1 4 0 2 7 9 8 6 2	2	14
4: 5 6 9 3 8 7 2 4 5 6 9 8 7 9 4	0	15
5: 8 9 5 6 7 4 3 5 7 9 8 4 7 1	1	14

about 6 hits

Glencoe Division, Macmillan/McGraw-Hill

NAME ______________________ DATE __________

9-7

Practice Worksheet

Conic Sections

Write the standard form of each equation. State whether the graph of the equation is a parabola, a circle, an ellipse, or a hyperbola. Then graph the equation.

1. $y^2 = -3x$

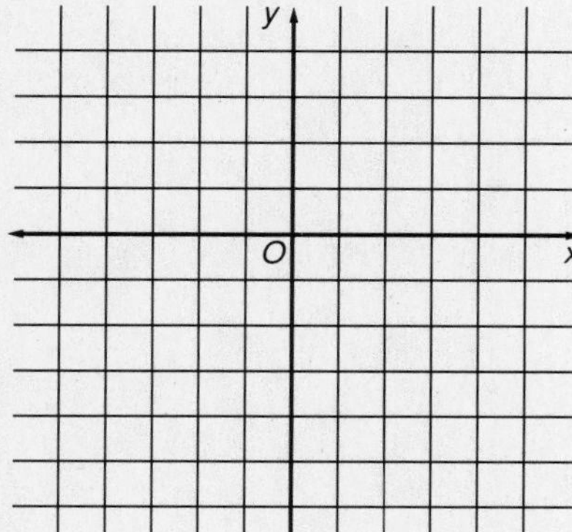

2. $x^2 + y^2 + 6x = 7$

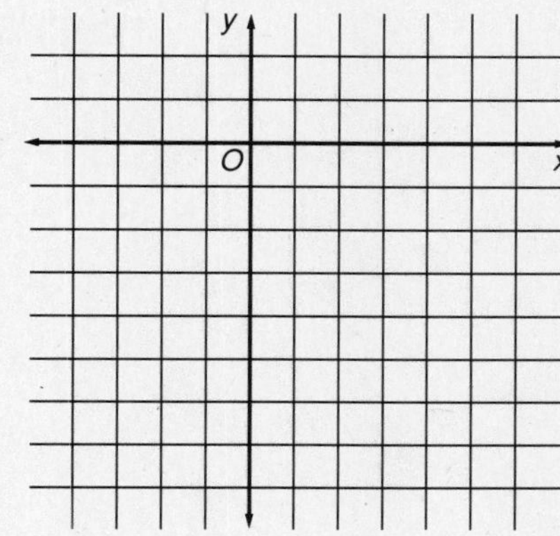

3. $5x^2 - 6y^2 - 30x - 12y + 9 = 0$

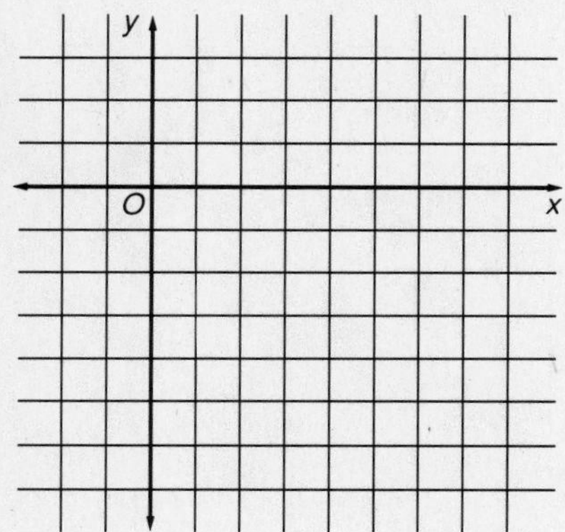

4. $3x^2 = 8 - 4y^2 - 8y$

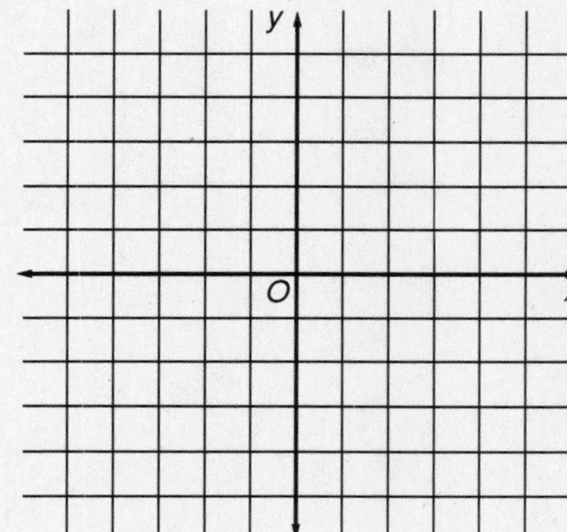

5. $5y^2 = 10 - 4x^2$

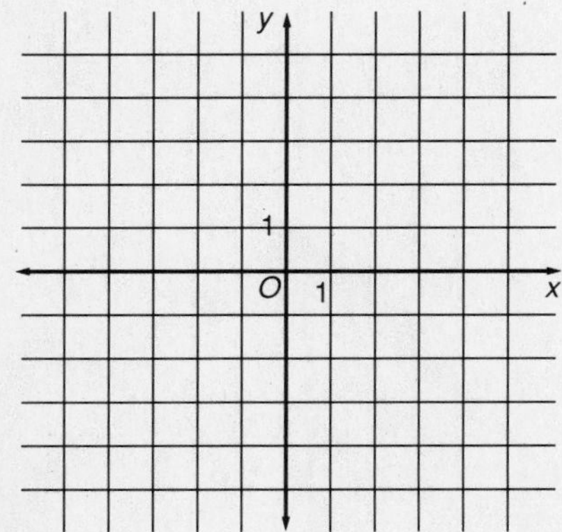

6. $5x^2 + 2y^2 + 30x - 16y + 67 = 0$

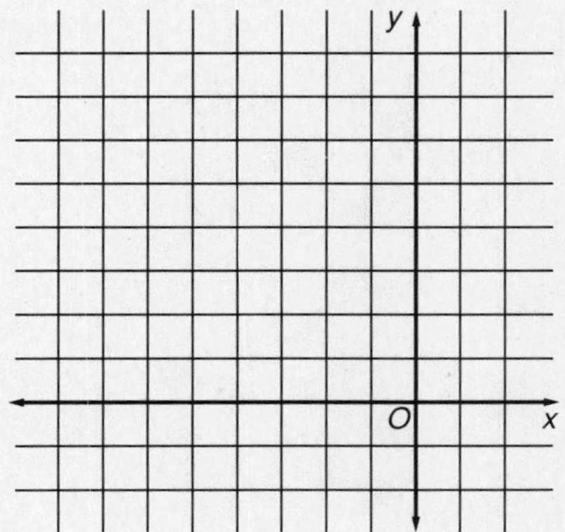

NAME ______________________ DATE ____________

9-7 Practice Worksheet

Conic Sections

Write the standard form of each equation. State whether the graph of the equation is a parabola, a circle, an ellipse, or a hyperbola. Then graph the equation.

1. $y^2 = -3x$ **$x = -\frac{1}{3}(y - 0)^2 + 0$; parabola**

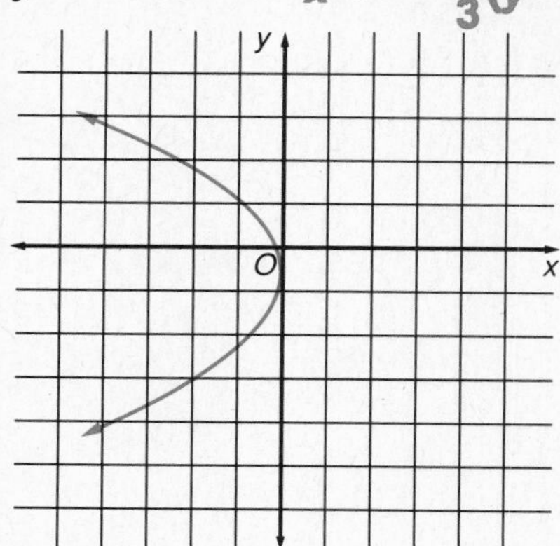

2. $x^2 + y^2 + 6x = 7$ **$(x - 3)^2 + (y - 0)^2 = 16$; circle**

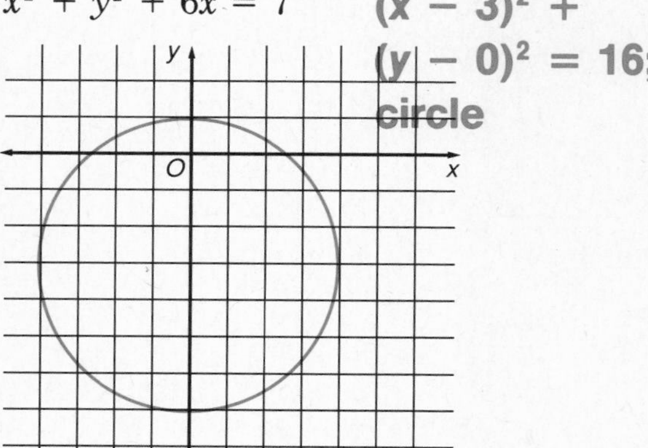

3. $5x^2 - 6y^2 - 30x - 12y + 9 = 0$ **$\frac{(x - 3)^2}{6} - \frac{(y + 1)^2}{5} = 1$; hyperbola**

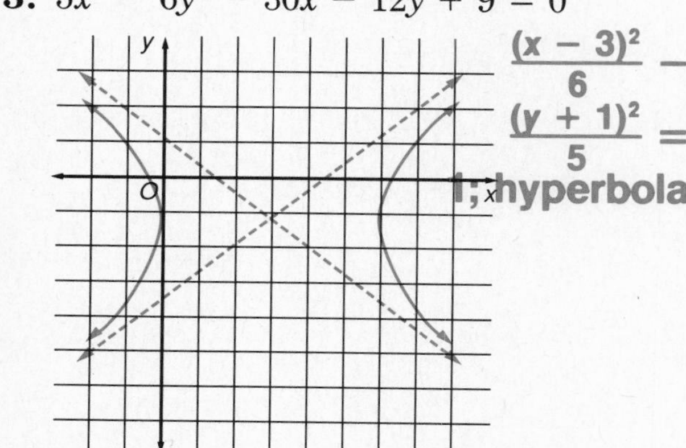

4. $3x^2 = 8 - 4y^2 - 8y$ **$\frac{(x - 0)^2}{4} + \frac{(y + 1)^2}{3} = 1$; ellipse**

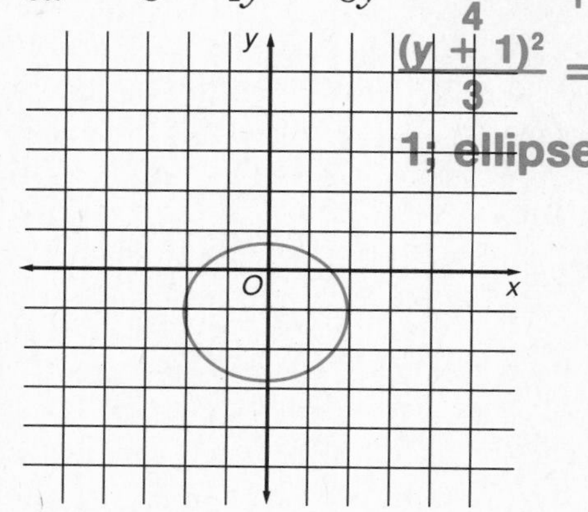

5. $5y^2 = 10 - 4x^2$ **$\frac{x^2}{\frac{5}{2}} + \frac{y^2}{2} = 1$; ellipse**

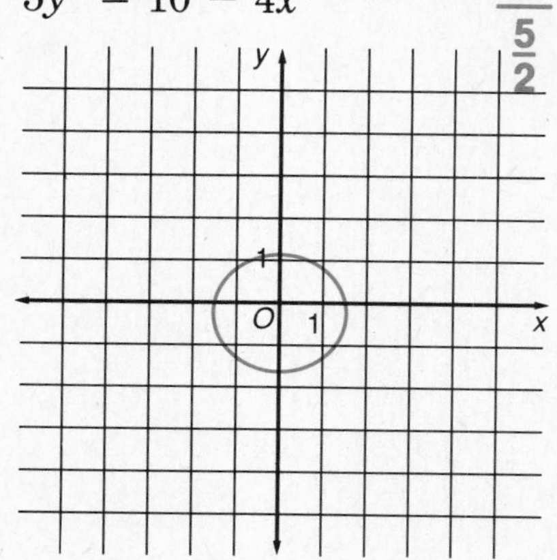

6. $5x^2 + 2y^2 + 30x - 16y + 67 = 0$ **$\frac{(x + 3)^2}{2} + \frac{(y - 4)^2}{5} = 1$; ellipse**

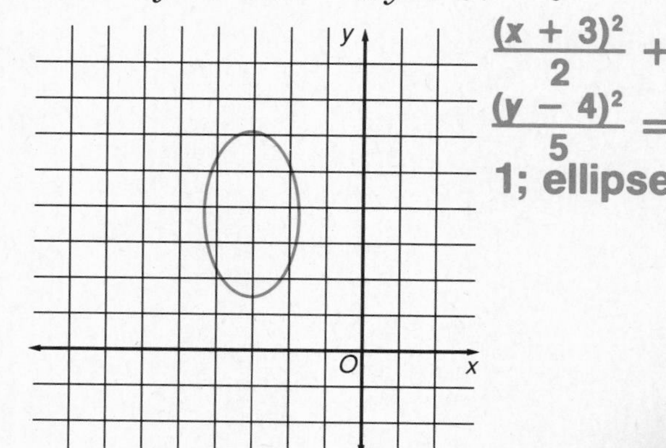

Glencoe Division, Macmillan/McGraw-Hill

NAME ____________________ DATE ____________

9-8 Practice Worksheet

Graphing Quadratic Systems

Graph each system of equations. Then find the solutions of each system.

1. $y = x^2$
$y = -x + 2$

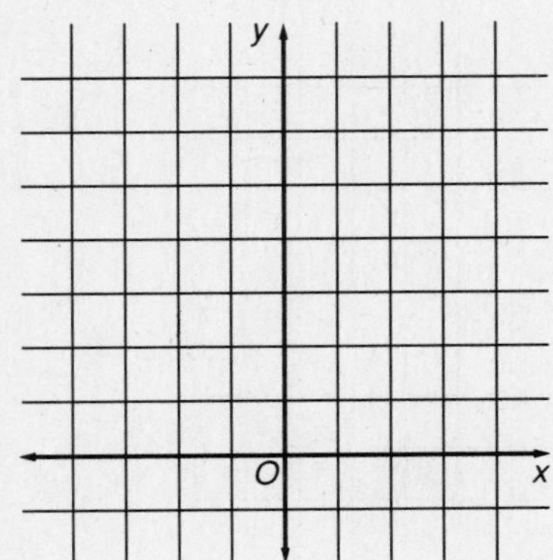

2. $x^2 + y^2 = 16$
$x - y = 4$

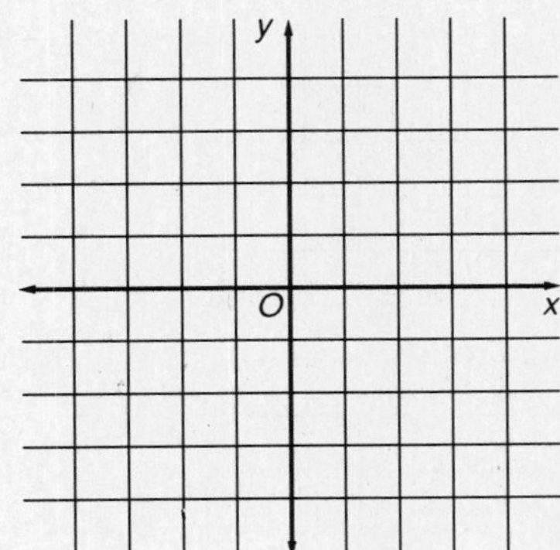

3. $4y^2 - 9x^2 = 36$
$4x^2 - 9y^2 = 36$

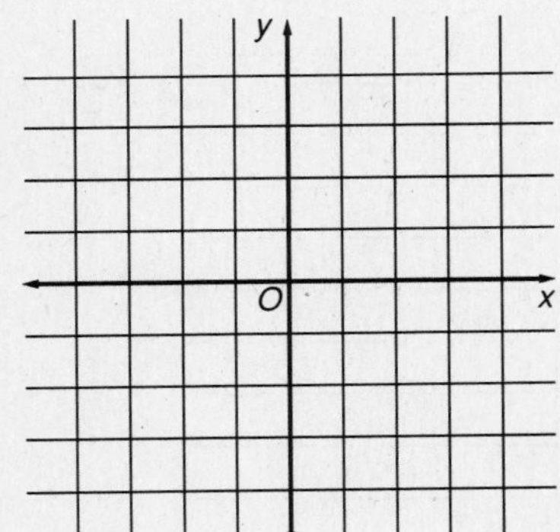

4. $y = -x^2 + 2x$
$y = x^2 - 2x$

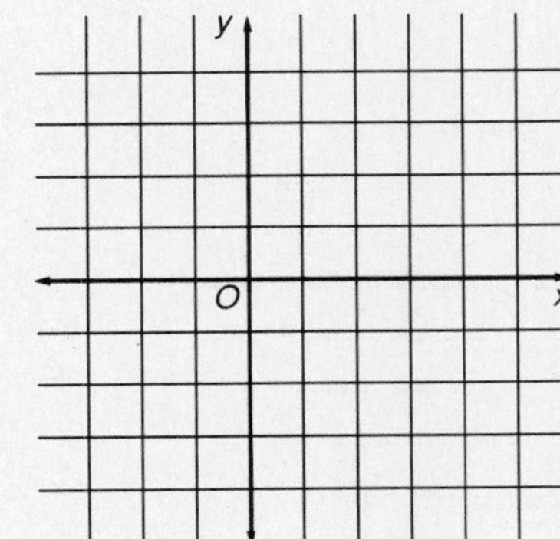

5. $xy = 8$
$y = x^2$

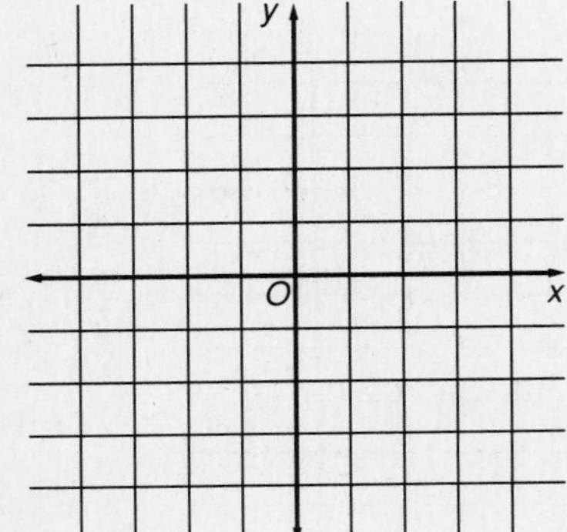

6. $(x - 3)^2 + 9(y - 3)^2 = 9$
$x = \frac{1}{4}(y - 3)^2 - 1$

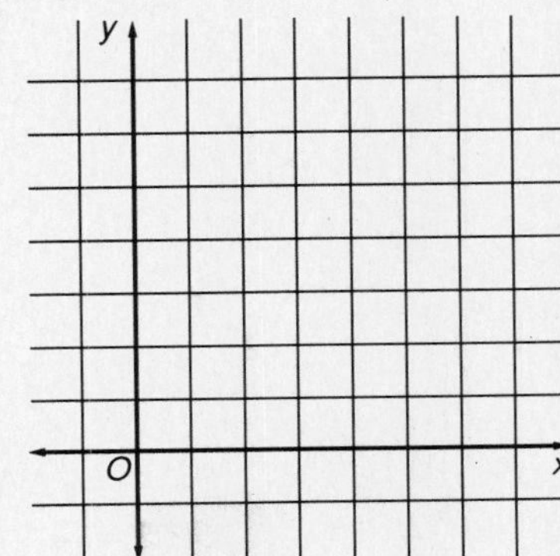

NAME ______________________ DATE ____________

9-8 Practice Worksheet

Graphing Quadratic Systems

Graph each system of equations. Then find the solutions of each system.

1. $y = x^2$
$y = -x + 2$ **(−2, 4), (1, 1)**

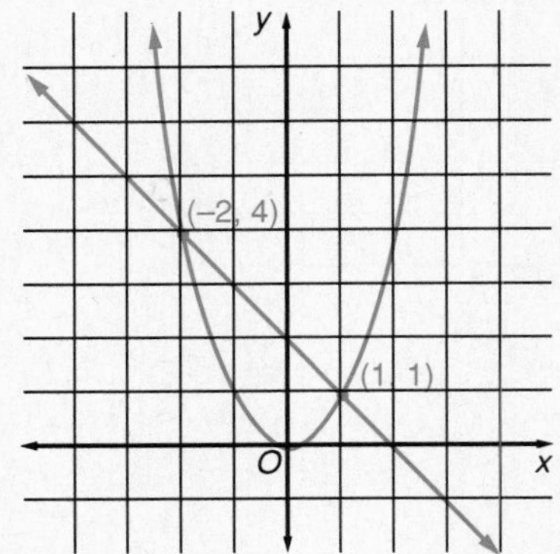

2. $x^2 + y^2 = 16$
$x - y = 4$ **(4, 0), (0, −4)**

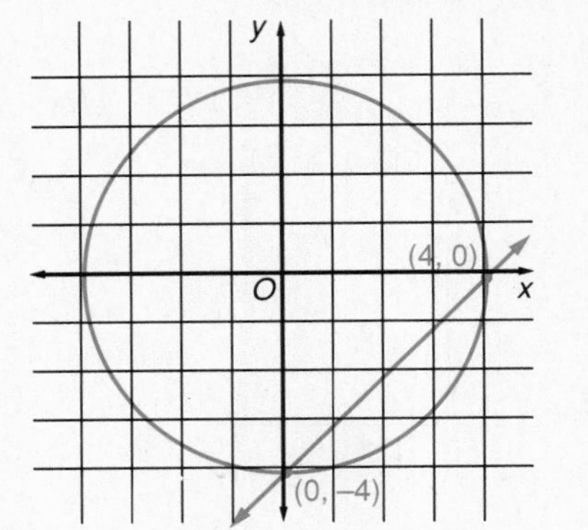

3. $4y^2 - 9x^2 = 36$
$4x^2 - 9y^2 = 36$ **No solutions**

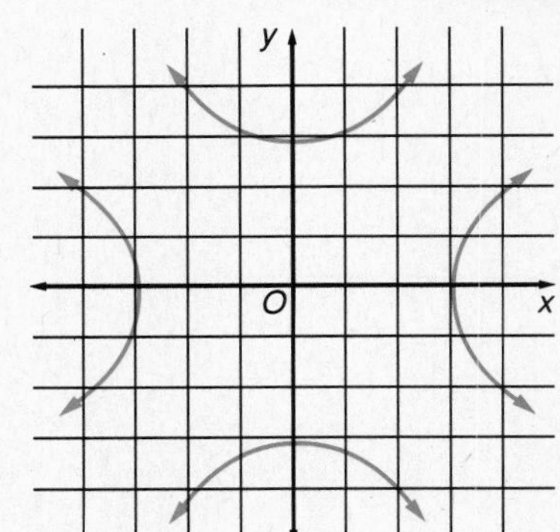

4. $y = -x^2 + 2x$
$y = x^2 - 2x$ **(0, 0), (2, 0)**

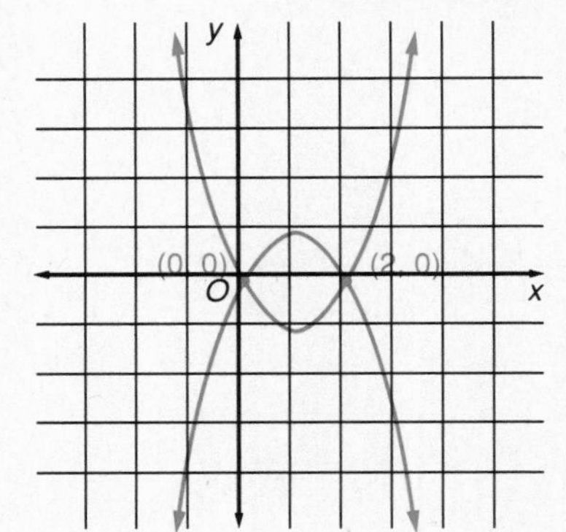

5. $xy = 8$
$y = x^2$ **(2, 4)**

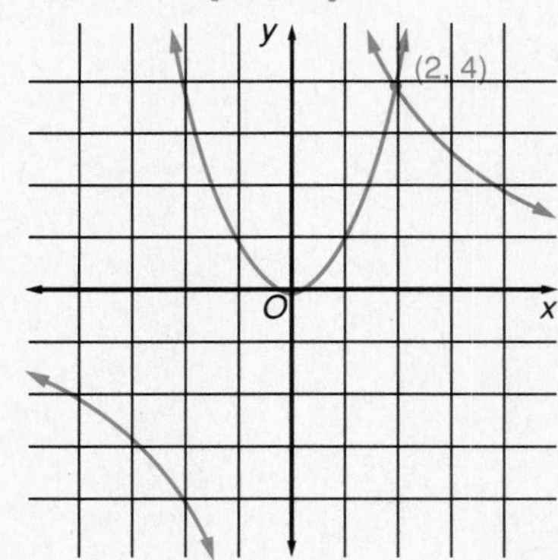

6. $(x - 3)^2 + 9(y - 3)^2 = 9$
$x = \frac{1}{4}(y - 3)^2 - 1$ **No solutions**

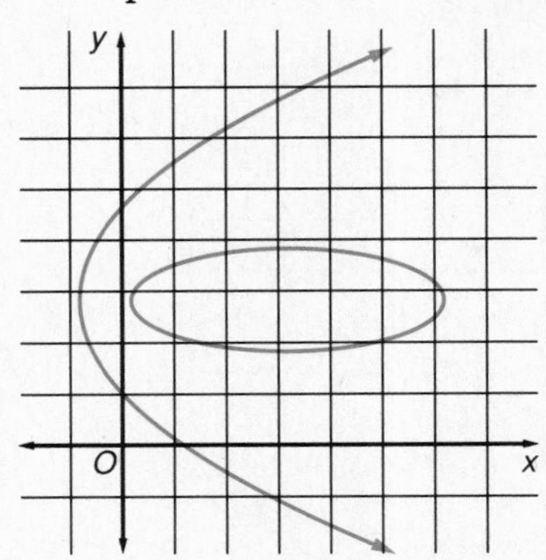

Glencoe Division, Macmillan/McGraw-Hill

NAME ______________________ DATE ____________

9-9 Practice Worksheet

Solving Quadratic Systems

Solve each system of equations.

1. $(x - 2)^2 + y^2 = 5$
$x - y = 1$

2. $x = 2(y + 1)^2 - 6$
$x + 3y = 5$

3. $y^2 - 3x^2 = 6$
$y = 2x - 1$

4. $x + 2y^2 = 4$
$y = -x + 1$

5. $x^2 = 8y$
$(x - 2)^2 = 8y$

6. $\frac{x^2}{4} + \frac{y^2}{9} = 1$
$y^2 = \frac{15}{4}x$

7. $2x^2 + 5y^2 = 53$
$3x^2 - 2y^2 = -6$

8. $x^2 + y^2 = 25$
$16x^2 + 25y^2 = 400$

Solve each system of inequalities by graphing.

9. $x^2 + y^2 < 36$
$x^2 + y^2 \geq 16$

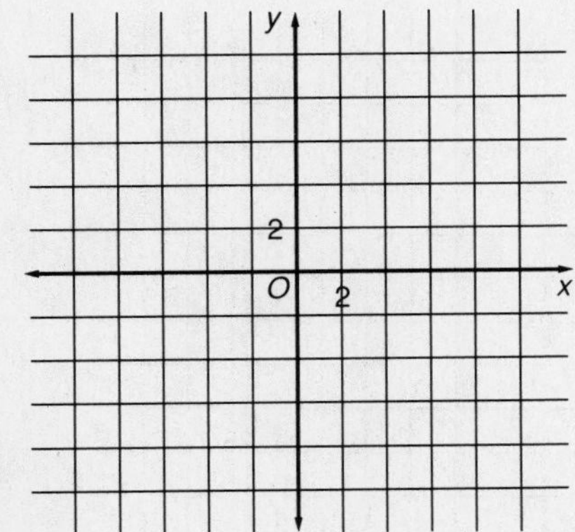

10. $\frac{(x + 2)^2}{4} + \frac{(y - 3)^2}{16} \leq 1$
$(x + 1)^2 + (y - 2)^2 \leq 4$

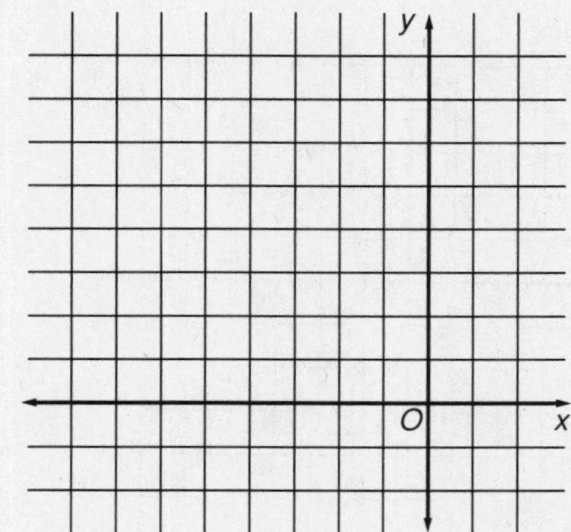

NAME ______________________ DATE ____________

9-9

Practice Worksheet

Solving Quadratic Systems

Solve each system of equations.

1. $(x - 2)^2 + y^2 = 5$
$x - y = 1$
(0, −1), (3, 2)

2. $x = 2(y + 1)^2 - 6$
$x + 3y = 5$
$(2, 1), \left(\frac{37}{2}, -\frac{9}{2}\right)$

3. $y^2 - 3x^2 = 6$
$y = 2x - 1$
(−1, −3), (5, 9)

4. $x + 2y^2 = 4$
$y = -x + 1$
$(2, -1), \left(-\frac{1}{2}, \frac{3}{2}\right)$

5. $x^2 = 8y$
$(x - 2)^2 = 8y$
$\left(1, \frac{1}{8}\right)$

6. $\frac{x^2}{4} + \frac{y^2}{9} = 1$
$y^2 = \frac{15}{4}x$
$\left(\frac{4}{3}, \pm\sqrt{5}\right)$

7. $2x^2 + 5y^2 = 53$
$3x^2 - 2y^2 = -6$
(2, ±3), (−2, ±3)

8. $x^2 + y^2 = 25$
$16x^2 + 25y^2 = 400$
(±5, 0)

Solve each system of inequalities by graphing.

9. $x^2 + y^2 < 36$
$x^2 + y^2 \geq 16$

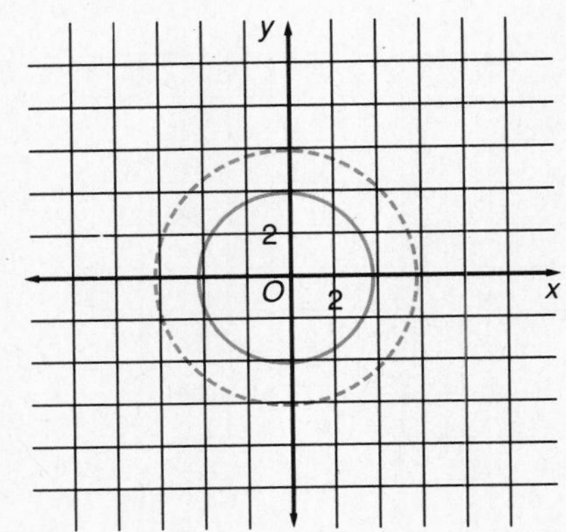

10. $\frac{(x + 2)^2}{4} + \frac{(y - 3)^2}{16} \leq 1$
$(x + 1)^2 + (y - 2)^2 \leq 4$

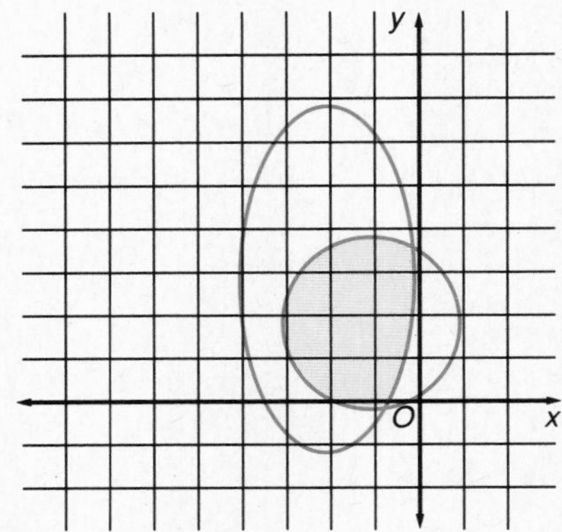

NAME ______________________ DATE ______________

10-1 Practice Worksheet

Polynomial Functions

Find f(3) for each function f(x).

1. $f(x) = x^2 - 6x + 2$

2. $f(x) = x^4 - x^2$

3. $f(x) = -5x^3 + 6x^2 - x - 4$

4. $f(x) = \frac{x^2}{6} + 4x - 10$

Find h(−2) for each function h(x).

5. $h(x) = x^3 - x^5$

6. $h(x) = -7x^2 + 5x + 9$

7. $h(x) = x^2 - \frac{5x}{4} + 6$

8. $h(x) = 3x^3 - 7x^2 + 2x - 5$

Find g(x + h) for each function g(x).

9. $g(x) = 6x - 7$

10. $g(x) = 3x^2 - 4x + 6$

11. $g(x) = -2x^2 + 5x - 4$

12. $g(x) = x^3 - 2x$

Find 5[f(x + 2)] for each function f(x).

13. $f(x) = 3x^2 - 4$

14. $f(x) = x + 8$

15. $f(x) = 3x - 4$

16. $f(x) = 2x^2 - 5x + 1$

Glencoe Division, Macmillan/McGraw-Hill

NAME ____________________ DATE __________

10-1 Practice Worksheet

Polynomial Functions

Find f(3) for each function f(x).

1. $f(x) = x^2 - 6x + 2$ **−7**

2. $f(x) = x^4 - x^2$ **72**

3. $f(x) = -5x^3 + 6x^2 - x - 4$ **−88**

4. $f(x) = \frac{x^2}{6} + 4x - 10$ $\frac{7}{2}$

Find h(−2) for each function h(x).

5. $h(x) = x^3 - x^5$ **24**

6. $h(x) = -7x^2 + 5x + 9$ **−29**

7. $h(x) = x^2 - \frac{5x}{4} + 6$ $\frac{25}{2}$

8. $h(x) = 3x^3 - 7x^2 + 2x - 5$ **−61**

Find g(x + h) for each function g(x).

9. $g(x) = 6x - 7$ $6x + 6h - 7$

10. $g(x) = 3x^2 - 4x + 6$
$3x^2 + 6xh + 3h^2 - 4x - 4h + 6$

11. $g(x) = -2x^2 + 5x - 4$
$-2x^2 - 4xh - 2h^2 + 5x + 5h - 4$

12. $g(x) = x^3 - 2x$
$x^3 + 3x^2h + 3xh^2 + h^3 - 2x - 2h$

Find 5[f(x + 2)] for each function f(x).

13. $f(x) = 3x^2 - 4$ $15x^2 + 60x + 40$

14. $f(x) = x + 8$ $5x + 50$

15. $f(x) = 3x - 4$
$15x + 10$

16. $f(x) = 2x^2 - 5x + 1$
$10x^2 + 15x - 5$

Glencoe Division, Macmillan/McGraw-Hill

NAME ______________________ DATE ____________

10-2 Practice Worksheet

The Remainder and Factor Theorems

Divide using synthetic division and write your answer in the form dividend = quotient · divisor + remainder. Is the binomial a factor of the polynomial?

1. $(4x^3 - 9x^2 - 10x - 2) \div (x - 3)$

2. $(2x^3 + 5x^2 - 9x + 20) \div (x + 4)$

3. $(x^4 - 6x^3 - 2x - 10) \div (x + 1)$

4. $(3x^4 - 9x^3 - 32x^2 + 54) \div (x - 5)$

Given a polynomial and one of its factors, find the remaining factors of the polynomial. Some factors may not be binomials.

5. $x^3 + 6x^2 - x - 30;\ x + 5$

6. $x^3 - 11x^2 + 36x - 36;\ x - 6$

7. $2x^3 + 3x^2 - 65x + 84;\ x - 4$

8. $2x^3 + 15x^2 - 14x - 48;\ x - 2$

9. $16x^5 + 32x^4 - x - 2;\ x + 2$

10. $x^4 - 3x^3 + 27x - 81;\ x - 3$

Find values for k so that each remainder is 5.

11. $(2x^2 - 8x + k) \div (x - 7)$

12. $(x^3 + 4x^2 + kx + 8) \div (x + 2)$

13. $(x^4 + kx^3 - 7x^2 + 8x + 25) \div (x - 2)$

14. $(x^2 + 2x + 6) \div (x + k)$

Glencoe Division, Macmillan/McGraw-Hill

NAME ______________________ DATE ______________

10-2 Practice Worksheet

The Remainder and Factor Theorems

Divide using synthetic division and write your answer in the form dividend = quotient · divisor + remainder. Is the binomial a factor of the polynomial?

1. $(4x^3 - 9x^2 - 10x - 2) \div (x - 3)$
$4x^3 - 9x^2 - 10x - 2 =$
$(4x^2 + 3x - 1)(x - 3) - 5;$
no

2. $(2x^3 + 5x^2 - 9x + 20) \div (x + 4)$
$2x^3 + 5x^2 - 9x + 20 =$
$(2x^2 - 3x + 3)(x + 4) + 8;$
no

3. $(x^4 - 6x^3 - 2x - 10) \div (x + 1)$
$x^4 - 6x^3 - 2x - 10 =$
$(x^3 - 7x^2 + 7x - 9)(x + 1) - 1;$
no

4. $(3x^4 - 9x^3 - 32x^2 + 54) \div (x - 5)$
$3x^4 - 9x^3 - 32x^2 + 54 =$
$(3x^3 + 6x^2 - 2x - 10)(x - 5) + 4;$
no

Given a polynomial and one of its factors, find the remaining factors of the polynomial. Some factors may not be binomials.

5. $x^3 + 6x^2 - x - 30;\ x + 5$
$x + 3, x - 2$

6. $x^3 - 11x^2 + 36x - 36;\ x - 6$
$x - 3, x - 2$

7. $2x^3 + 3x^2 - 65x + 84;\ x - 4$
$2x - 3, x + 7$

8. $2x^3 + 15x^2 - 14x - 48;\ x - 2$
$2x + 3, x + 8$

9. $16x^5 + 32x^4 - x - 2;\ x + 2$
$4x^2 + 1, 2x + 1, 2x - 1$

10. $x^4 - 3x^3 + 27x - 81;\ x - 3$
$x + 3, x^2 - 3x + 9$

Find values for k so that each remainder is 5.

11. $(2x^2 - 8x + k) \div (x - 7)$
-37

12. $(x^3 + 4x^2 + kx + 8) \div (x + 2)$
5.5

13. $(x^4 + kx^3 - 7x^2 + 8x + 25) \div (x - 2)$
-3

14. $(x^2 + 2x + 6) \div (x + k)$
1

10-3 NAME ______________________ DATE ______________

Practice Worksheet

Problem Solving

Use any strategy.

1. Alyson purchased a total of 12 muffins at a bakery and paid $7.80 (not including tax). Some of the muffins were bran muffins and cost $0.60 apiece. The other muffins were banana nut muffins and cost $0.75 apiece. How many muffins of each kind did she buy?

2. On the first day of school, Kyle lost his class schedule. He remembers that Math is not the first class. History is before English and Band. Band is after History and English. Neither Math or English is the fourth class, and Math is before English. Reconstruct Kyle's class schedule.

Glencoe Division, Macmillan/McGraw-Hill

NAME ______________________ DATE ______________

10-3 Practice Worksheet

Problem Solving

Use any strategy.

1. Alyson purchased a total of 12 muffins at a bakery and paid $7.80 (not including tax). Some of the muffins were bran muffins and cost $0.60 apiece. The other muffins were banana nut muffins and cost $0.75 apiece. How many muffins of each kind did she buy?
8 bran muffins, 4 banana nut muffins

2. On the first day of school, Kyle lost his class schedule. He remembers that Math is not the first class. History is before English and Band. Band is after History and English. Neither Math or English is the fourth class, and Math is before English. Reconstruct Kyle's class schedule.
1st: History
2nd: Math
3rd: English
4th: Band

Glencoe Division, Macmillan/McGraw-Hill

NAME ______________________ DATE ______________

10-4 Practice Worksheet

Roots and Zeros

For each function, state the number of positive real zeros, negative real zeros, and imaginary zeros.

1. $f(x) = 2x^4 - 2x^3 + 2x^2 - x - 1$

2. $f(x) = 4x^3 - 2x^2 + x + 3$

3. $f(x) = 3x^4 + x^3 - 3x^2 + 7x + 5$

4. $f(x) = 7x^4 + 3x^3 - 2x^2 - x + 1$

5. $f(x) = x^3 + 2x^2 - 6x - 7$

6. $f(x) = x^5 - x^4 + x^3 + x - 7$

7. $f(x) = x^5 + x^4 - x^2 - x + 1$

8. $f(x) = 3x^4 + x^3 + 4x^2 - x - 4$

9. $f(x) = 3x^4 + 2x^3 + 4x + 7$

10. $f(x) = 5x^6 + 7x^4 + 8x^2 + 3$

Given a function and one of its zeros, find all of the zeros of the function.

11. $f(x) = x^3 - 7x^2 + 17x - 15;\ 2 + i$

12. $f(x) = x^3 + 6x + 20;\ 1 - 3i$

13. $g(x) = x^4 - 6x^3 + 6x^2 + 24x - 40;\ 3 + i$

14. $g(x) = x^3 - 3x^2 + 9x - 7;\ 1$

Write the polynomial function of least degree with integral coefficients that has the given zeros.

15. $6,\ 2i$

16. $4,\ -1,\ -3i$

17. $i,\ -5i$

18. $1 + 2i,\ 1 - i$

NAME ________________________ DATE ____________

10-4 Practice Worksheet

Roots and Zeros

For each function, state the number of positive real zeros, negative real zeros, and imaginary zeros.

1. $f(x) = 2x^4 - 2x^3 + 2x^2 - x - 1$
3 or 1; 1; 0 or 2

2. $f(x) = 4x^3 - 2x^2 + x + 3$
2 or 0; 1; 0 or 2

3. $f(x) = 3x^4 + x^3 - 3x^2 + 7x + 5$
2 or 0; 2 or 0; 0, 2, or 4

4. $f(x) = 7x^4 + 3x^3 - 2x^2 - x + 1$
2 or 0; 2 or 0; 0, 2, or 4

5. $f(x) = x^3 + 2x^2 - 6x - 7$
1; 2 or 0; 0 or 2

6. $f(x) = x^5 - x^4 + x^3 + x - 7$
3 or 1; 0; 2 or 4

7. $f(x) = x^5 + x^4 - x^2 - x + 1$
2 or 0; 3 or 1; 0, 2, or 4

8. $f(x) = 3x^4 + x^3 + 4x^2 - x - 4$
1; 3 or 1; 0 or 2

9. $f(x) = 3x^4 + 2x^3 + 4x + 7$
0; 2 or 0; 4 or 2

10. $f(x) = 5x^6 + 7x^4 + 8x^2 + 3$
0; 0; 6

Given a function and one of its zeros, find all of the zeros of the function.

11. $f(x) = x^3 - 7x^2 + 17x - 15;\ 2 + i$
$2 - i, 3$

12. $f(x) = x^3 + 6x + 20;\ 1 - 3i$
$1 + 3i, -2$

13. $g(x) = x^4 - 6x^3 + 6x^2 + 24x - 40;\ 3 + i$
$3 - i, 2, -2$

14. $g(x) = x^3 - 3x^2 + 9x - 7;\ 1$
$1 + i\sqrt{6}, 1 - i\sqrt{6}$

Write the polynomial function of least degree with integral coefficients that has the given zeros.

15. $6, 2i$
$f(x) = x^3 - 6x^2 + 4x - 24$

16. $4, -1, -3i$
$f(x) = x^4 - 3x^3 + 5x^2 - 27x - 36$

17. $i, -5i$
$f(x) = x^4 + 26x^2 + 25$

18. $1 + 2i, 1 - i$
$f(x) = x^4 - 4x^3 + 11x^2 - 14x + 10$

NAME ______________________ DATE ____________

10-5 Practice Worksheet

The Rational Zero Theorem

State all possible rational zeros for each function.

1. $f(x) = x^3 - 5x^2 + 2x + 12$

2. $f(x) = x^4 - 8x^3 + 7x - 14$

3. $f(x) = 5x^4 - 2x - 4$

4. $f(x) = 3x^5 - 7x^2 + x + 6$

Find all the rational zeros for each function.

5. $f(x) = x^3 + 3x^2 - 6x - 8$

6. $f(x) = x^3 + 7x^2 + 7x - 15$

7. $f(x) = x^3 - 9x^2 + 27x - 27$

8. $f(x) = x^3 - x^2 - 8x + 12$

9. $f(x) = x^4 - 3x^3 - 11x^2 + 3x + 10$

10. $f(x) = x^4 - 4x^3 - 7x^2 + 34x - 24$

11. $f(x) = x^4 - 2x^3 - 4x^2 + 11x - 6$

12. $f(x) = x^3 + 4x^2 - 2x + 15$

Find all zeros of each function.

13. $f(x) = 3x^3 - 4x^2 - 17x + 6$

14. $f(x) = 4x^3 - 12x^2 - x + 3$

15. $f(x) = 18x^3 + 9x^2 - 2x - 1$

16. $f(x) = 2x^3 + 3x^2 + 5x + 2$

17. $f(x) = 2x^4 + 7x^3 - 2x^2 - 19x - 12$

18. $f(x) = x^4 - 4x^3 + x^2 + 16x - 20$

NAME ______________________ DATE ____________

10-5

Practice Worksheet

The Rational Zero Theorem

State all possible rational zeros for each function.

1. $f(x) = x^3 - 5x^2 + 2x + 12$
$\pm 1, \pm 2, \pm 3, \pm 4, \pm 6, \pm 12$

2. $f(x) = x^4 - 8x^3 + 7x - 14$
$\pm 1, \pm 2, \pm 7, \pm 14$

3. $f(x) = 5x^4 - 2x - 4$
$\pm 1, \pm \frac{1}{5}; \pm 2, \pm \frac{2}{5}, \pm 4, \pm \frac{4}{5}$

4. $f(x) = 3x^5 - 7x^2 + x + 6$
$\pm 1, \pm \frac{1}{3}, \pm 2, \pm \frac{2}{3}, \pm 3, \pm 6$

Find all the rational zeros for each function.

5. $f(x) = x^3 + 3x^2 - 6x - 8$
$2, -1, -4$

6. $f(x) = x^3 + 7x^2 + 7x - 15$
$1, -3, -5$

7. $f(x) = x^3 - 9x^2 + 27x - 27$
3

8. $f(x) = x^3 - x^2 - 8x + 12$
$2, -3$

9. $f(x) = x^4 - 3x^3 - 11x^2 + 3x + 10$
$1, 5, -1, -2$

10. $f(x) = x^4 - 4x^3 - 7x^2 + 34x - 24$
$1, 2, 4, -3$

11. $f(x) = x^4 - 2x^3 - 4x^2 + 11x - 6$
$1, 2$

12. $f(x) = x^3 + 4x^2 - 2x + 15$
-5

Find all zeros of each function.

13. $f(x) = 3x^3 - 4x^2 - 17x + 6$
$-2, 3, \frac{1}{3}$

14. $f(x) = 4x^3 - 12x^2 - x + 3$
$3, \frac{1}{2}, -\frac{1}{2}$

15. $f(x) = 18x^3 + 9x^2 - 2x - 1$
$-\frac{1}{2}, \frac{1}{3}, -\frac{1}{3}$

16. $f(x) = 2x^3 + 3x^2 + 5x + 2$
$-\frac{1}{2}, \frac{-1 \pm i\sqrt{7}}{2}$

17. $f(x) = 2x^4 + 7x^3 - 2x^2 - 19x - 12$
$-1, -3, \frac{1 \pm \sqrt{33}}{4}$

18. $f(x) = x^4 - 4x^3 + x^2 + 16x - 20$
$2, -2, 2 \pm i$

Glencoe Division, Macmillan/McGraw-Hill

NAME ________________________ DATE ____________

10-6 Practice Worksheet

Graphing Polynomials and Approximating Zeros

Approximate to the nearest tenth the real zeros of each function.

1. $f(x) = x^3 - 3x^2 + 4$

2. $f(x) = x^3 - 7x + 6$

3. $f(x) = x^3 + 6x^2 + 11x + 3$

4. $f(x) = x^3 - 6x^2 + 8x - 2$

5. $f(x) = x^3 + 3x^2 - 4x - 6$

6. $f(x) = x^3 + x^2 - x + 15$

7. $f(x) = x^4 - 2x^3 + 2x^2 - 5x + 4$

8. $f(x) = x^6 + 2x^4 - x^2 - 4$

Graph each function.

9. $f(x) = (x - 2)^3$

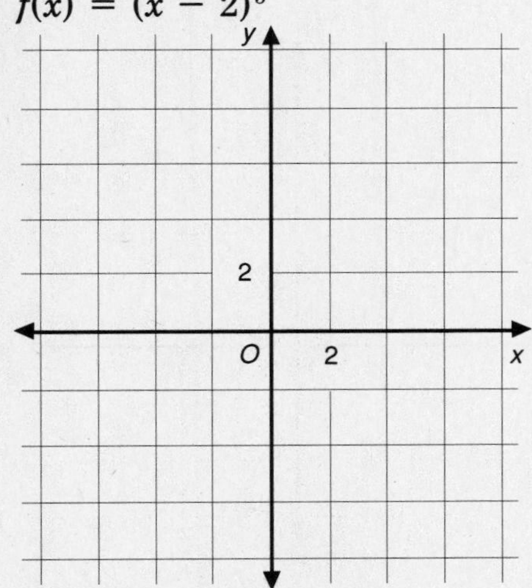

10. $f(x) = (x + 1)^4 - 3$

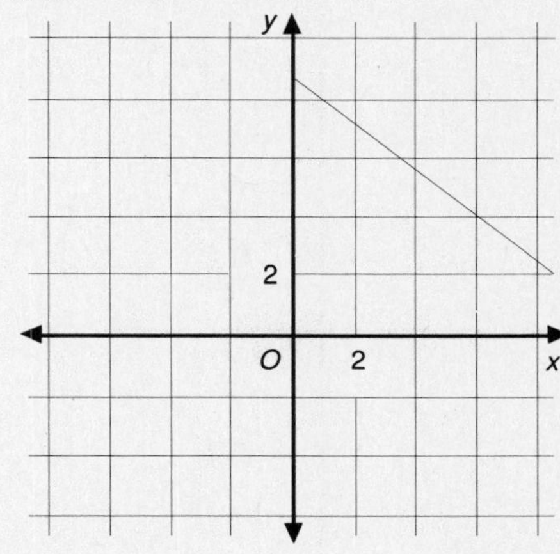

11. $f(x) = x^3 - 3x^2 - x + 3$

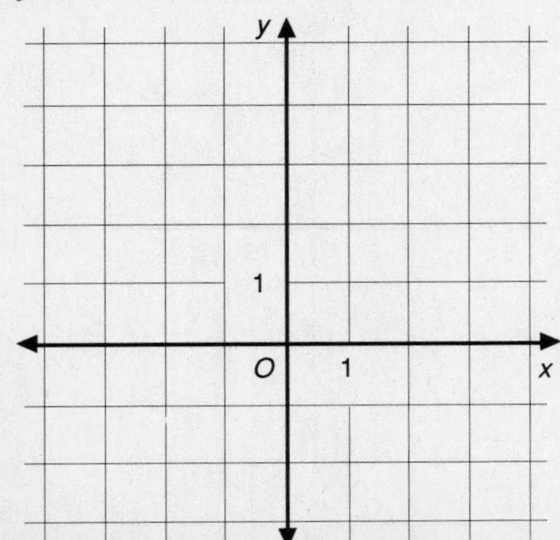

12. $f(x) = x^4 - 9x^2$

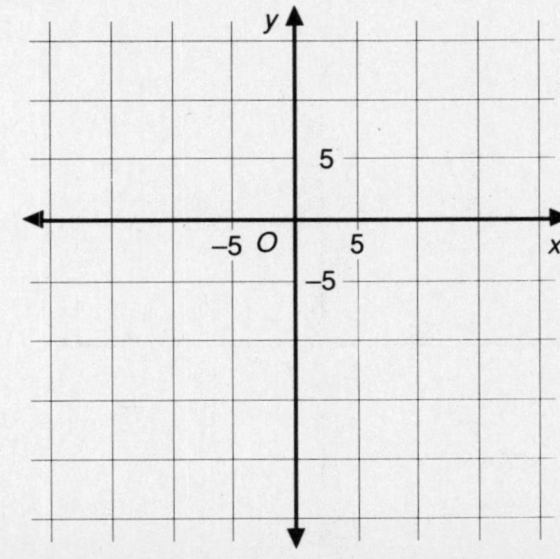

NAME ______________________ DATE ____________

10-6 Practice Worksheet

Graphing Polynomials and Approximating Zeros

Approximate to the nearest tenth the real zeros of each function.

1. $f(x) = x^3 - 3x^2 + 4$
   −1.0, 2.0

2. $f(x) = x^3 - 7x + 6$
   −3.0, 1.0, 2.0

3. $f(x) = x^3 + 6x^2 + 11x + 3$
   −0.3

4. $f(x) = x^3 - 6x^2 + 8x - 2$
   0.3, 1.5, 4.2

5. $f(x) = x^3 + 3x^2 - 4x - 6$
   −3.6, −1, 1.6

6. $f(x) = x^3 + x^2 - x + 15$
   −3.0

7. $f(x) = x^4 - 2x^3 + 2x^2 - 5x + 4$
   1.0, 1.7

8. $f(x) = x^6 + 2x^4 - x^2 - 4$
   −1.1, 1.1

Graph each function.

9. $f(x) = (x - 2)^3$

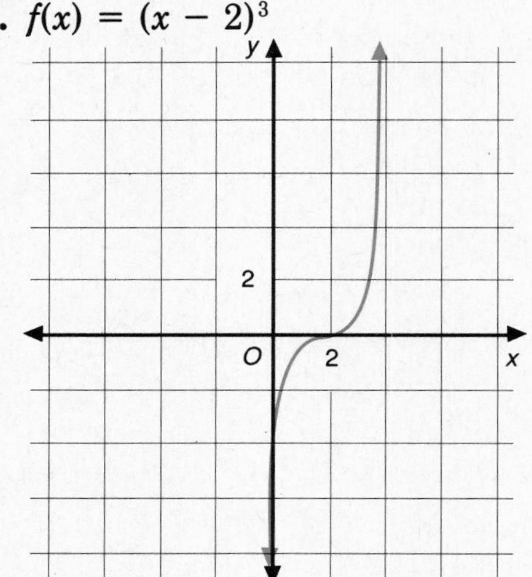

10. $f(x) = (x + 1)^4 - 3$

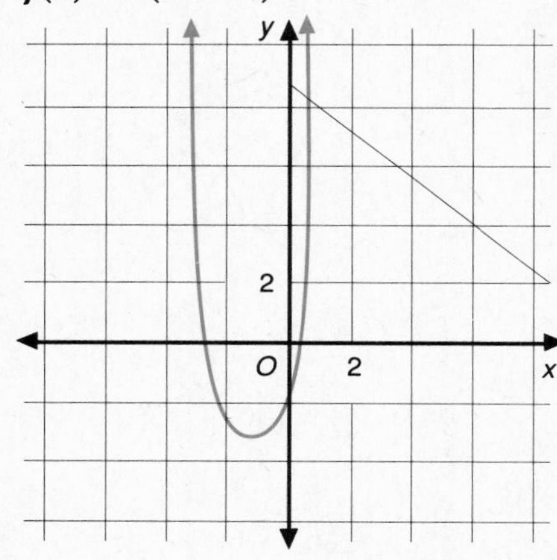

11. $f(x) = x^3 - 3x^2 - x + 3$

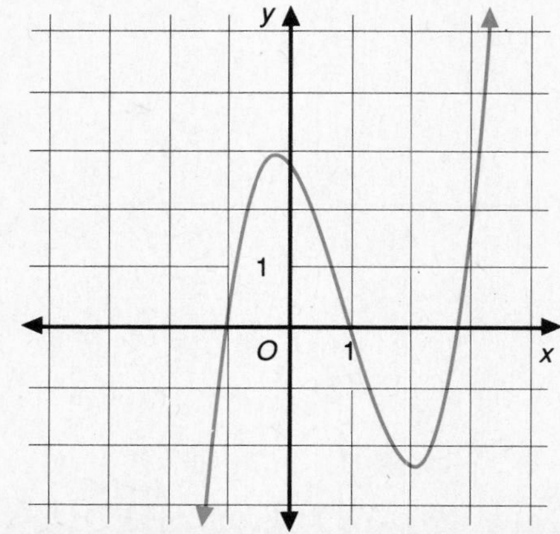

12. $f(x) = x^4 - 9x^2$

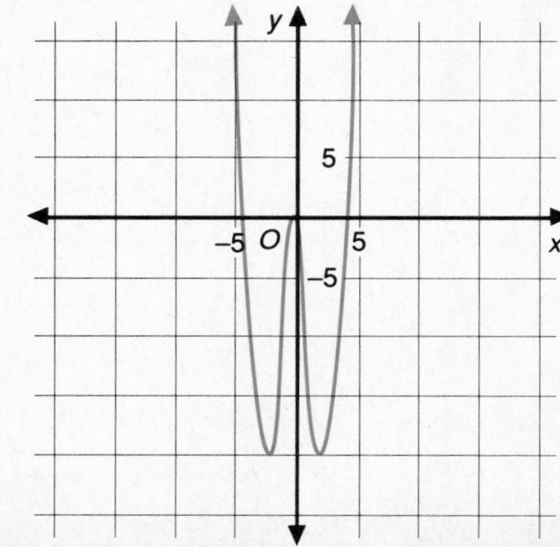

NAME ____________________ DATE ____________

10-7

Practice Worksheet

Composition of Functions

For each pair of functions, find [f ∘ g](2) and [g ∘ f](2).

1. $f(x) = 2x - 1$
$g(x) = -3x$

2. $f(x) = x^2 - 5$
$g(x) = 3x^2 + 1$

For each pair of functions, find f[g(x)] and g[f(x)].

3. $f(x) = x - 8$
$g(x) = x + 8$

4. $f(x) = x^2 - x + 3$
$g(x) = |x|$

For each pair of functions, find f[g(−3)] and g[f(−3)].

5. $f(x) = 9$
$g(x) = \frac{1}{x}$

6. $f(x) = \sqrt{x + 5}$
$g(x) = 2x + 8$

If f(x) = x^2, g(x) = 5x, and h(x) = x + 4, find each value.

7. $f[g(1)]$

8. $g[h(-2)]$

9. $h[f(4)]$

10. $f[h(-9)]$

Express g ∘ f and f ∘ g, if they exist, as sets of ordered pairs.

11. $f = \{(3, 8), (2, 5), (4, -5), (9, 3)\}$
$g = \{(9, 2), (-5, 3), (5, 9), (8, 10), (1, 9)\}$

12. $f = \{(1, 4), (10, 5), (6, -3)\}$
$g = \{(5, 1), (4, 6), (-3, 10)\}$

NAME ______________________ DATE ____________

10-7 **Practice Worksheet**

Composition of Functions

For each pair of functions, find $[f \circ g](2)$ and $[g \circ f](2)$.

1. $f(x) = 2x - 1$
   $g(x) = -3x$ **−13; −9**

2. $f(x) = x^2 - 5$
   $g(x) = 3x^2 + 1$ **164; 4**

For each pair of functions, find $f[g(x)]$ and $g[f(x)]$.

3. $f(x) = x - 8$
   $g(x) = x + 8$ **x; x**

4. $f(x) = x^2 - x + 3$
   $g(x) = |x|$ **$x^2 - |x| + 3$; $|x^2 - x + 3|$**

For each pair of functions, find $f[g(-3)]$ and $g[f(-3)]$.

5. $f(x) = 9$
   $g(x) = \frac{1}{x}$ **9; $\frac{1}{9}$**

6. $f(x) = \sqrt{x + 5}$
   $g(x) = 2x + 8$ **$\sqrt{7}$; $2\sqrt{2} + 8$**

If $f(x) = x^2$, $g(x) = 5x$, and $h(x) = x + 4$, find each value.

7. $f[g(1)]$ **25**

8. $g[h(-2)]$ **10**

9. $h[f(4)]$ **20**

10. $f[h(-9)]$ **25**

Express $g \circ f$ and $f \circ g$, if they exist, as sets of ordered pairs.

11. $f = \{(3, 8), (2, 5), (4, -5), (9, 3)\}$
    $g = \{(9, 2), (-5, 3), (5, 9), (8, 10), (1, 9)\}$
    $g \circ f$ doesn't exist
    $f \circ g$ doesn't exist

12. $f = \{(1, 4), (10, 5), (6, -3)\}$
    $g = \{(5, 1), (4, 6), (-3, 10)\}$
    $g \circ f = \{(1, 6), (10, 1), (6, 10)\}$
    $f \circ g = \{(5, 4), (4, -3), (-3, 5)\}$

Glencoe Division, Macmillan/McGraw-Hill

NAME ______________________ DATE __________

10-8 **Practice Worksheet**

Inverse Functions and Relations

Find the inverse of each function.

1. $f(x) = 2x + 5$

2. $y = 7$

3. $y = 3 - x$

4. $f(x) = x^2 - 1$

Determine whether each pair of functions are inverse functions.

5. $f(x) = x + 5$
   $g(x) = x - 5$

6. $f(x) = \frac{1}{2}x + 2$
   $g(x) = 2x - 4$

7. $f(x) = 4 - x$
   $g(x) = 4 + x$

8. $f(x) = 3x - 9$
   $g(x) = -3x + 9$

Graph each function and its inverse.

9. $y = x^2 - 3$

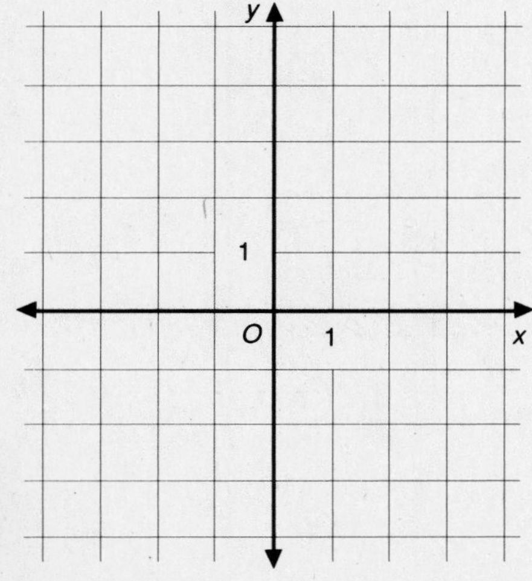

10. $f(x) = -4x$

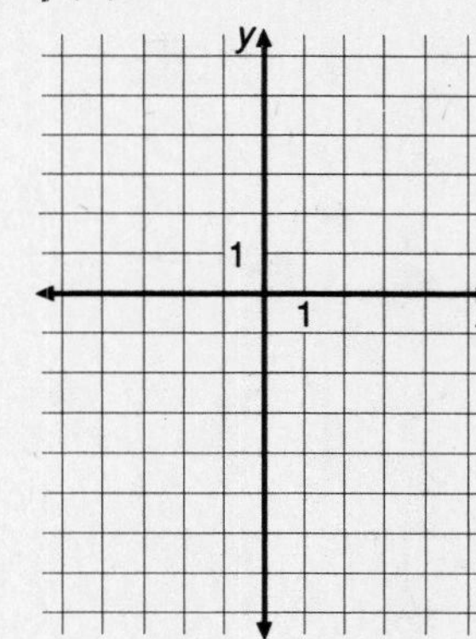

NAME ______________________ DATE ____________

10-8 **Practice Worksheet**

Inverse Functions and Relations

Find the inverse of each function.

1. $f(x) = 2x + 5$ $f^{-1}(x) = \frac{1}{2}x - \frac{5}{2}$

2. $y = 7$ $x = 7$

3. $y = 3 - x$ $y = 3 - x$

4. $f(x) = x^2 - 1$ $f^{-1}(x) = \pm\sqrt{x + 1}$

Determine whether each pair of functions are inverse functions.

5. $f(x) = x + 5$
   $g(x) = x - 5$ Yes

6. $f(x) = \frac{1}{2}x + 2$
   $g(x) = 2x - 4$ Yes

7. $f(x) = 4 - x$
   $g(x) = 4 + x$ No

8. $f(x) = 3x - 9$
   $g(x) = -3x + 9$ No

Graph each function and its inverse.

9. $y = x^2 - 3$

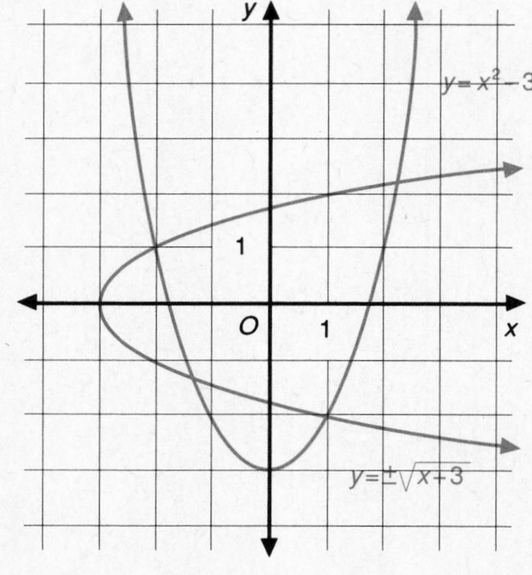

10. $f(x) = -4x$

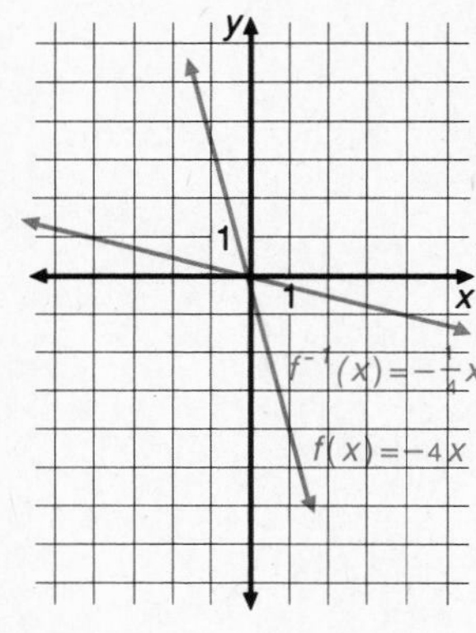

Glencoe Division, Macmillan/McGraw-Hill

NAME ______________________ DATE ____________

11-1 Practice Worksheet

Graphing Rational Functions

Graph each rational function.

1. $y = \dfrac{-4}{x - 2}$

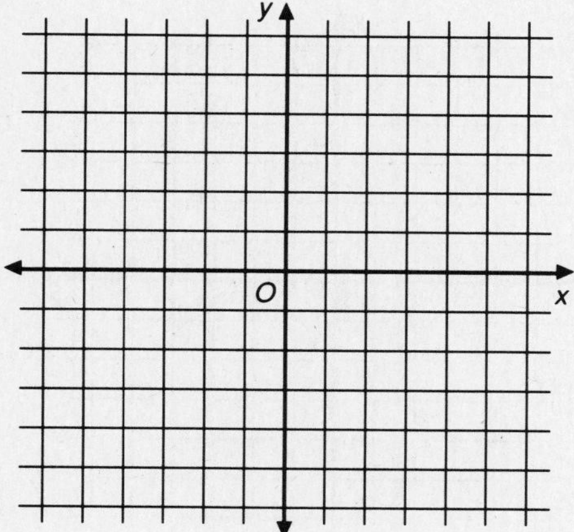

2. $y = \dfrac{3}{(x + 1)(x - 1)}$

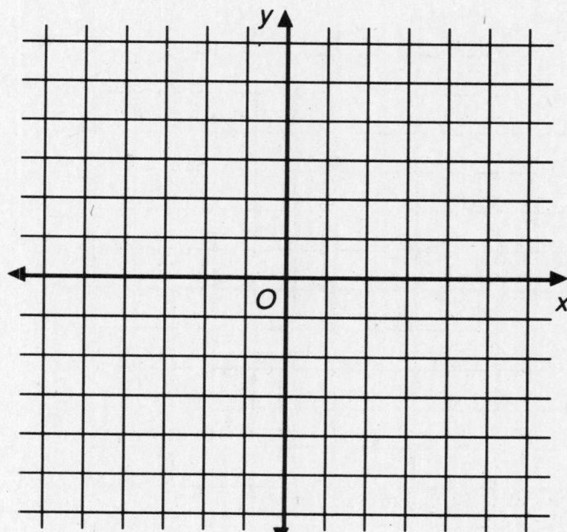

3. $y = \dfrac{x}{x + 3}$

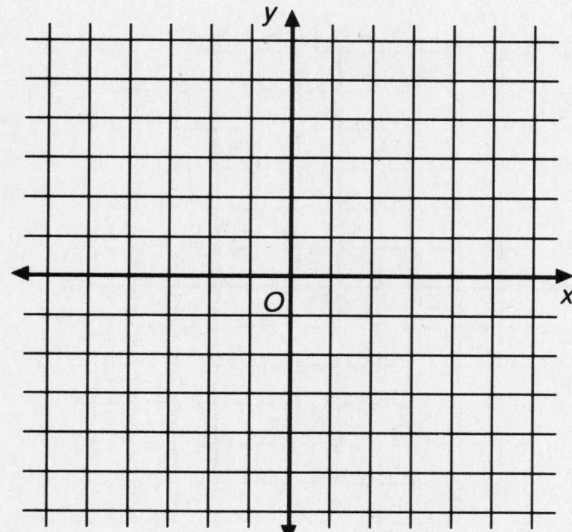

4. $y = \dfrac{-5}{x + 1}$

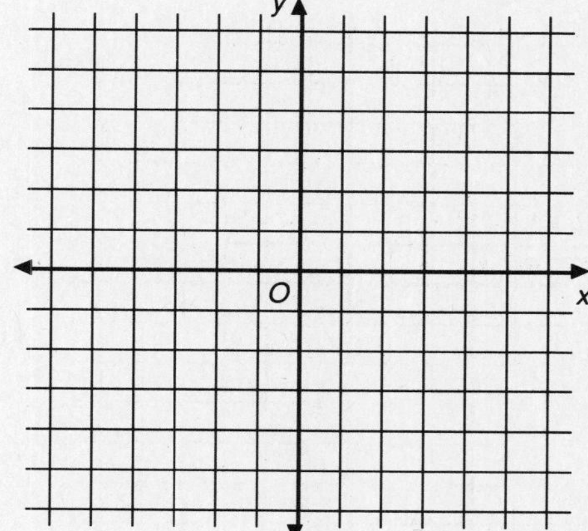

5. $y = \dfrac{3x}{(x + 3)^2}$

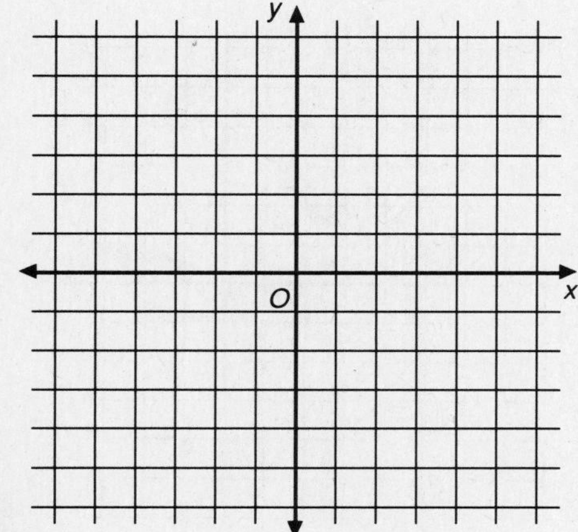

6. $y = \dfrac{x - 3}{x - 2}$

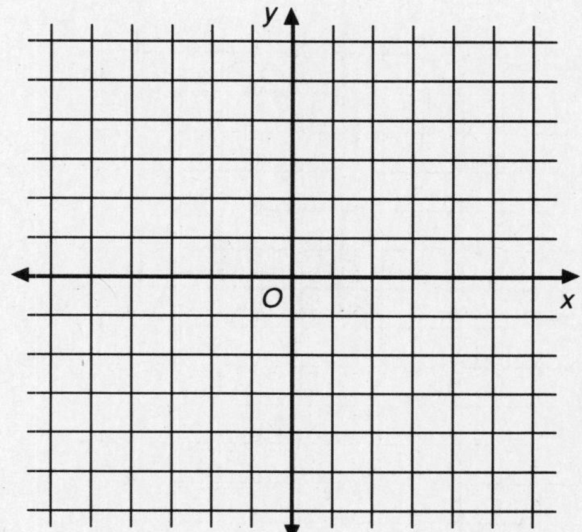

NAME ______________________ DATE ____________

11-1 Practice Worksheet

Graphing Rational Functions

Graph each rational function.

1. $y = \frac{-4}{x - 2}$

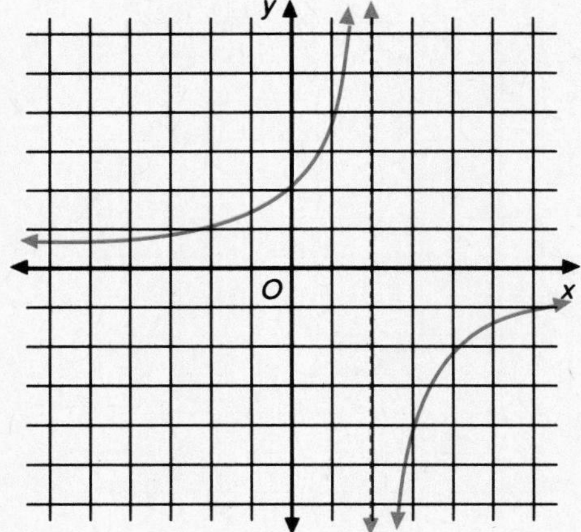

2. $y = \frac{3}{(x + 1)(x - 1)}$

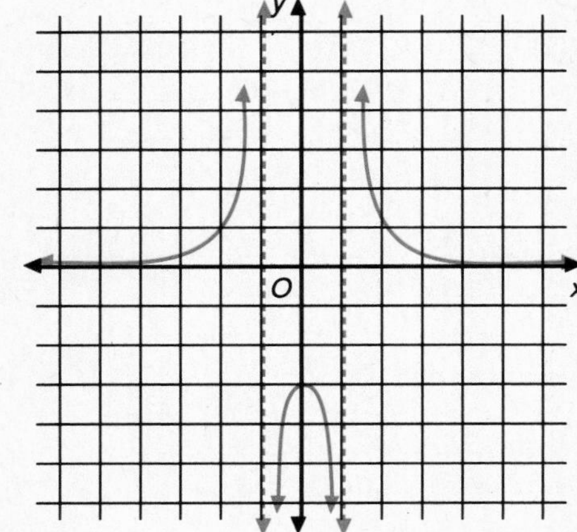

3. $y = \frac{x}{x + 3}$

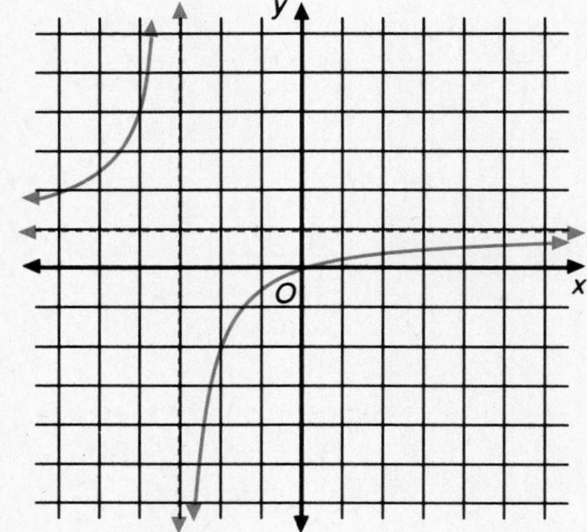

4. $y = \frac{-5}{x + 1}$

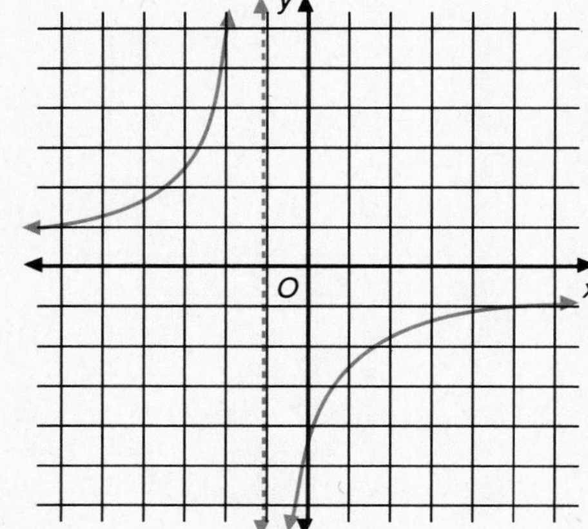

5. $y = \frac{3x}{(x + 3)^2}$

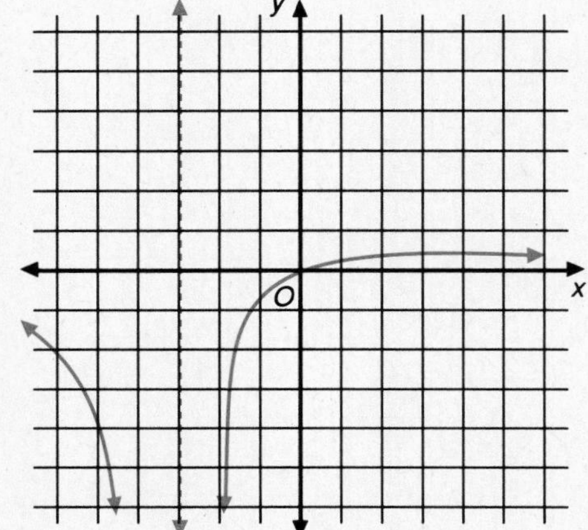

6. $y = \frac{x - 3}{x - 2}$

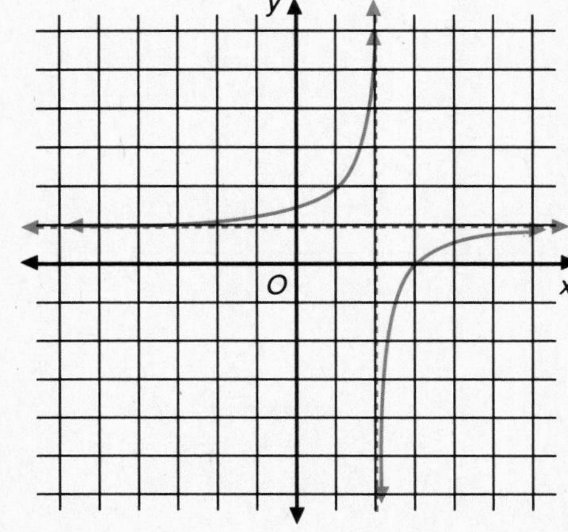

Glencoe Division, Macmillan/McGraw-Hill

NAME ______________________ DATE ____________

11-2 Practice Worksheet

Direct, Inverse, and Joint Variation

Write an equation for each statement and then solve the equation.

1. Find y when $x = 6$, if y varies directly as x and $y = 8$ when $x = 2$.

2. Find y when $x = 1.5$, if y varies directly as x and $y = -16$ when $x = 6$.

3. Find y when $x = 4$, if y varies directly as x and $y = 7$ when $x = 1.5$.

4. Find y when $x = 5$, if y varies directly as x and $y = 5$ when $x = 3.5$.

5. Find x when $y = 3$, if y varies inversely as x and $x = 4$, when $y = 16$.

6. Find x when $y = 5$, if y varies inversely as x and $x = 6$ when $y = -18$.

7. Find y when $x = 2\frac{1}{2}$, if y varies inversely as x and $x = 5$ when $y = 3$.

8. Find y when $x = 10$, if y varies inversely as x and $x = 7.5$ when $y = 6$.

9. Find y when $x = 4$ and $z = 15$, if y varies jointly as x and z and $y = 5$ when $z = 8$ and $x = 10$.

10. Find y when $x = 12$ and $z = 2$, if y varies jointly as x and z and $y = 24$ when $z = 2$ and $x = 1$.

11. Find y when $x = 6$ and $z = 8$, if y varies jointly as x and z and $y = 60$ when $x = 3$ and $z = 4$.

12. Find y when $x = 4$ and $z = -1$, if y varies jointly as x and z and $y = 12$ when $x = -2$ and $z = 3$.

Glencoe Division, Macmillan/McGraw-Hill

NAME ______________________ DATE ____________

11-2 Practice Worksheet

Direct, Inverse, and Joint Variation

Write an equation for each statement and then solve the equation.

1. Find y when $x = 6$, if y varies directly as x and $y = 8$ when $x = 2$. **24**

2. Find y when $x = 1.5$, if y varies directly as x and $y = -16$ when $x = 6$. **−4**

3. Find y when $x = 4$, if y varies directly as x and $y = 7$ when $x = 1.5$. $\frac{56}{3}$

4. Find y when $x = 5$, if y varies directly as x and $y = 5$ when $x = 3.5$. $\frac{50}{7}$

5. Find x when $y = 3$, if y varies inversely as x and $x = 4$, when $y = 16$. $\frac{64}{3}$

6. Find x when $y = 5$, if y varies inversely as x and $x = 6$ when $y = -18$. **−21.6**

7. Find y when $x = 2\frac{1}{2}$, if y varies inversely as x and $x = 5$ when $y = 3$. **6**

8. Find y when $x = 10$, if y varies inversely as x and $x = 7.5$ when $y = 6$. **4.5**

9. Find y when $x = 4$ and $z = 15$, if y varies jointly as x and z and $y = 5$ when $z = 8$ and $x = 10$. $\frac{15}{4}$

10. Find y when $x = 12$ and $z = 2$, if y varies jointly as x and z and $y = 24$ when $z = 2$ and $x = 1$. **288**

11. Find y when $x = 6$ and $z = 8$, if y varies jointly as x and z and $y = 60$ when $x = 3$ and $z = 4$. **240**

12. Find y when $x = 4$ and $z = -1$, if y varies jointly as x and z and $y = 12$ when $x = -2$ and $z = 3$. **8**

NAME ______________________ DATE ______________

11-3 Practice Worksheet

Multiplying and Dividing Rational Expressions

Simplify each expression.

1. $\frac{a+y}{6} \cdot \frac{4}{y+a}$

2. $\frac{a-y}{w+n} \cdot \frac{w^2-n^2}{y-a}$

3. $\frac{x^2-5x-24}{6x+2x^2} \cdot \frac{5x^2}{8-x}$

4. $\frac{n^5}{n-6} \cdot \frac{n^2-6n}{n^8}$

5. $\frac{a^5y^3}{wy^7} \div \frac{a^3w^2}{w^5y^2}$

6. $\left(\frac{2xy}{w^2}\right)^3 \div \frac{24x^2}{w^5}$

7. $\frac{x+y}{6} \div \frac{x^2-y^2}{3}$

8. $\frac{3x+6}{x^2-9} \div \frac{6x^2+12x}{4x+12}$

9. $\dfrac{\frac{x^2-9}{4}}{\frac{3-x}{8}}$

10. $\dfrac{\frac{1}{x}+2}{\frac{4}{x}-1}$

11. $\dfrac{\frac{y^4-81}{xy+4y+3x+12}}{y^2+9}$

12. $\dfrac{\frac{x^3+2^3}{x^2-2x}}{\frac{(x+2)^3}{x^2+4x+4}}$

Glencoe Division, Macmillan/McGraw-Hill

NAME ________________________ DATE ____________

11-3 Practice Worksheet

Multiplying and Dividing Rational Expressions

Simplify each expression.

1. $\frac{a+y}{6} \cdot \frac{4}{y+a}$ $\frac{2}{3}$

2. $\frac{a-y}{w+n} \cdot \frac{w^2-n^2}{y-a}$ $n - w$

3. $\frac{x^2-5x-24}{6x+2x^2} \cdot \frac{5x^2}{8-x}$ $-\frac{5x}{2}$

4. $\frac{n^5}{n-6} \cdot \frac{n^2-6n}{n^8}$ $\frac{1}{n^2}$

5. $\frac{a^5y^3}{wy^7} \div \frac{a^3w^2}{w^5y^2}$ $\frac{a^2w^2}{y^2}$

6. $\left(\frac{2xy}{w^2}\right)^3 \div \frac{24x^2}{w^5}$ $\frac{xy^3}{3w}$

7. $\frac{x+y}{6} \div \frac{x^2-y^2}{3}$ $\frac{1}{2(x-y)}$

8. $\frac{3x+6}{x^2-9} \div \frac{6x^2+12x}{4x+12}$ $\frac{2}{x(x-3)}$

9. $\frac{\frac{x^2-9}{4}}{\frac{3-x}{8}}$ $-2(x+3)$

10. $\frac{\frac{1}{x}+2}{\frac{4}{x}-1}$ $\frac{1+2x}{4-x}$

11. $\frac{\frac{y^4-81}{xy+4y+3x+12}}{y^2+9}$ $\frac{y-3}{x+4}$

12. $\frac{\frac{x^3+2^3}{x^2-2x}}{\frac{(x+2)^3}{x^2+4x+4}}$ $\frac{x^2-2x+4}{x(x-2)}$

NAME ______________________ DATE ____________

11-4

Practice Worksheet

Adding and Subtracting Rational Expressions

Simplify each expression.

1. $\frac{5}{6ab} - \frac{7}{8a}$

2. $2x - 5 - \frac{x - 8}{x + 4}$

3. $\frac{4}{a - 3} + \frac{9}{a - 5}$

4. $\frac{16}{x^2 - 16} + \frac{2}{x + 4}$

5. $\frac{5}{2x - 12} - \frac{20}{x^2 - 4x - 12}$

6. $\frac{2 - 5m}{m - 9} + \frac{4m - 5}{9 - m}$

7. $\frac{2p - 3}{p^2 - 5p + 6} - \frac{5}{p^2 - 9}$

8. $\frac{1}{5n} - \frac{3}{4} + \frac{7}{10n}$

9. $\dfrac{\frac{r + 6}{r} - \frac{1}{r + 2}}{\frac{r^2 + 4r + 3}{r^2 + r}}$

10. $\dfrac{n + 5 - \frac{12}{n + 1}}{\frac{n + 9}{n + 1} - \frac{5}{n}}$

11. $\dfrac{\frac{2}{x - y} + \frac{1}{x + y}}{\frac{1}{x - y}}$

12. $\dfrac{x - \frac{5x}{x + 2}}{\frac{x - 3}{x}}$

NAME ______________________ DATE ____________

11-4 Practice Worksheet

Adding and Subtracting Rational Expressions

Simplify each expression.

1. $\frac{5}{6ab} - \frac{7}{8a}$

   $\frac{20 - 21b}{24ab}$

2. $2x - 5 - \frac{x - 8}{x + 4}$

   $\frac{2(x + 3)(x - 2)}{x + 4}$

3. $\frac{4}{a - 3} + \frac{9}{a - 5}$

   $\frac{13a - 47}{(a - 3)(a - 5)}$

4. $\frac{16}{x^2 - 16} + \frac{2}{x + 4}$

   $\frac{2}{x - 4}$

5. $\frac{5}{2x - 12} - \frac{20}{x^2 - 4x - 12}$

   $\frac{5}{2(x + 2)}$

6. $\frac{2 - 5m}{m - 9} + \frac{4m - 5}{9 - m}$

   $\frac{7 - 9m}{m - 9}$

7. $\frac{2p - 3}{p^2 - 5p + 6} - \frac{5}{p^2 - 9}$

   $\frac{2p^2 - 2p + 1}{(p - 2)(p + 3)(p - 3)}$

8. $\frac{1}{5n} - \frac{3}{4} + \frac{7}{10n}$

   $\frac{3(6 - 5n)}{20n}$

9. $\dfrac{\frac{r + 6}{r} - \frac{1}{r + 2}}{\frac{r^2 + 4r + 3}{r^2 + r}}$

   $\frac{r + 4}{r + 2}$

10. $\dfrac{n + 5 - \frac{12}{n + 1}}{\frac{n + 9}{n + 1} - \frac{5}{n}}$

    $\frac{n(n + 7)}{n + 5}$

11. $\dfrac{\frac{2}{x - y} + \frac{1}{x + y}}{\frac{1}{x - y}}$

    $\frac{3x + y}{x + y}$

12. $\dfrac{x - \frac{5x}{x + 2}}{\frac{x - 3}{x}}$

    $\frac{x^2}{x + 2}$

NAME ______________________ DATE ______________

11-5 Practice Worksheet

Solving Rational Equations

Solve each equation. Check your solutions.

1. $\frac{12}{x} + \frac{3}{4} = \frac{3}{2}$

2. $\frac{x^2}{8} - 4 = \frac{x}{2}$

3. $\frac{x + 10}{x^2 - 2} = \frac{4}{x}$

4. $\frac{x}{x + 2} + x = \frac{5x + 8}{x + 2}$

5. $\frac{5}{x - 5} = \frac{x}{x - 5} - 1$

6. $\frac{1}{3x - 2} + \frac{5}{x} = 0$

7. $\frac{1}{x + 3} = \frac{2}{x} - \frac{3}{4x}$

8. $\frac{5}{x + 6} = \frac{9x + 6}{x^2 + 6x} + \frac{2}{x}$

9. $\frac{6}{x - 1} = \frac{4}{x - 2} + \frac{2}{x + 1}$

10. $\frac{x + 1}{x - 3} = 4 - \frac{12}{x^2 - 2x - 3}$

11. $\frac{1}{x - 1} = \frac{2}{x + 1} - \frac{1}{x + 3}$

12. $\frac{1}{x + 2} + \frac{1}{x - 2} = \frac{3}{x + 1}$

Glencoe Division, Macmillan/McGraw-Hill

NAME ____________________ DATE __________

11-5 Practice Worksheet

Solving Rational Equations

Solve each equation. Check your solutions.

1. $\frac{12}{x} + \frac{3}{4} = \frac{3}{2}$ **16**

2. $\frac{x^2}{8} - 4 = \frac{x}{2}$ **−4, 8**

3. $\frac{x + 10}{x^2 - 2} = \frac{4}{x}$ $-\frac{2}{3}$, **4**

4. $\frac{x}{x + 2} + x = \frac{5x + 8}{x + 2}$ **4**

5. $\frac{5}{x - 5} = \frac{x}{x - 5} - 1$ **all reals except 5**

6. $\frac{1}{3x - 2} + \frac{5}{x} = 0$ $\frac{5}{8}$

7. $\frac{1}{x + 3} = \frac{2}{x} - \frac{3}{4x}$ **−15**

8. $\frac{5}{x + 6} = \frac{9x + 6}{x^2 + 6x} + \frac{2}{x}$ **−3**

9. $\frac{6}{x - 1} = \frac{4}{x - 2} + \frac{2}{x + 1}$ **Ø**

10. $\frac{x + 1}{x - 3} = 4 - \frac{12}{x^2 - 2x - 3}$ $-\frac{5}{3}$, **5**

11. $\frac{1}{x - 1} = \frac{2}{x + 1} - \frac{1}{x + 3}$ **Ø**

12. $\frac{1}{x + 2} + \frac{1}{x - 2} = \frac{3}{x + 1}$ $1 \pm \sqrt{13}$

Glencoe Division, Macmillan/McGraw-Hill

NAME ______________________ DATE ____________

11-6 Practice Worksheet

Problem Solving Strategy: Organizing Data

Solve. Use any strategy.

1. Write the digits 1-9 in the circles so that the sum along any straight path is the same.

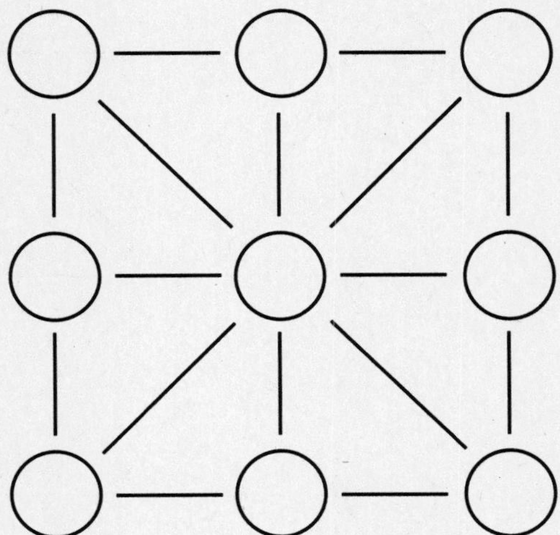

2. The sum of the last four digits of Kathy's telephone number is 7, and none of the digits is 0. If the probability of guessing Kathy's phone number is $\frac{1}{n}$, where n is the number of possible numbers, what is the probability of guessing Kathy's number on the first try?

3. The view of the rectangular box at the right shows three faces of the box. The areas of two of the faces are 30 cm^2 and 48 cm^2. The volume of the box is 240 cm^3. What is the area of the third face?

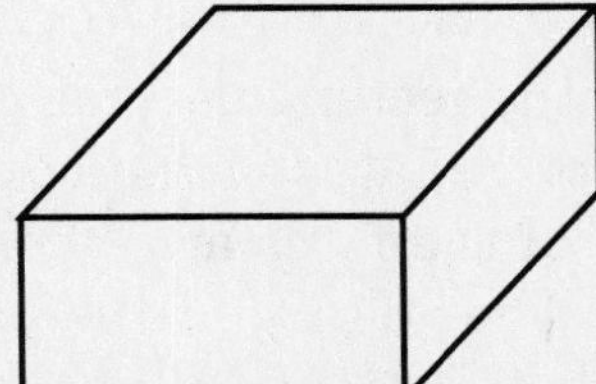

NAME ______________________ DATE ____________

11-6 Practice Worksheet

Problem Solving Strategy: Organizing Data

Solve. Use any strategy.

1. Write the digits 1-9 in the circles so that the sum along any straight path is the same.

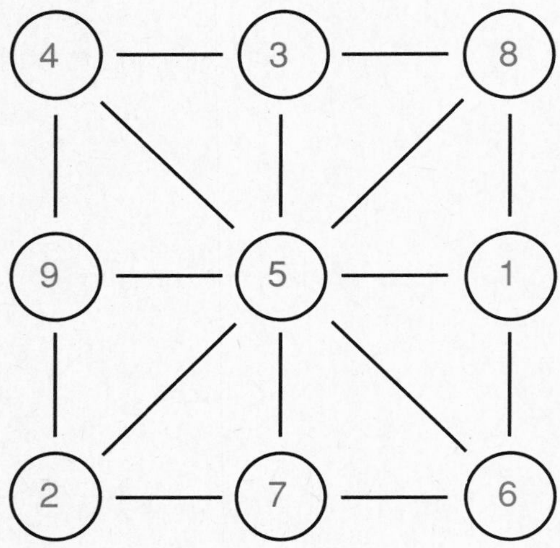

2. The sum of the last four digits of Kathy's telephone number is 7, and none of the digits is 0. If the probability of guessing Kathy's phone number is $\frac{1}{n}$, where n is the number of possible numbers, what is the probability of guessing Kathy's number on the first try? $\frac{1}{20}$

3. The view of the rectangular box at the right shows three faces of the box. The areas of two of the faces are 30 cm^2 and 48 cm^2. The volume of the box is 240 cm^3. What is the area of the third face? 40 cm^2

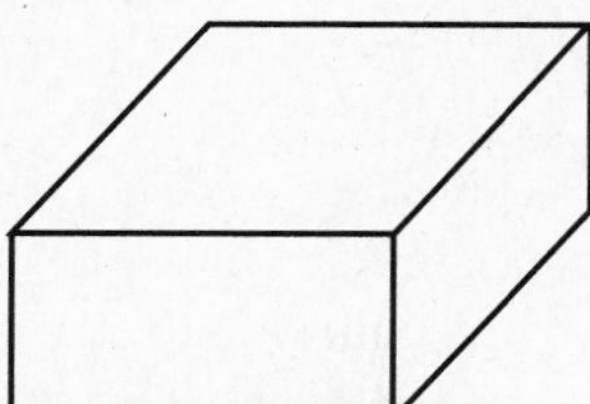

NAME ________________ DATE ________

11-7 Practice Worksheet

Applications of Rational Equations

Solve each problem.

1. It takes Angus three days to cultivate the garden. It takes Helga four days to do the same job. How long does it take them to do the job if they work together?

2. A tank can be filled by a hose in 15 hours. It can be emptied by a drainpipe in 25 hours. If the drainpipe is open while the tank is being filled, how long does it take to fill the tank?

3. Carlos can run to Ingrid's house in 30 minutes. Ingrid can run to Carlos' house in 40 minutes. If they start from their houses at the same time, in how many minutes will they meet?

4. The denominator of a fraction is one less than three times the numerator. If 12 is added to both numerator and denominator, the resulting fraction has a value of $\frac{3}{4}$. Find the original fraction.

5. Increasing the average speed of a car by 12 mph results in a 189-mile trip taking an hour less than before. What was the original average speed of the car?

6. In one hour, Steve drives 25 miles farther in his car than John can cycle on his bike. If it takes John $1\frac{1}{2}$ hours longer to cycle 75 miles than it takes Steve in his car, how fast can John cycle?

NAME ______________________ DATE ____________

11-7

Practice Worksheet

Applications of Rational Equations

Solve each problem.

1. It takes Angus three days to cultivate the garden. It takes Helga four days to do the same job. How long does it take them to do the job if they work together?

$1\frac{5}{7}$ days

2. A tank can be filled by a hose in 15 hours. It can be emptied by a drainpipe in 25 hours. If the drainpipe is open while the tank is being filled, how long does it take to fill the tank?

$37\frac{1}{2}$ h

3. Carlos can run to Ingrid's house in 30 minutes. Ingrid can run to Carlos' house in 40 minutes. If they start from their houses at the same time, in how many minutes will they meet?

$17\frac{1}{7}$ min

4. The denominator of a fraction is one less than three times the numerator. If 12 is added to both numerator and denominator, the resulting fraction has a value of $\frac{3}{4}$. Find the original fraction.

$\frac{3}{8}$

5. Increasing the average speed of a car by 12 mph results in a 189-mile trip taking an hour less than before. What was the original average speed of the car?

42 mi/h

6. In one hour, Steve drives 25 miles farther in his car than John can cycle on his bike. If it takes John $1\frac{1}{2}$ hours longer to cycle 75 miles than it takes Steve in his car, how fast can John cycle?

25 mi/h

Glencoe Division, Macmillan/McGraw-Hill

NAME ______________________ DATE ______________

12-1

Practice Worksheet

Real Exponents and Exponential Functions

Simplify each expression.

1. $(2^{\sqrt{2}})^{\sqrt{18}}$

2. $13^{\sqrt{6}} \cdot 13^{\sqrt{24}}$

3. $125^{\sqrt{11}} \div 5^{\sqrt{11}}$

4. $(n^{\sqrt{3}})^{\sqrt{75}}$

5. $32^{\sqrt{3}} \cdot 16^{\sqrt{2}}$

6. $(r^{\sqrt{3}} + p^{\sqrt{5}})^2$

7. $(n^{\sqrt{6}} + w^{\sqrt{3}})(n^{\sqrt{6}} - w^{\sqrt{3}})$

8. $(r^{\sqrt{3}} \cdot p^{\sqrt{5}})^2$

Solve each equation.

9. $7^{6x} = 7^{2x-20}$

10. $3^{6x-5} = 9^{4x-3}$

11. $9^{2x-1} = 27^{x+4}$

12. $5^{2x+3} = (\sqrt{5})^{x+4}$

13. $2^{3x-1} = \left(\frac{1}{8}\right)^x$

14. $\left(\frac{1}{16}\right)^{x+1} = \left(\frac{1}{8}\right)^{2x-1}$

NAME ____________________ DATE ____________

12-1 **Practice Worksheet**

Real Exponents and Exponential Functions

Simplify each expression.

1. $(2^{\sqrt{2}})^{\sqrt{18}}$ 2^6 or 64

2. $13^{\sqrt{6}} \cdot 13^{\sqrt{24}}$ $13^{3\sqrt{6}}$

3. $125^{\sqrt{11}} \div 5^{\sqrt{11}}$ $5^{2\sqrt{11}}$

4. $(n^{\sqrt{3}})^{\sqrt{75}}$ n^{15}

5. $32^{\sqrt{3}} \cdot 16^{\sqrt{2}}$ $2^{5\sqrt{3}+4\sqrt{2}}$

6. $(r^{\sqrt{3}} + p^{\sqrt{5}})^2$
$r^{2\sqrt{3}} + 2r^{\sqrt{3}}p^{\sqrt{5}} + p^{2\sqrt{5}}$

7. $(n^{\sqrt{6}} + w^{\sqrt{3}})(n^{\sqrt{6}} - w^{\sqrt{3}})$
$n^{2\sqrt{6}} - w^{2\sqrt{3}}$

8. $(r^{\sqrt{3}} \cdot p^{\sqrt{5}})^2$ $r^{2\sqrt{3}} \cdot p^{2\sqrt{5}}$

Solve each equation.

9. $7^{6x} = 7^{2x-20}$ -5

10. $3^{6x-5} = 9^{4x-3}$ $\frac{1}{2}$

11. $9^{2x-1} = 27^{x+4}$ 14

12. $5^{2x+3} = (\sqrt{5})^{x+4}$ $-\frac{2}{3}$

13. $2^{3x-1} = \left(\frac{1}{8}\right)^x$ $\frac{1}{6}$

14. $\left(\frac{1}{16}\right)^{x+1} = \left(\frac{1}{8}\right)^{2x-1}$ $\frac{7}{2}$

NAME ____________________ DATE ____________

12-2 Practice Worksheet

Logarithms and Logarithmic Functions

Write each equation in logarithmic form.

1. $5^3 = 125$

2. $27^{\frac{4}{3}} = 81$

Write each equation in exponential form.

3. $\log_{10} 0.00001 = -5$

4. $\log_{\frac{3}{2}} \frac{\sqrt{6}}{3} = -\frac{1}{2}$

Evaluate each expression.

5. $\log_3 81$

6. $\log_{10} 0.0001$

7. $\log_2 \frac{1}{16}$

8. $\log_{\frac{1}{3}} 27$

9. $\log_9 1$

10. $\log_8 4$

Solve each equation.

11. $\log_4 x = \frac{3}{2}$

12. $\log_y 16 = -4$

13. $\log_a \frac{1}{8} = -3$

14. $\log_7 n = -\frac{1}{2}$

15. $\log_{\sqrt{5}} y = \frac{4}{3}$

16. $\log_x \sqrt[3]{9} = \frac{1}{6}$

17. $\log_8(3x + 7) = \log_8(7x + 4)$

18. $\log_7(8x + 20) = \log_7(x + 6)$

19. $\log_3(9x - 1) = \log_3(4x - 16)$

20. $\log_{12}(x - 9) = \log_{12}(3x - 13)$

21. $\log_5(x^2 - 30) = \log_5 6$

22. $\log_4(x^2 + 6) = \log_4 5x$

Glencoe Division, Macmillan/McGraw-Hill

NAME ______________________ DATE ____________

12-2

Practice Worksheet

Logarithms and Logarithmic Functions

Write each equation in logarithmic form.

1. $5^3 = 125$ $\log_5 125 = 3$

2. $27^{\frac{4}{3}} = 81$ $\log_{27} 81 = \frac{4}{3}$

Write each equation in exponential form.

3. $\log_{10} 0.00001 = -5$ $10^{-5} = 0.00001$

4. $\log_{\frac{3}{2}} \frac{\sqrt{6}}{3} = -\frac{1}{2}$ $\left(\frac{3}{2}\right)^{-\frac{1}{2}} = \frac{\sqrt{6}}{3}$

Evaluate each expression.

5. $\log_3 81$ 4

6. $\log_{10} 0.0001$ -4

7. $\log_2 \frac{1}{16}$ -4

8. $\log_{\frac{1}{3}} 27$ -3

9. $\log_9 1$ 0

10. $\log_8 4$ $\frac{2}{3}$

Solve each equation.

11. $\log_4 x = \frac{3}{2}$ 8

12. $\log_y 16 = -4$ $\frac{1}{2}$

13. $\log_a \frac{1}{8} = -3$ 2

14. $\log_7 n = -\frac{1}{2}$ $\frac{\sqrt{7}}{7}$

15. $\log_{\sqrt{5}} y = \frac{4}{3}$ $5^{\frac{2}{3}}$ or $\sqrt[3]{25}$

16. $\log_x \sqrt[3]{9} = \frac{1}{6}$ 81

17. $\log_8(3x + 7) = \log_8(7x + 4)$ $\frac{3}{4}$

18. $\log_7(8x + 20) = \log_7(x + 6)$ -2

19. $\log_3(9x - 1) = \log_3(4x - 16)$
no solution

20. $\log_{12}(x - 9) = \log_{12}(3x - 13)$
no solution

21. $\log_5(x^2 - 30) = \log_5 6$ ± 6

22. $\log_4(x^2 + 6) = \log_4 5x$ $2, 3$

NAME ______________________ DATE ____________

12-3 Practice Worksheet

Properties of Logarithms

Evaluate each expression.

1. $n^{\log_n 3}$

2. $14^{\log_{14} 6}$

Use $\log_{10} 5 = 0.6990$ and $\log_{10} 7 = 0.8451$ to evaluate each expression.

3. $\log_{10} 35$

4. $\log_{10} \frac{7}{5}$

5. $\log_{10} 25$

6. $\log_{10} 490$

7. $\log_{10} \left(1\frac{3}{7}\right)$

8. $\log_{10} 0.05$

Solve each equation.

9. $\log_6 x + \log_6 9 = \log_6 54$

10. $\log_8 48 - \log_8 w = \log_8 4$

11. $\log_7 n = \frac{2}{3} \log_7 8$

12. $\log_3 y = \frac{1}{4} \log_3 16 + \frac{1}{3} \log_3 64$

13. $\log_9 (3u + 14) - \log_9 5 = \log_9 2u$

14. $\log_7 x + \log_7 x - \log_7 3 = \log_7 12$

15. $4 \log_2 x + \log_2 5 = \log_2 405$

16. $\log_6(2x - 5) + 1 = \log_6(7x + 10)$

17. $\log_{16}(9x + 5) - \log_{16}(x^2 - 1) = \frac{1}{2}$

18. $\log_8(n - 3) + \log_8(n + 4) = 1$

19. $\log_6(3m + 7) - \log_6(m + 4) = 2 \log_6 6 - 3 \log_6 3$

20. $\log_2(2x + 8) - \log_2(2x^2 + 21x + 61) = -3$

Glencoe Division, Macmillan/McGraw-Hill

NAME ______________________ DATE ____________

12-3 Practice Worksheet

Properties of Logarithms

Evaluate each expression.

1. $n^{\log_n 3}$ **3**

2. $14^{\log_{14} 6}$ **6**

Use $\log_{10} 5 = 0.6990$ and $\log_{10} 7 = 0.8451$ to evaluate each expression.

3. $\log_{10} 35$ **1.5441**

4. $\log_{10} \frac{7}{5}$ **0.1461**

5. $\log_{10} 25$ **1.3980**

6. $\log_{10} 490$ **2.6902**

7. $\log_{10} \left(1\frac{3}{7}\right)$ **0.1549**

8. $\log_{10} 0.05$ **−1.3010**

Solve each equation.

9. $\log_6 x + \log_6 9 = \log_6 54$ **6**

10. $\log_8 48 - \log_8 w = \log_8 4$ **12**

11. $\log_7 n = \frac{2}{3} \log_7 8$ **4**

12. $\log_3 y = \frac{1}{4} \log_3 16 + \frac{1}{3} \log_3 64$ **8**

13. $\log_9 (3u + 14) - \log_9 5 = \log_9 2u$ **2**

14. $\log_7 x + \log_7 x - \log_7 3 = \log_7 12$ **6**

15. $4 \log_2 x + \log_2 5 = \log_2 405$ **3**

16. $\log_6(2x - 5) + 1 = \log_6(7x + 10)$ **8**

17. $\log_{16}(9x + 5) - \log_{16}(x^2 - 1) = \frac{1}{2}$ **3**

18. $\log_8(n - 3) + \log_8(n + 4) = 1$ **4**

19. $\log_6(3m + 7) - \log_6(m + 4) = 2 \log_6 6 - 3 \log_6 3$ **−1**

20. $\log_2(2x + 8) - \log_2(2x^2 + 21x + 61) = -3$ $\frac{1}{2}$**, −3**

NAME ______________________ DATE ____________

12-4 **Practice Worksheet**

Common Logarithms

Use a calculator to find the logarithm of each number, rounded to four decimal places. Then state the characteristic and the mantissa.

1. 95

2. 0.233

3. 4920

4. 30,700

5. 211.3

6. 4.321

7. 8.125

8. 17.654

9. 0.0004764

10. 1.8519

11. 6.437×10^{-9}

12. 0.0125

Use a calculator to find the antilogarithm of each logarithm, rounded to four decimal places.

13. 2.63

14. -0.4089

15. 2.9484

16. -2.2168

17. 3.6940

18. $0.6456 - 3$

19. 4.8503

20. $0.6164 - 2$

21. 5.3

22. 2.384

23. -1.55

24. -3.2479

Glencoe Division, Macmillan/McGraw-Hill

NAME ______________________ DATE ______________

12-4 Practice Worksheet

Common Logarithms

Use a calculator to find the logarithm of each number, rounded to four decimal places. Then state the characteristic and the mantissa.

1. 95 **1.9777; 1; 0.9777**

2. 0.233 **−0.6326; −1; 0.3674**

3. 4920 **3.6920; 3; 0.6920**

4. 30,700 **4.4871; 4; 0.4871**

5. 211.3 **2.3249; 2; 0.3249**

6. 4.321 **0.6356; 0; 0.6356**

7. 8.125 **0.9098; 0; 0.9098**

8. 17.654 **1.2468; 1; 0.2468**

9. 0.0004764 **−3.3220; −4; 0.6780**

10. 1.8519 **0.2676; 0; 0.2676**

11. 6.437×10^{-9} **−8.1913; −9; 0.8086**

12. 0.0125 **−1.9031; −2; 0.0969**

Use a calculator to find the antilogarithm of each logarithm, rounded to four decimal places.

13. 2.63 **426.5795**

14. −0.4089 **0.3900**

15. 2.9484 **887.9735**

16. −2.2168 **0.0061**

17. 3.6940 **4943.1069**

18. 0.6456 − 3 **0.0044**

19. 4.8503 **70,843.4985**

20. 0.6164 − 2 **0.0413**

21. 5.3 **199,526.2315**

22. 2.384 **242.1029**

23. −1.55 **0.0282**

24. −3.2479 **0.0006**

NAME ______________________ DATE ______________

12-5 Practice Worksheet

Natural Logarithms

Use your calculator to find each value, rounded to four decimal places.

1. ln 4.76

2. ln 3.98

3. ln 26.9

4. ln 72.34

5. ln 0.478

6. ln 0.0025

7. ln 894

8. ln 526

9. ln 0.406

10. ln 0.0243

11. antiln 0.8926

12. antiln 0.247

13. antiln 0.9425

14. antiln −0.8679

15. antiln −0.5427

16. antiln 1.876

17. antiln 2.741

18. antiln −1.478

19. antiln 9.42

20. antiln −2.791

Glencoe Division, Macmillan/McGraw-Hill

NAME ______________________ DATE ______________

12-5 Practice Worksheet

Natural Logarithms

Use your calculator to find each value, rounded to four decimal places.

1. ln 4.76
1.5602

2. ln 3.98
1.3813

3. ln 26.9
3.2921

4. ln 72.34
4.2814

5. ln 0.478
−0.7381

6. ln 0.0025
−5.9915

7. ln 894
6.7957

8. ln 526
6.2653

9. ln 0.406
−0.9014

10. ln 0.0243
−3.7173

11. antiln 0.8926
2.4415

12. antiln 0.247
1.2802

13. antiln 0.9425
2.5664

14. antiln −0.8679
0.4198

15. antiln −0.5427
0.5812

16. antiln 1.876
6.5273

17. antiln 2.741
15.5025

18. antiln −1.478
0.2281

19. antiln 9.42
12,332.5822

20. antiln −2.791
0.0614

Glencoe Division, Macmillan/McGraw-Hill

NAME ______________________ DATE ______________

12-6 Practice Worksheet

Problem Solving Strategy: Using Estimation

Solve. Use any strategy.

1. Marita invested $5200 in a 2-year certificate of deposit that has an annual yield of 9.8%. Estimate the amount of interest she will earn and then check your estimate against the answer you obtain, using $I = prt$.

2. Jim wants to paint the walls of a room that is 15 feet wide and 20 feet long. The ceiling is 8 feet high. How many gallons of paint will he need if each gallon covers 350 square feet and he wants to give the room two coats of paint?

3. Use the following clues to find a year important in history.

(1) The thousands digit is half the ones digit, which is half the hundreds digit.
(2) The sum of the digits is 16.
(3) No two digits are the same.

Glencoe Division, Macmillan/McGraw-Hill

NAME ____________________ DATE ____________

12-6 Practice Worksheet

Problem Solving Strategy: Using Estimation

Solve. Use any strategy.

1. Marita invested $5200 in a 2-year certificate of deposit that has an annual yield of 9.8%. Estimate the amount of interest she will earn and then check your estimate against the answer you obtain, using $I = prt$.
   less than $1040; $1019.20

2. Jim wants to paint the walls of a room that is 15 feet wide and 20 feet long. The ceiling is 8 feet high. How many gallons of paint will he need if each gallon covers 350 square feet and he wants to give the room two coats of paint?
   4 gallons

3. Use the following clues to find a year important in history.
   (1) The thousands digit is half the ones digit, which is half the hundreds digit.
   (2) The sum of the digits is 16.
   (3) No two digits are the same.
   1492

Glencoe Division, Macmillan/McGraw-Hill

NAME ______________________ DATE ______________

12-7 Practice Worksheet

Exponential Equations

Use logarithms to solve each equation.

1. $3.5^x = 47.9$

2. $8.2^y = 64.5$

3. $7.2^{a-4} = 8.21$

4. $2^{b+1} = 7.31$

5. $y = \log_3 78.5$

6. $k = \log_4 91.8$

7. $4^{2x} = 9^{x-1}$

8. $7^{3b} = 12^{b+2}$

9. $6^{s-2} = 4^{3-s}$

10. $3^{4r} = 5^{r-1}$

11. $17c^{\frac{2}{3}} = 44$

12. $7x^{\frac{9}{8}} = 111$

13. $x = \log_7 30$

14. $n = \log_3 152$

15. $5^{x^2-3} = 72$

16. $\sqrt[4]{3^{4x+5}} = 7^x$

NAME ______________________ DATE ______________

12-7 Practice Worksheet

Exponential Equations

Use logarithms to solve each equation.

1. $3.5^x = 47.9$ **3.0885**

2. $8.2^y = 64.5$ **1.9802**

3. $7.2^{a-4} = 8.21$ **5.0665**

4. $2^{b+1} = 7.31$ **1.8699**

5. $y = \log_3 78.5$ **3.9715**

6. $k = \log_4 91.8$ **3.2602**

7. $4^{2x} = 9^{x-1}$ **−3.8188**

8. $7^{3b} = 12^{b+2}$ **1.4823**

9. $6^{s-2} = 4^{3-s}$ **2.4362**

10. $3^{4r} = 5^{r-1}$ **−0.5779**

11. $17c^{\frac{2}{3}} = 44$ **4.1640**

12. $7x^{\frac{9}{8}} = 111$ **11.6645**

13. $x = \log_7 30$ **1.7479**

14. $n = \log_3 152$ **4.5729**

15. $5^{x^2-3} = 72$ **±2.3785**

16. $\sqrt[4]{3^{4x+5}} = 7^x$ **1.6208**

NAME ______________________ DATE ______________

12-8 Practice Worksheet

Applications of Logarithms

Solve each problem.

1. Suppose \$500 is invested at 6% annual interest compounded twice a year. When will the investment be worth \$1000?

2. Suppose \$500 is invested at 6% annual interest compounded continuously. When will the investment be worth \$1000?

3. An organism of a certain type can grow from 30 to 195 organisms in 5 hours. Find k for the growth formula.

4. For a certain strain of bacteria, k is 0.825 when t is measured in days. How long will it take 20 bacteria to increase to 2000?

5. An investment service promises to triple your money in 12 years. Assuming continuous compounding of interest, what rate of interest is needed?

6. A substance decomposes radioactively. Its half-life is 32 years. Find the constant k in the decay formula.

7. A piece of machinery valued at \$250,000 depreciates at 12% per year by the fixed rate method. After how many years will the value have depreciated to \$100,000?

8. Dave bought a new car 8 years ago for \$5400. To buy a new car comparably equipped now would cost \$12,500. Assuming a steady rate of increase, what was the yearly rate of inflation in car prices over the 8-year period?

12-8

NAME ____________________ DATE ____________

Practice Worksheet

Applications of Logarithms

Solve each problem.

1. Suppose \$500 is invested at 6% annual interest compounded twice a year. When will the investment be worth \$1000?
   11.72 years

2. Suppose \$500 is invested at 6% annual interest compounded continuously. When will the investment be worth \$1000?
   11.55 years

3. An organism of a certain type can grow from 30 to 195 organisms in 5 hours. Find k for the growth formula.
   0.3744

4. For a certain strain of bacteria, k is 0.825 when t is measured in days. How long will it take 20 bacteria to increase to 2000?
   5.582 days

5. An investment service promises to triple your money in 12 years. Assuming continuous compounding of interest, what rate of interest is needed?
   9.155%

6. A substance decomposes radioactively. Its half-life is 32 years. Find the constant k in the decay formula.
   −0.02166

7. A piece of machinery valued at \$250,000 depreciates at 12% per year by the fixed rate method. After how many years will the value have depreciated to \$100,000?
   7.168 years

8. Dave bought a new car 8 years ago for \$5400. To buy a new car comparably equipped now would cost \$12,500. Assuming a steady rate of increase, what was the yearly rate of inflation in car prices over the 8-year period?
   11.06%

Glencoe Division, Macmillan/McGraw-Hill

13-1

NAME ____________ DATE ____________

Practice Worksheet

Problem Solving Strategy: Look for a Pattern

Solve. Use any strategy.

1. Find n if $n(n - 1)(n - 2)(n - 3)(n - 4) = 360{,}360$.

2. Tires are on sale for 20% off. Karla has a coupon for 5% off. She gets another 4% off for not charging the tires on a credit card. These discounts are taken one after another. If the final price of a set of four tires is $162.85, what was the original price?

3. Find the missing terms in the sequence.

4, 9, 25, 36, 49, ______, ______

4. Find the missing terms in the sequence.

1, 1, 1, 3, 5, 9, 17, ______, ______

NAME ______________________ DATE ______________

13-1 Practice Worksheet

Problem Solving Strategy: Look for a Pattern

Solve. Use any strategy.

1. Find n if $n(n - 1)(n - 2)(n - 3)(n - 4) = 360{,}360$. **15**

2. Tires are on sale for 20% off. Karla has a coupon for 5% off. She gets another 4% off for not charging the tires on a credit card. These discounts are taken one after another. If the final price of a set of four tires is $162.85, what was the original price? **$223.20**

3. Find the missing terms in the sequence.

4, 9, 25, 36, 49, __64__, __81__

4. Find the missing terms in the sequence.

1, 1, 1, 3, 5, 9, 17, __31__, __57__

Glencoe Division, Macmillan/McGraw-Hill

NAME ______________________ DATE ____________

13-2 Practice Worksheet

Arithmetic Sequences

Find the nth term of each arithmetic sequence.

1. $a_1 = -5, d = 4, n = 9$

2. $a_1 = 13, d = -\frac{5}{2}, n = 29$

3. $a_1 = 3, d = -4, n = 6$

4. $a_1 = -5, d = \frac{1}{2}, n = 10$

Complete each statement.

5. 97 is the ___?___th term of $-3, 1, 5, 9, \ldots$.

6. -10 is the ___?___th term of $14, 12.5, 11, 9.5, \ldots$.

Find the indicated term in each arithmetic sequence.

7. a_{15} for $-3, 3, 9, \ldots$

8. a_{19} for $17, 12, 7, \ldots$

9. a_{26} for $1, \frac{7}{3}, \frac{11}{3}, \ldots$

10. a_{35} for $17, 16\frac{2}{3}, 16\frac{1}{3}, \ldots$

Find the missing terms in each arithmetic sequence.

11. 3, ______, ______, 20

12. ______, −10, ______, ______, ______, 14

13. 5, ______, ______, 27

14. ______, 4, ______, ______, ______, 29

15. How many multiples of 11 are there between 13 and 384?

Glencoe Division, Macmillan/McGraw-Hill

NAME ______________________ DATE ______________

13-2 Practice Worksheet

Arithmetic Sequences

Find the nth term of each arithmetic sequence.

1. $a_1 = -5, d = 4, n = 9$
27

2. $a_1 = 13, d = -\frac{5}{2}, n = 29$
−57

3. $a_1 = 3, d = -4, n = 6$
−17

4. $a_1 = -5, d = \frac{1}{2}, n = 10$
$-\frac{1}{2}$

Complete each statement.

5. 97 is the __?__th term of −3, 1, 5, 9, ... 26

6. −10 is the __?__th term of 14, 12.5, 11, 9.5, ... 17

Find the indicated term in each arithmetic sequence.

7. a_{15} for −3, 3, 9, . . .
81

8. a_{19} for 17, 12, 7, . . .
−73

9. a_{26} for $1, \frac{7}{3}, \frac{11}{3}, \ldots$
$\frac{103}{3}$

10. a_{35} for $17, 16\frac{2}{3}, 16\frac{1}{3}, \ldots$
$\frac{17}{3}$

Find the missing terms in each arithmetic sequence.

11. 3, ______, ______, 20
$8\frac{2}{3}, 14\frac{1}{3}$

12. ______, −10, ______, ______, ______, 14
−16, −4, 2, 8

13. 5, ______, ______, 27
$12\frac{1}{3}, 19\frac{2}{3}$

14. ______, 4, ______, ______, ______, 29
$-2\frac{1}{4}, 10\frac{1}{4}, 16\frac{1}{2}, 22\frac{3}{4}$

15. How many multiples of 11 are there between 13 and 384?
33

Glencoe Division, Macmillan/McGraw-Hill

NAME ______________________ DATE ____________

13-3 Practice Worksheet

Arithmetic Series

Find S_n for each arithmetic series described.

1. $a_1 = 16, a_n = 98, n = 13$

2. $a_1 = 13, d = -6, n = 21$

3. $d = -\frac{2}{3}, n = 16, a_n = 44$

4. $a_1 = -121, d = 3, a_n = 5$

Find the sum of each arithmetic series.

5. 5, 7, 9, . . . , 27

6. −4, 1, 6, . . . , 91

7. 13, 20, 27, . . . , 272

8. 89, 86, 83, . . . , 20

9. $\sum_{k=3}^{8} (5k - 10)$

10. $\sum_{p=4}^{10} (2p + 1)$

11. $\sum_{n=1}^{6} (3n + 5)$

12. $\sum_{j=1}^{5} (9 - 4j)$

Find the first three terms of each arithmetic series described.

13. $a_1 = 14, a_n = -85, S_n = -1207$

14. $n = 16, a_n = 15, S_n = -120$

15. A display in a grocery store has 1 can on the top row, 2 cans on the 2nd row, 3 cans on the 3rd row, and so on. How many cans are needed to make 25 rows?

Glencoe Division, Macmillan/McGraw-Hill

NAME ______________________ DATE __________

13-3 Practice Worksheet

Arithmetic Series

Find S_n for each arithmetic series described.

1. $a_1 = 16$, $a_n = 98$, $n = 13$ **741**

2. $a_1 = 13$, $d = -6$, $n = 21$ **−987**

3. $d = -\frac{2}{3}$, $n = 16$, $a_n = 44$ **784**

4. $a_1 = -121$, $d = 3$, $a_n = 5$ **−2494**

Find the sum of each arithmetic series.

5. 5, 7, 9, . . . , 27
192

6. −4, 1, 6, . . . , 91
870

7. 13, 20, 27, . . . , 272
5415

8. 89, 86, 83, . . . , 20
1308

9. $\sum_{k=3}^{8} (5k - 10)$
105

10. $\sum_{p=4}^{10} (2p + 1)$
105

11. $\sum_{n=1}^{6} (3n + 5)$
93

12. $\sum_{j=1}^{5} (9 - 4j)$
−15

Find the first three terms of each arithmetic series described.

13. $a_1 = 14$, $a_n = -85$, $S_n = -1207$
14, 11, 8

14. $n = 16$, $a_n = 15$, $S_n = -120$
−30, −27, −24

15. A display in a grocery store has 1 can on the top row, 2 cans on the 2nd row, 3 cans on the 3rd row, and so on. How many cans are needed to make 25 rows? **325**

Glencoe Division, Macmillan/McGraw-Hill

NAME ______________________ DATE ______________

13-4 Practice Worksheet

Geometric Sequences

Find the first four terms of each geometric sequence described.

1. $a_1 = -6,\ r = -\frac{2}{3}$

2. $a_1 = 2,\ r = \sqrt{3}$

3. $a_1 = -\frac{5}{2},\ r = 2$

4. $a_1 = \sqrt{2},\ r = \sqrt{3}$

Find the nth term of each geometric sequence described.

5. $a_1 = 5,\ n = 4,\ r = 3$

6. $a_4 = 20,\ n = 6,\ r = -3$

7. $a_1 = -4,\ n = 6,\ r = -2$

8. $a_6 = 8,\ n = 12,\ r = \frac{1}{2}$

9. Each foot of water screens out 60% of the light above. What percent of the light remains after passing through 5 feet of water?

Find the missing geometric means. Then graph each sequence, using the x-axis for the number of the term and the y-axis for the term itself.

10. ______, ______, 2, ______, ______, 54

11. 32, ______, ______, ______, 162

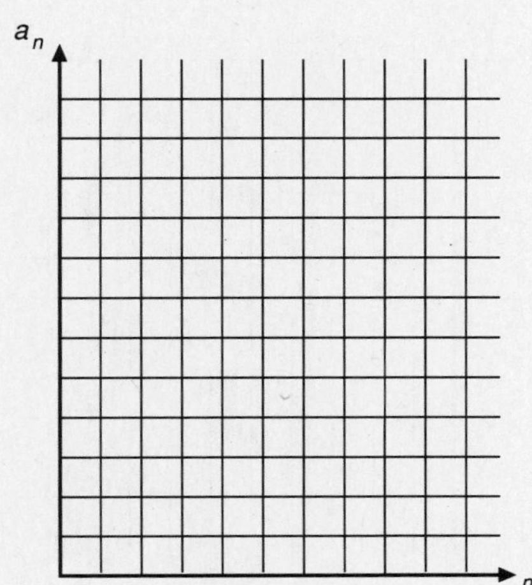

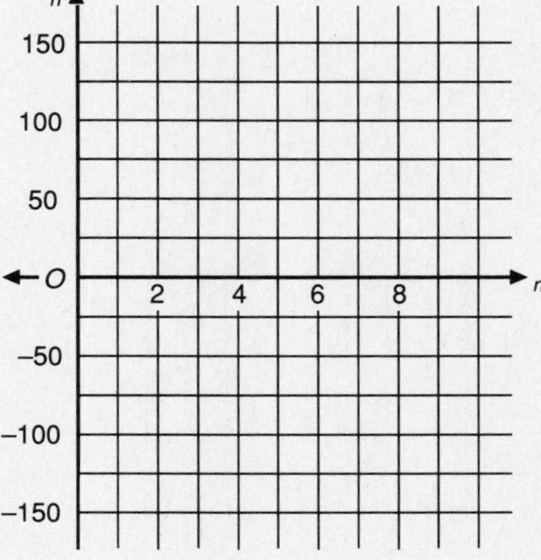

NAME ______________________ DATE ____________

13-4 Practice Worksheet

Geometric Sequences

Find the first four terms of each geometric sequence described.

1. $a_1 = -6, r = -\frac{2}{3}$
$-6, 4, -\frac{8}{3}, \frac{16}{9}$

2. $a_1 = 2, r = \sqrt{3}$
$2, 2\sqrt{3}, 6, 6\sqrt{3}$

3. $a_1 = -\frac{5}{2}, r = 2$
$-\frac{5}{2}, -5, -10, -20$

4. $a_1 = \sqrt{2}, r = \sqrt{3}$
$\sqrt{2}, \sqrt{6}, 3\sqrt{2}, 3\sqrt{6}$

Find the nth term of each geometric sequence described.

5. $a_1 = 5, n = 4, r = 3$ **135**

6. $a_4 = 20, n = 6, r = -3$ **180**

7. $a_1 = -4, n = 6, r = -2$ **128**

8. $a_6 = 8, n = 12, r = \frac{1}{2}$ $\frac{1}{8}$

9. Each foot of water screens out 60% of the light above. What percent of the light remains after passing through 5 feet of water? **1.024%**

Find the missing geometric means. Then graph each sequence, using the x-axis for the number of the term and the y-axis for the term itself.

10. ______, ______, 2, ______, ______, 54
$\frac{2}{9}, \frac{2}{3}, 6, 18$

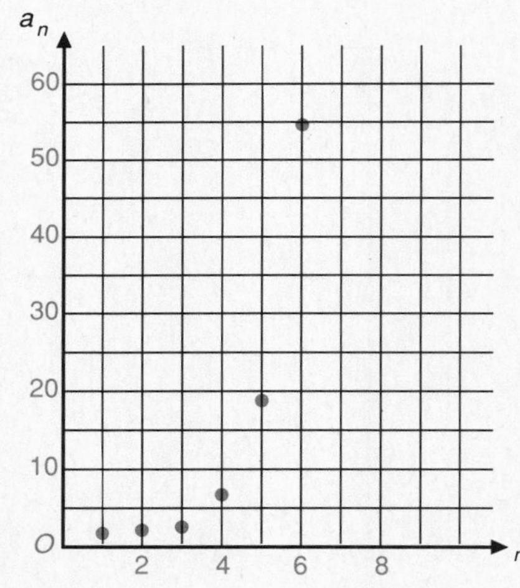

11. 32, ______, ______, ______, 162
48, 72, 108, or −48, 72, −108

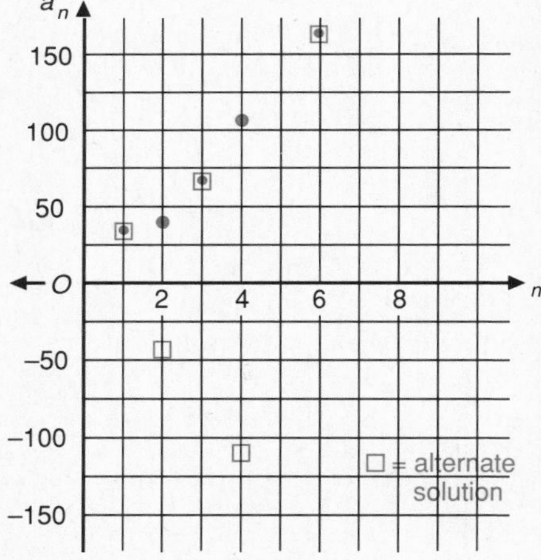

Glencoe Division, Macmillan/McGraw-Hill

NAME ______________________ DATE ____________

13-5

Practice Worksheet

Geometric Series

Find the sum of each geometric series described.

1. $160 + 80 + 40 + \ldots, n = 6$

2. $a_1 = 5, r = -\frac{1}{2}, n = 7$

3. $a_2 = \frac{-3}{8}, a_3 = \frac{1}{4}, n = 5$

4. $a_3 = 8, a_5 = 2, n = 6$

Use sigma notation to express each series.

5. $54 + 18 + 6 + 2 + \frac{2}{3} + \frac{2}{9}$

6. $16 - 24 + 36 - 54 + 81 - 121.5 + 182.25$

Find a_1 for each geometric series described.

7. $S_n = -55, r = -\frac{2}{3}, n = 5$

8. $S_n = 2457, a_n = 3072, r = -4$

9. A pile driver drives a post 9 feet into the ground on its first hit. Each additional hit drives the post $\frac{2}{3}$ the distance of the prior hit. Find the total distance the post has been driven after 4 hits.

10. In problem 9, what is the greatest distance the pole could be driven into the ground?

11. Hugh Moore makes up a joke and tells it to his 5 closest friends on Sunday morning. Each of those friends tells his or her 5 closest friends on Monday morning, and so on. Assuming no duplication, how many people will have heard the joke by the end of Saturday?

NAME ______________________________ DATE ______________

13-5

Practice Worksheet

Geometric Series

Find the sum of each geometric series described.

1. $160 + 80 + 40 + \ldots, n = 6$ **315**

2. $a_1 = 5, r = -\frac{1}{2}, n = 7$ $\frac{215}{64}$

3. $a_2 = \frac{-3}{8}, a_3 = \frac{1}{4}, n = 5$ $\frac{58}{144}$

4. $a_3 = 8, a_5 = 2, n = 6$ **21 or 63**

Use sigma notation to express each series.

5. $54 + 18 + 6 + 2 + \frac{2}{3} + \frac{2}{9}$ $\sum_{n=1}^{6} 54\left(\frac{1}{3}\right)^{n-1}$

6. $16 - 24 + 36 - 54 + 81 - 121.5 + 182.25$ $\sum_{n=1}^{7} 16\left(-\frac{3}{2}\right)^{n-1}$

Find a_1 for each geometric series described.

7. $S_n = -55, r = -\frac{2}{3}, n = 5$ **−81**

8. $S_n = 2457, a_n = 3072, r = -4$ **−3**

9. A pile driver drives a post 9 feet into the ground on its first hit. Each additional hit drives the post $\frac{2}{3}$ the distance of the prior hit. Find the total distance the post has been driven after 4 hits. $21\frac{2}{3}$ **ft**

10. In problem 9, what is the greatest distance the pole could be driven into the ground? **27 ft**

11. Hugh Moore makes up a joke and tells it to his 5 closest friends on Sunday morning. Each of those friends tells his or her 5 closest friends on Monday morning, and so on. Assuming no duplication, how many people will have heard the joke by the end of Saturday? **97,655; 97,656 if Hugh is included**

NAME ______________________ DATE ____________

13-6 Practice Worksheet

Infinite Geometric Series

Find the sum of each infinite geometric series, if it exists.

1. $a_1 = 35, r = \frac{2}{7}$

2. $18 - 6 + 2 - \ldots$

3. $\frac{4}{25} + \frac{2}{5} + 1 + \ldots$

4. $6 + 4 + \frac{8}{3} + \ldots$

5. $10 + 1 + 0.1 + \ldots$

6. $2 + 6 + 18 + \ldots$

7. $a_1 = 26, r = \frac{1}{2}$

8. $a_1 = 108, r = -\frac{3}{4}$

9. $a_1 = 42, r = \frac{6}{5}$

10. $a_1 = 50, r = \frac{2}{5}$

Express each decimal as an infinite geometric series. Then find the ratio it represents.

11. $0.4\overline{9}$

12. $0.\overline{164}$

13. $0.2\overline{8}$

14. $0.6\overline{41}$

Find the first three terms of each infinite geometric series.

15. $S = 64, r = -\frac{3}{4}$

16. $S = 625, r = \frac{1}{5}$

17. $S = 90, r = -\frac{1}{2}$

18. $S = 4, r = \frac{1}{3}$

Glencoe Division, Macmillan/McGraw-Hill

NAME ______________________ DATE ____________

13-6 Practice Worksheet

Infinite Geometric Series

Find the sum of each infinite geometric series, if it exists.

1. $a_1 = 35, r = \frac{2}{7}$ **49**

2. $18 - 6 + 2 - \ldots$ $\mathbf{\frac{27}{2}}$

3. $\frac{4}{25} + \frac{2}{5} + 1 + \ldots$ **does not exist**

4. $6 + 4 + \frac{8}{3} + \ldots$ **18**

5. $10 + 1 + 0.1 + \ldots$ $\mathbf{\frac{100}{9}}$

6. $2 + 6 + 18 + \ldots$ **does not exist**

7. $a_1 = 26, r = \frac{1}{2}$ **52**

8. $a_1 = 108, r = -\frac{3}{4}$ $\mathbf{\frac{432}{7}}$

9. $a_1 = 42, r = \frac{6}{5}$ **does not exist**

10. $a_1 = 50, r = \frac{2}{5}$ $\mathbf{\frac{250}{3}}$

Express each decimal as an infinite geometric series. Then find the ratio it represents.

11. $0.4\overline{9}$ **0.49 + 0.009 + 0.0009 + . . . ;** $\mathbf{\frac{1}{2}}$

12. $0.\overline{164}$ **0.164 + 0.000164 + 0.000000164 + . . . ;** $\mathbf{\frac{164}{999}}$

13. $0.2\overline{8}$ **0.28 + 0.008 + 0.0008 + . . . ;** $\mathbf{\frac{13}{45}}$

14. $0.6\overline{41}$ **0.641 + 0.00041 + 0.0000041 + . . . ;** $\mathbf{\frac{127}{198}}$

Find the first three terms of each infinite geometric series.

15. $S = 64, r = -\frac{3}{4}$ **112 − 84 + 63**

16. $S = 625, r = \frac{1}{5}$ **500 + 100 + 20**

17. $S = 90, r = -\frac{1}{2}$
135 − 67.5 + 33.75

18. $S = 4, r = \frac{1}{3}$
$\mathbf{\frac{8}{3} + \frac{8}{9} + \frac{8}{27}}$

Glencoe Division, Macmillan/McGraw-Hill

NAME ______________________ DATE ____________

13-7 Practice Worksheet

The Binomial Theorem

Use your calculator to evaluate each expression.

1. $7!$

2. $6!4!$

3. $\frac{8!}{6!2!}$

4. $\frac{8!}{5!3!}$

5. $(3! - 2!)!$

6. $\left(\frac{0! + 1! + 3!}{2!}\right)!$

Expand each binomial.

7. $(x + 3)^4$

8. $(2m - y)^4$

9. $(2x - y)^5$

10. $(r + 3)^5$

11. $(n + v)^8$

12. $(x - y)^7$

Find the indicated term of each expansion.

13. fourth term of $(x - 3y)^6$

14. fifth term of $(2x - 1)^9$

15. seventh term of $(x + y)^{10}$

16. tenth term of $(2x + y)^{12}$

17. Find the sixth element in the tenth row of Pascal's triangle.

18. Find the ninth element in the fourteenth row of Pascal's triangle.

Glencoe Division, Macmillan/McGraw-Hill

NAME ______________________ DATE ____________

13-7

Practice Worksheet

The Binomial Theorem

Use your calculator to evaluate each expression.

1. $7!$ 5040

2. $6!4!$ 17,280

3. $\frac{8!}{6!2!}$ 28

4. $\frac{8!}{5!3!}$ 56

5. $(3! - 2!)!$ 24

6. $\left(\frac{0! + 1! + 3!}{2!}\right)!$ 24

Expand each binomial.

7. $(x + 3)^4$
$x^4 + 12x^3 + 54x^2 + 108x + 81$

8. $(2m - y)^4$
$16m^4 - 32m^3y + 24m^2y^2 - 8my^3 + y^4$

9. $(2x - y)^5$ $32x^5 - 80x^4y + 80x^3y^2 - 40x^2y^3 + 10xy^4 - y^5$

10. $(r + 3)^5$ $r^5 + 15r^4 + 90r^3 + 270r^2 + 405r + 243$

11. $(n + v)^8$ $n^8 + 8n^7v + 28n^6v^2 + 56n^5v^3 + 70n^4v^4 + 56n^3v^5 + 28n^2v^6 + 8nv^7 + v^8$

12. $(x - y)^7$ $x^7 - 7x^6y + 21x^5y^2 - 35x^4y^3 + 35x^3y^4 - 21x^2y^5 + 7xy^6 - y^7$

Find the indicated term of each expansion.

13. fourth term of $(x - 3y)^6$
$-540x^3y^3$

14. fifth term of $(2x - 1)^9$
$4032x^5$

15. seventh term of $(x + y)^{10}$
$210x^4y^6$

16. tenth term of $(2x + y)^{12}$
$1760x^3y^9$

17. Find the sixth element in the tenth row of Pascal's triangle. 126

18. Find the ninth element in the fourteenth row of Pascal's triangle. 1287

NAME ______________________ DATE ____________

14-1 Practice Worksheet

Problem Solving Strategy: Organize Data and Make a Graph

The following chart gives the earned run average leaders for the National and American Leagues.

Year	National League	ERA	American League	ERA
1981	Nolan Ryan, Houston	1.69	Steve McCatty, Oakland	2.32
1982	Steve Rogers, Montreal	2.40	Rick Sutcliffe, Cleveland	2.96
1983	Atlee Hammaker, San Francisco	2.25	Rick Honeycutt, Texas	2.42
1984	Alejandro Pena, Los Angeles	2.48	Mike Boddicker, Baltimore	2.79
1985	Dwight Gooden, New York	1.53	Dave Stieb, Toronto	2.48
1986	Mike Scott, Houston	2.22	Roger Clemens, Boston	2.48
1987	Nolan Ryan, Houston	2.76	Jimmy Key, Toronto	2.76
1988	Joe Magrane, St. Louis	2.18	Alan Anderson, Minnesota	2.45
1989	Scott Garrelts, San Francisco	2.28	Bret Saberhagen, Kansas City	2.16
1990	Danny Darwin, Houston	2.21	Roger Clemens, Boston	1.93

1. Who had the lowest earned run average from 1981 to 1990?

2. Make a line graph showing the lowest earned run average for each year in the National League.

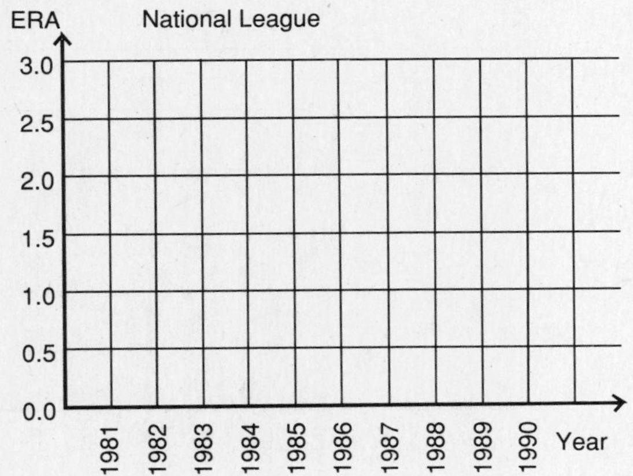

3. Make a bar graph showing the lowest earned run average for each year in the American League.

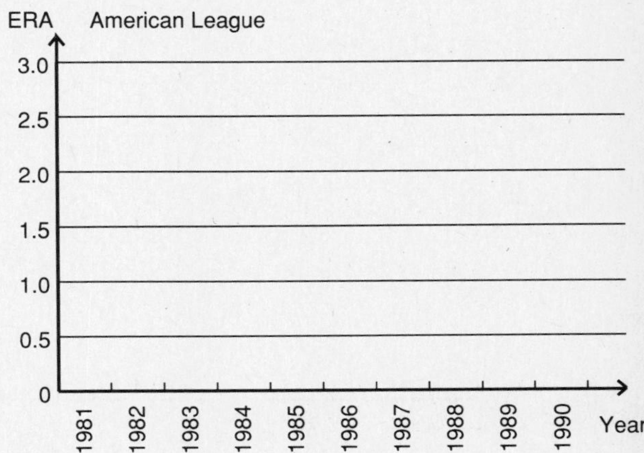

4. Nina has a part-time job and makes $80 per week. She spends $10 of her earnings each week to buy her lunches. Find the percent of a circle graph that represents the amount Nina spends on her lunches.

5. Find the number of degrees of a circle graph that represents the amount Nina spends on her lunches. (See problem 4.)

6. Each week Nina saves $35. Find the number of degrees of a circle graph that represents the amount Nina saves. (See problem 4.)

Glencoe Division, Macmillan/McGraw-Hill

NAME ______________________________ DATE ______________

14-1 **Practice Worksheet**

Problem Solving Strategy: Organize Data and Make a Graph

The following chart gives the earned run average leaders for the National and American Leagues.

Year	National League	ERA	American League	ERA
1981	Nolan Ryan, Houston	1.69	Steve McCatty, Oakland	2.32
1982	Steve Rogers, Montreal	2.40	Rick Sutcliffe, Cleveland	2.96
1983	Atlee Hammaker, San Francisco	2.25	Rick Honeycutt, Texas	2.42
1984	Alejandro Pena, Los Angeles	2.48	Mike Boddicker, Baltimore	2.79
1985	Dwight Gooden, New York	1.53	Dave Stieb, Toronto	2.48
1986	Mike Scott, Houston	2.22	Roger Clemens, Boston	2.48
1987	Nolan Ryan, Houston	2.76	Jimmy Key, Toronto	2.76
1988	Joe Magrane, St. Louis	2.18	Alan Anderson, Minnesota	2.45
1989	Scott Garrelts, San Francisco	2.28	Bret Saberhagen, Kansas City	2.16
1990	Danny Darwin, Houston	2.21	Roger Clemens, Boston	1.93

1. Who had the lowest earned run average from 1981 to 1990? **Dwight Gooden**

2. Make a line graph showing the lowest earned run average for each year in the National League.

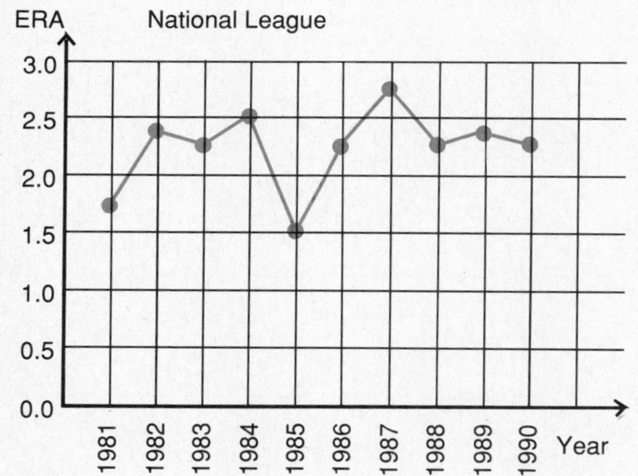

3. Make a bar graph showing the lowest earned run average for each year in the American League.

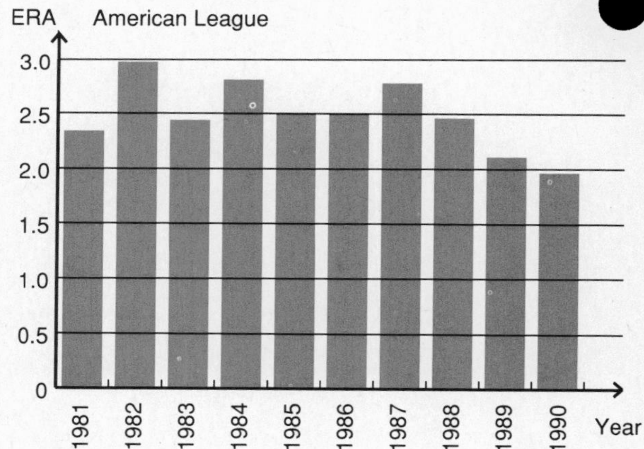

4. Nina has a part-time job and makes $80 per week. She spends $10 of her earnings each week to buy her lunches. Find the percent of a circle graph that represents the amount Nina spends on her lunches. **12.5%**

5. Find the number of degrees of a circle graph that represents the amount Nina spends on her lunches. (See problem 4.) **45°**

6. Each week Nina saves $35. Find the number of degrees of a circle graph that represents the amount Nina saves. (See problem 4.) **157.5°**

Glencoe Division, Macmillan/McGraw-Hill

NAME ________________________ DATE ____________

14-2 Practice Worksheet

Line Plots and Stem-and-Leaf Plots

Each number below represents the weight of each person in Mr. Miller's math class.

134	116	146	152	124	110	137	108	110	132
98	221	86	143	114	104	121	127	137	110

1. Make a line plot of the weights of the people in the class.

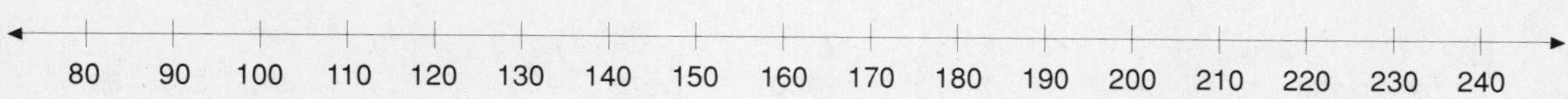

2. What is the weight of the heaviest person?

3. What is the weight of the lightest person?

4. Which weight(s) occur most frequently?

The following tables give the number of games bowled and total points scored for two bowling teams for the season.

Pin Struck		
Player	No. of games	Points
Bob	111	17,316
Cindy	93	11,625
Steve	87	11,832
Cheri	110	15,070
Juan	108	19,008

Bowl Downers		
Player	No. of games	Points
Kiko	96	10,752
Paul	84	12,348
Clarice	111	14,319
Bethany	105	10,290
Jarrod	99	16,731

5. Make a stem-and-leaf plot of the number of games bowled by the 10 players.

6. Who had the highest average?

7. Who had the lowest average?

NAME ____________________ DATE ____________

14-2 Practice Worksheet

Line Plots and Stem-and-Leaf Plots

Each number below represents the weight of each person in Mr. Miller's math class.

134	116	146	152	124	110	137	108	110	132
98	221	86	143	114	104	121	127	137	110

1. Make a line plot of the weights of the people in the class.

```
                  X
                  X                          X
    X        X  X XX  XX XXX  XX X  XX  X                              X
<---+----+----+----+----+----+----+----+----+----+----+----+----+----+----+----+----+--->
   80   90  100  110  120  130  140  150  160  170  180  190  200  210  220  230  240
```

2. What is the weight of the heaviest person? **221**

3. What is the weight of the lightest person? **86**

4. Which weight(s) occur most frequently? **110**

The following tables give the number of games bowled and total points scored for two bowling teams for the season.

Pin Struck		
Player	No. of games	Points
Bob	111	17,316
Cindy	93	11,625
Steve	87	11,832
Cheri	110	15,070
Juan	108	19,008

Bowl Downers		
Player	No. of games	Points
Kiko	96	10,752
Paul	84	12,348
Clarice	111	14,319
Bethany	105	10,290
Jarrod	99	16,731

5. Make a stem-and-leaf plot of the number of games bowled by the 10 players.

Stem	Leaf
8	4 7
9	3 6 9
10	5 8
11	0 1 1

6. Who had the highest average? **Juan**

7. Who had the lowest average? **Bethany**

Glencoe Division, Macmillan/McGraw-Hill

NAME ______________________ DATE ____________

14-3 Practice Worksheet

Central Tendency: Median, Mode, and Mean

The following chart gives the number of airline fatalities in the United States during the years 1981 to 1989.

	Fatalities		Fatalities
1981	4	1986	1
1982	233	1987	231
1983	15	1988	285
1984	4	1989	278
1985	197		

1. Find the mean of the data.

2. Find the median of the data.

3. Find the mode of the data.

The following chart gives the average number of points per game scored by members of a basketball team during a recent year.

37.1	8.5	4.2
14.5	8.5	3.5
11.3	8.3	2.8
9.7	6.9	1.9

4. Find the mean of the data.

5. Find the median of the data.

6. Find the mode of the data.

The following chart gives the number of students present at each of the monthly club meetings.

August	146	January	121
September	138	February	93
October	120	March	118
November	132	April	129
December	146	May	136

7. Find the mean of the data.

8. Find the median of the data.

9. Find the mode of the data.

Glencoe Division, Macmillan/McGraw-Hill

NAME ______________________ DATE ____________

14-3 Practice Worksheet

Central Tendency: Median, Mode, and Mean

The following chart gives the number of airline fatalities in the United States during the years 1981 to 1989.

	Fatalities		Fatalities
1981	4	1986	1
1982	233	1987	231
1983	15	1988	285
1984	4	1989	278
1985	197		

1. Find the mean of the data. **138.7**

2. Find the median of the data. **197**

3. Find the mode of the data. **4**

The following chart gives the average number of points per game scored by members of a basketball team during a recent year.

37.1	8.5	4.2
14.5	8.5	3.5
11.3	8.3	2.8
9.7	6.9	1.9

4. Find the mean of the data. **9.8**

5. Find the median of the data. **8.4**

6. Find the mode of the data. **8.5**

The following chart gives the number of students present at each of the monthly club meetings.

August	146	January	121
September	138	February	93
October	120	March	118
November	132	April	129
December	146	May	136

7. Find the mean of the data. **127.9**

8. Find the median of the data. **130.5**

9. Find the mode of the data. **146**

Glencoe Division, Macmillan/McGraw-Hill

NAME ________________________________ DATE ______________

14-4 Practice Worksheet

Variation: Range, Interquartile Range, and Outliers

Find the range, quartiles, and interquartile range for each set of data. Find any outliers in each set of data.

1. {4, 7, 9, 2, 8, 16, 21, 10, 5, 11}

2. {25, 46, 39, 27, 50, 56, 92, 48, 56, 10}

3. {43, 26, 92, 11, 8, 49, 52, 126, 86, 42, 63, 78, 91, 79, 86}

4. {1.6, 9.8, 4.5, 6.2, 8.7, 5.6, 3.9, 6.8, 9.7, 1.1, 4.7, 3.8, 7.5, 2.8, 0.1}

5. {146, 289, 121, 146, 212, 98, 86, 153, 128, 136, 181, 142}

6. {1592, 1486, 1479, 1682, 1720, 1104, 1486, 1895, 1890, 2687, 3542}

7. {506, 612, 789, 412, 814, 583, 102, 881, 457, 826}

8. {26.8, 15.7, 98.4, 27.3, 14.1, 81.6, 19.4, 21.5, 46.5, 23.7, 16.7, 29.8}

9.

Stem	Leaf
1	0 1 5 9
2	2 4 6
3	7 8
4	5 5 7 8

10.

Stem	Leaf
2	26 43 59
4	02 87 93
5	16 20
7	98

NAME ______________________ DATE ____________

14-4 Practice Worksheet

Variation: Range, Interquartile Range, and Outliers

Find the range, quartiles, and interquartile range for each set of data. Find any outliers in each set of data.

1. {4, 7, 9, 2, 8, 16, 21, 10, 5, 11}
19; 5, 8.5, 11; 6; 21

2. {25, 46, 39, 27, 50, 56, 92, 48, 56, 10}
82; 27, 47, 56; 29; none

3. {43, 26, 92, 11, 8, 49, 52, 126, 86, 42, 63, 78, 91, 79, 86}
118; 42, 63, 86; 44; none

4. {1.6, 9.8, 4.5, 6.2, 8.7, 5.6, 3.9, 6.8, 9.7, 1.1, 4.7, 3.8, 7.5, 2.8, 0.1}
9.7; 2.8, 4.7, 7.5; 4.7; none

5. {146, 289, 121, 146, 212, 98, 86, 153, 128, 136, 181, 142}
203; 124.5, 144, 167; 42.5; 289

6. {1592, 1486, 1479, 1682, 1720, 1104, 1486, 1895, 1890, 2687, 3542}
2438; 1486, 1682, 1895; 409; 2687 and 3542

7. {506, 612, 789, 412, 814, 583, 102, 881, 457, 826}
779; 457, 597.5, 814; 357; none

8. {26.8, 15.7, 98.4, 27.3, 14.1, 81.6, 19.4, 21.5, 46.5, 23.7, 16.7, 29.8}
84.3; 18.05, 25.25, 38.15; 20.1; 10.6 and 98.4

9.

Stem	Leaf
1	0 1 5 9
2	2 4 6
3	7 8
4	5 5 7 8

38; 17, 26, 45; 28; none

10.

Stem	Leaf
2	26 43 59
4	02 87 93
5	16 20
7	98

572; 251, 487, 518; 267; none

Glencoe Division, Macmillan/McGraw-Hill

NAME ______________________ DATE ______________

14-5 Practice Worksheet

Box and Whisker Plots

The following chart gives the number of motorcycle fatalities in the United States by state and federal district in a recent year.

AL	39	FL	235	LA	45	NE	31	OK	46	VT	12
AK	1	GA	63	ME	21	NV	22	OR	70	VA	56
AZ	91	HI	13	MD	65	NH	24	PA	150	WA	90
AR	50	ID	27	MA	62	NJ	49	RI	18	WV	27
CA	767	IL	174	MI	105	NM	37	SC	56	WI	88
CO	62	IN	131	MN	54	NY	181	SD	14	WY	5
CT	65	IA	57	MS	30	NC	91	TN	83		
DE	14	KS	42	MO	60	ND	7	TX	297		
DC	4	KY	40	MT	26	OH	199	UT	30		

1. Make a box-and-whisker plot of the data.

2. Identify any outliers.

The following chart gives the heights of forty presidents of the United States.

Washington	74″	Buchanan	72″	Harding	72″
J. Adams	67″	Lincoln	76″	Coolidge	70″
Jefferson	74″	A. Johnson	70″	Hoover	71″
Madison	64″	Grant	68″	F. Roosevelt	74″
Monroe	72″	Hayes	68″	Truman	69″
J. Q. Adams	67″	Garfield	72″	Eisenhower	70″
Jackson	73″	Arthur	74″	Kennedy	72″
Van Buren	66″	Cleveland	71″	L. Johnson	74″
W. H. Harrison	66″	B. Harrison	66″	Nixon	72″
Tyler	72″	Cleveland	71″	Ford	72″
Polk	68″	McKinley	70″	Carter	70″
Taylor	68″	T. Roosevelt	70″	Reagan	73″
Fillmore	69″	Taft	72″		
Pierce	70″	Wilson	71″		

3. Make a box-and-whisker plot of the data.

4. Identify any outliers.

Glencoe Division, Macmillan/McGraw-Hill

NAME ______________________ DATE ______________

14-5 Practice Worksheet

Box and Whisker Plots

The following chart gives the number of motorcycle fatalities in the United States by state and federal district in a recent year.

AL	39	FL	235	LA	45	NE	31	OK	46	VT	12
AK	1	GA	63	ME	21	NV	22	OR	70	VA	56
AZ	91	HI	13	MD	65	NH	24	PA	150	WA	90
AR	50	ID	27	MA	62	NJ	49	RI	18	WV	27
CA	767	IL	174	MI	105	NM	37	SC	56	WI	88
CO	62	IN	131	MN	54	NY	181	SD	14	WY	5
CT	65	IA	57	MS	30	NC	91	TN	83		
DE	14	KS	42	MO	60	ND	7	TX	297		
DC	4	KY	40	MT	26	OH	199	UT	30		

1. Make a box-and-whisker plot of the data.

2. Identify any outliers. **199, 235, 297, 767**

The following chart gives the heights of forty presidents of the United States.

Washington	74″	Buchanan	72″	Harding	72″
J. Adams	67″	Lincoln	76″	Coolidge	70″
Jefferson	74″	A. Johnson	70″	Hoover	71″
Madison	64″	Grant	68″	F. Roosevelt	74″
Monroe	72″	Hayes	68″	Truman	69″
J. Q. Adams	67″	Garfield	72″	Eisenhower	70″
Jackson	73″	Arthur	74″	Kennedy	72″
Van Buren	66″	Cleveland	71″	L. Johnson	74″
W. H. Harrison	66″	B. Harrison	66″	Nixon	72″
Tyler	72″	Cleveland	71″	Ford	72″
Polk	68″	McKinley	70″	Carter	70″
Taylor	68″	T. Roosevelt	70″	Reagan	73″
Fillmore	69″	Taft	72″		
Pierce	70″	Wilson	71″		

3. Make a box-and-whisker plot of the data.

4. Identify any outliers. **no outliers**

Glencoe Division, Macmillan/McGraw-Hill

NAME ______________________ DATE ______________

14-6 Practice Worksheet

Variation: Standard Deviation

Find the standard deviation for each set of data.

1. {3, 5, 2, 6, 5, 9, 5, 2, 8, 6}

2. {6.1, 2.5, 4.8, 3.8, 7.1, 6.1, 5.9}

3. {0.050, 0.048, 0.051, 0.047, 0.048, 0.053, 0.044, 0.048, 0.052, 0.046}

4. {26, 37, 89, 42, 56, 43, 27, 18, 72, 83}

5. {156, 283, 102, 127, 136, 145, 154, 129, 110, 152, 181, 193}

6. {1246, 8492, 5673, 1491, 2467, 4531, 3798, 1288, 4543, 5896}

7.

Stem	Leaf
2	5 6 8
3	0 4
5	3 8
7	2
9	4 7 9

8.

Stem	Leaf
2	00 46
3	23 79 86
4	51 80
5	32 49 97

9.

Stem	Leaf
42	1 3 7 9
48	2 4
50	9
52	0 3 5

10.

Stem	Leaf
11	00 23 59
12	27 63
13	42 57
14	14 98 99

Glencoe Division, Macmillan/McGraw-Hill

NAME ______________________ DATE ______________

14-6 Practice Worksheet

Variation: Standard Deviation

Find the standard deviation for each set of data.

Accept answers reasonably close to those given here. Slight variations can result from differences in calculator models.

1. {3, 5, 2, 6, 5, 9, 5, 2, 8, 6} **2.21**

2. {6.1, 2.5, 4.8, 3.8, 7.1, 6.1, 5.9} **1.47**

3. {0.050, 0.048, 0.051, 0.047, 0.048, 0.053, 0.044, 0.048, 0.052, 0.046} **0.002665**

4. {26, 37, 89, 42, 56, 43, 27, 18, 72, 83} **23.23**

5. {156, 283, 102, 127, 136, 145, 154, 129, 110, 152, 181, 193} **45.88**

6. {1246, 8492, 5673, 1491, 2467, 4531, 3798, 1288, 4543, 5896} **2252.58**

7.

Stem	Leaf
2	5 6 8
3	0 4
5	3 8
7	2
9	4 7 9

28.68

8.

Stem	Leaf
2	00 46
3	23 79 86
4	51 80
5	32 49 97

124.77

9.

Stem	Leaf
42	1 3 7 9
48	2 4
50	9
52	0 3 5

42.60

10.

Stem	Leaf
11	00 23 59
12	27 63
13	42 57
14	14 98 99

139.53

NAME ______________________ DATE ____________

14-7

Practice Worksheet

The Normal Distribution

The weights of eggs produced on a farm are normally distributed with a mean of 1.4 ounces and a standard deviation of 0.4 ounces.

1. What percent of the eggs weigh at least 1 ounce?

2. How many of 1200 eggs are within 2 standard deviations of the mean?

3. To be graded extra large, an egg must weigh at least 2.2 ounces. What is the probability that an egg from this farm will be graded extra large?

A bottle of fruit punch must contain at least 16 fluid ounces. The machine that fills the bottles is set so that the mean volume is 16.4 fluid ounces. The volumes in the bottles are normally distributed.

4. What percent of the bottles are underfilled if the standard deviation is 0.2 fluid ounces?

5. What percent of the bottles are underfilled if the standard deviation is 0.4 fluid ounces?

6. If the standard deviation is 0.2 fluid ounces, find the mean volume that will ensure only 0.5% of the bottles will be underfilled.

A battery has an average life span of 50 hours, with a standard deviation of 3 hours. The life span of the batteries is normally distributed.

7. What percent of the batteries last at least 44 hours?

8. How many of 1500 batteries are within 1 standard deviation of the mean?

9. What percent of the batteries will last at least 53 hours?

NAME ______ DATE ______

14-7 Practice Worksheet

The Normal Distribution

The weights of eggs produced on a farm are normally distributed with a mean of 1.4 ounces and a standard deviation of 0.4 ounces.

1. What percent of the eggs weigh at least 1 ounce? **84%**

2. How many of 1200 eggs are within 2 standard deviations of the mean? **1140 eggs**

3. To be graded extra large, an egg must weigh at least 2.2 ounces. What is the probability that an egg from this farm will be graded extra large? **0.025**

A bottle of fruit punch must contain at least 16 fluid ounces. The machine that fills the bottles is set so that the mean volume is 16.4 fluid ounces. The volumes in the bottles are normally distributed.

4. What percent of the bottles are underfilled if the standard deviation is 0.2 fluid ounces? **2.5%**

5. What percent of the bottles are underfilled if the standard deviation is 0.4 fluid ounces? **16%**

6. If the standard deviation is 0.2 fluid ounces, find the mean volume that will ensure only 0.5% of the bottles will be underfilled. **16.6 fluid ounces**

A battery has an average life span of 50 hours, with a standard deviation of 3 hours. The life span of the batteries is normally distributed.

7. What percent of the batteries last at least 44 hours? **97.5%**

8. How many of 1500 batteries are within 1 standard deviation of the mean? **1020 batteries**

9. What percent of the batteries will last at least 53 hours? **16%**

15-1

NAME ______________________ DATE ____________

Practice Worksheet

Problem Solving Strategy: Using Models

Solve. Use any strategy.

1. A deli has 6 types of meat, 4 types of cheese, and 3 types of bread. How many different sandwiches can you make if you use one type of meat, one type of cheese, and one type of bread for each sandwich?

2. Tina, Tom, and Teri all volunteer at the hospital. Tina works every fourth day. Tom works every sixth day. Teri works every eighth day. They all work May 1. What is the next day that all three will work together?

3. A desk drawer contains three pencils. The pencils have either #2, #2$\frac{1}{2}$, or #3 leads. They are either yellow, blue or red in color. They write with either fine, medium, or thick points. A randomly selected pencil is either a #2, or blue, or has a fine point. Another pencil is either a #3, or yellow, or has a thick point. The yellow pencil has a thicker point than the #2$\frac{1}{2}$ pencil. What size lead, what color, and what size point does each pencil have?

Glencoe Division, Macmillan/McGraw-Hill

NAME ____________________ DATE ____________

15-1 Practice Worksheet

Problem Solving Strategy: Using Models

Solve. Use any strategy.

1. A deli has 6 types of meat, 4 types of cheese, and 3 types of bread. How many different sandwiches can you make if you use one type of meat, one type of cheese, and one type of bread for each sandwich?

72

2. Tina, Tom, and Teri all volunteer at the hospital. Tina works every fourth day. Tom works every sixth day. Teri works every eighth day. They all work May 1. What is the next day that all three will work together?

May 25

3. A desk drawer contains three pencils. The pencils have either #2, #$2\frac{1}{2}$, or #3 leads. They are either yellow, blue or red in color. They write with either fine, medium, or thick points. A randomly selected pencil is either a #2, or blue, or has a fine point. Another pencil is either a #3, or yellow, or has a thick point. The yellow pencil has a thicker point than the #$2\frac{1}{2}$ pencil. What size lead, what color, and what size point does each pencil have?

#2—yellow—thick
#$2\frac{1}{2}$—blue—medium
#3—red—fine

NAME ______________________ DATE ____________

15-2

Practice Worksheet

The Counting Principle

Solve each problem.

1. A briefcase lock has 3 rotating cylinders, each containing 10 digits. How many numerical codes are possible?

2. A golf club manufacturer makes irons with 7 different shaft lengths, 3 different grips, 5 different lies, and 2 different club head materials. How many different combinations are offered?

3. There are five different routes that a commuter can take from her home to the office. In how many ways can she make a round trip if she uses a different route coming than going?

4. In how many ways can the 4 call letters of a radio station be arranged if the first letter must be W or K and no letters repeat?

5. How many 7-digit phone numbers can be formed if the first digit cannot be 0 or 1?

6. How many 7-digit phone numbers can be formed if the first digit cannot be 0 or 1 and if no digit can be repeated?

Glencoe Division, Macmillan/McGraw-Hill

NAME ______________________ DATE ____________

15-2 Practice Worksheet

The Counting Principle

Solve each problem.

1. A briefcase lock has 3 rotating cylinders, each containing 10 digits. How many numerical codes are possible? **1000**

2. A golf club manufacturer makes irons with 7 different shaft lengths, 3 different grips, 5 different lies, and 2 different club head materials. How many different combinations are offered? **210**

3. There are five different routes that a commuter can take from her home to the office. In how many ways can she make a round trip if she uses a different route coming than going? **20**

4. In how many ways can the 4 call letters of a radio station be arranged if the first letter must be W or K and no letters repeat? **27,600**

5. How many 7-digit phone numbers can be formed if the first digit cannot be 0 or 1? **8,000,000**

6. How many 7-digit phone numbers can be formed if the first digit cannot be 0 or 1 and if no digit can be repeated? **483,840**

Glencoe Division, Macmillan/McGraw-Hill

NAME ______________________ DATE ____________

15-3 Practice Worksheet

Linear Permutations

Evaluate each expression.

1. $\frac{8!}{6!}$

2. $P(8, 6)$

3. $\frac{P(7, 5)}{P(4, 3)}$

4. $\frac{P(6, 5)P(4, 4)}{P(5, 1)P(9, 2)}$

How many different ways can the letters of each word be arranged?

5. CANADA

6. ILLINI

7. ANNUALLY

8. MEMBERS

Solve each problem.

9. A photographer is taking a picture of a bride and groom together with 6 attendants. How many ways can he arrange the 8 people in a line if the bride and groom stand in the middle?

10. A person playing a word game has the following letters on her tray: QUOUNNTAGGRA. How many 12-letter arrangements could she make to see if a single word could be formed from all the letters?

11. How many ways can 3 identical pen sets and 5 identical watches be given to 8 graduates if each receives one item?

12. Three different hardcover books and five different paperbacks are placed on a shelf. How many ways can they be arranged if all the hardcover books are together?

NAME ______________________ DATE ____________

15-3

Practice Worksheet

Linear Permutations

Evaluate each expression.

1. $\frac{8!}{6!}$ 56

2. $P(8, 6)$ 20, 160

3. $\frac{P(7, 5)}{P(4, 3)}$ 105

4. $\frac{P(6, 5)P(4, 4)}{P(5, 1)P(9, 2)}$ 48

How many different ways can the letters of each word be arranged?

5. CANADA 120

6. ILLINI 60

7. ANNUALLY 5040

8. MEMBERS 1260

Solve each problem.

9. A photographer is taking a picture of a bride and groom together with 6 attendants. How many ways can he arrange the 8 people in a line if the bride and groom stand in the middle? 1440

10. A person playing a word game has the following letters on her tray: QUOUNNTAGGRA. How many 12-letter arrangements could she make to see if a single word could be formed from all the letters? 29,937,600

11. How many ways can 3 identical pen sets and 5 identical watches be given to 8 graduates if each receives one item? 56

12. Three different hardcover books and five different paperbacks are placed on a shelf. How many ways can they be arranged if all the hardcover books are together? 4320

Glencoe Division, Macmillan/McGraw-Hill

NAME ______________________ DATE ______________

15-4 Practice Worksheet

Circular Permutations

Evaluate each expression.

1. $\frac{5!}{5}$

2. $\frac{7!}{2!5!}$

3. $\frac{P(8, 3)}{7!}$

4. $\frac{P(6, 3) \cdot P(4, 2)}{4!}$

5. $\frac{P(7, 4) \cdot P(5, 3)}{P(6, 5)}$

6. $\frac{P(8, 5)}{P(9, 2) \cdot P(7, 3)}$

Solve each problem.

7. How many ways can 4 charms be arranged on a bracelet that has no clasp?

8. How many ways can 4 charms be arranged on a bracelet that has a clasp?

9. How many ways can 8 charms be arranged on a bracelet that has a clasp?

10. How many ways can 8 charms be arranged on a bracelet that has no clasp?

11. How many ways can 5 men and 5 women be seated alternately at a round table?

12. How many ways can 6 red beads and 6 white beads be placed alternately on a necklace with no clasp?

13. How many ways can 6 red beads and 6 white beads be placed alternately on a necklace that has a clasp?

14. How many ways can Laura and her 6 friends be seated around a table if Laura sits at the head of the table?

Glencoe Division, Macmillan/McGraw-Hill

NAME ______________________ DATE ____________

15-4 Practice Worksheet

Circular Permutations

Evaluate each expression.

1. $\frac{5!}{5}$ **24**

2. $\frac{7!}{2!5!}$ **21**

3. $\frac{P(8, 3)}{7!}$ $\mathbf{\frac{1}{15}}$

4. $\frac{P(6, 3) \cdot P(4, 2)}{4!}$ **60**

5. $\frac{P(7, 4) \cdot P(5, 3)}{P(6, 5)}$ **70**

6. $\frac{P(8, 5)}{P(9, 2) \cdot P(7, 3)}$ $\mathbf{\frac{4}{9}}$

Solve each problem.

7. How many ways can 4 charms be arranged on a bracelet that has no clasp? **3**

8. How many ways can 4 charms be arranged on a bracelet that has a clasp? **12**

9. How many ways can 8 charms be arranged on a bracelet that has a clasp? **20,160**

10. How many ways can 8 charms be arranged on a bracelet that has no clasp? **2520**

11. How many ways can 5 men and 5 women be seated alternately at a round table? **1440**

12. How many ways can 6 red beads and 6 white beads be placed alternately on a necklace with no clasp? **21,600**

13. How many ways can 6 red beads and 6 white beads be placed alternately on a necklace that has a clasp? **129,600**

14. How many ways can Laura and her 6 friends be seated around a table if Laura sits at the head of the table? **720**

Glencoe Division, Macmillan/McGraw-Hill

NAME ______________________ DATE ______________

15-5 Practice Worksheet

Combinations

Evaluate each expression.

1. $C(8, 2)$

2. $C(11, 3)$

3. $C(20, 18)$

4. $C(9, 3) \cdot C(6, 2)$

Find the value of x.

5. $C(x, 7) = C(x, 2)$

6. $C(11, 2) = C(x, 9)$

Solve each problem.

7. How many 4-person bobsled teams can be chosen from a group of 9 athletes?

8. From a dessert cart in a fine restaurant, customers are allowed to pick 3 desserts from the 10 that are displayed. How many combinations are possible?

9. How many diagonals does a polygon with 12 sides have?

10. How many 5-sided polygons can be formed by joining any 5 of 11 points located on a circle?

An urn contains 8 white, 6 blue, and 9 red balls. How many ways can 6 balls be selected to meet each condition?

11. All balls are red.

12. Three are blue, 2 are white, and 1 is red.

13. Two are blue, and 4 are red.

14. Exactly 4 balls are white.

NAME ______________________ DATE ______________

15-5 Practice Worksheet

Combinations

Evaluate each expression.

1. $C(8, 2)$ **28**

2. $C(11, 3)$ **165**

3. $C(20, 18)$ **190**

4. $C(9, 3) \cdot C(6, 2)$ **1260**

Find the value of x.

5. $C(x, 7) = C(x, 2)$ **9**

6. $C(11, 2) = C(x, 9)$ **11**

Solve each problem.

7. How many 4-person bobsled teams can be chosen from a group of 9 athletes? **126**

8. From a dessert cart in a fine restaurant, customers are allowed to pick 3 desserts from the 10 that are displayed. How many combinations are possible? **120**

9. How many diagonals does a polygon with 12 sides have? **54**

10. How many 5-sided polygons can be formed by joining any 5 of 11 points located on a circle? **462**

An urn contains 8 white, 6 blue, and 9 red balls. How many ways can 6 balls be selected to meet each condition?

11. All balls are red. **84**

12. Three are blue, 2 are white, and 1 is red. **5040**

13. Two are blue, and 4 are red. **1890**

14. Exactly 4 balls are white. **7350**

NAME ________________________ DATE ____________

15-6 Practice Worksheet

Probability

State the odds of an event occurring given the probability of the event.

1. $\frac{4}{11}$ **2.** $\frac{2}{3}$ **3.** $\frac{5}{99}$

4. $\frac{1}{1000}$ **5.** $\frac{5}{16}$ **6.** $\frac{3}{95}$

State the probability of an event occurring given the odds of the event.

7. $\frac{2}{23}$ **8.** $\frac{3}{5}$ **9.** $\frac{4}{1}$

10. $\frac{9}{7}$ **11.** $\frac{11}{14}$ **12.** $\frac{1000}{1}$

Solve each problem.

A bag contains 1 green, 4 red, and 5 yellow balls. Two balls are selected at random. Find each probability.

13. P(2 red) **14.** P(1 red and 1 yellow)

15. P(1 green and 1 yellow) **16.** P(2 green)

A bank contains 3 pennies, 8 nickels, 4 dimes, and 10 quarters. Two coins are selected at random. Find each probability.

17. P(2 pennies) **18.** P(2 dimes)

19. P(1 nickel and 1 dime) **20.** P(1 quarter and 1 penny)

Glencoe Division, Macmillan/McGraw-Hill

NAME ______________________ DATE ____________

15-6 **Practice Worksheet**

Probability

State the odds of an event occurring given the probability of the event.

1. $\frac{4}{11}$ $\frac{4}{7}$

2. $\frac{2}{3}$ $\frac{2}{1}$

3. $\frac{5}{99}$ $\frac{5}{94}$

4. $\frac{1}{1000}$ $\frac{1}{999}$

5. $\frac{5}{16}$ $\frac{5}{11}$

6. $\frac{3}{95}$ $\frac{3}{92}$

State the probability of an event occurring given the odds of the event.

7. $\frac{2}{23}$ $\frac{2}{25}$

8. $\frac{3}{5}$ $\frac{3}{8}$

9. $\frac{4}{1}$ $\frac{4}{5}$

10. $\frac{9}{7}$ $\frac{9}{16}$

11. $\frac{11}{14}$ $\frac{11}{25}$

12. $\frac{1000}{1}$ $\frac{1000}{1001}$

Solve each problem.

A bag contains 1 green, 4 red, and 5 yellow balls. Two balls are selected at random. Find each probability.

13. P(2 red) $\frac{2}{15}$

14. P(1 red and 1 yellow) $\frac{4}{9}$

15. P(1 green and 1 yellow) $\frac{1}{9}$

16. P(2 green) 0

A bank contains 3 pennies, 8 nickels, 4 dimes, and 10 quarters. Two coins are selected at random. Find each probability.

17. P(2 pennies) $\frac{1}{100}$

18. P(2 dimes) $\frac{1}{50}$

19. P(1 nickel and 1 dime) $\frac{8}{75}$

20. P(1 quarter and 1 penny) $\frac{1}{10}$

Glencoe Division, Macmillan/McGraw-Hill

NAME ______________________ DATE ____________

15-7 **Practice Worksheet**

Multiplying Probabilities

There are 3 nickels, 2 dimes, and 5 quarters in a purse. Three coins are selected in succession at random.

1. Find the probability of selecting 1 nickel, 1 dime, and 1 quarter in that order without replacement.

2. Find the probability of selecting 1 nickel, 1 dime, and 1 quarter in that order with replacement.

3. Find the probability of selecting 1 nickel, 1 dime, and 1 quarter in any order with replacement.

4. Find the probability of selecting 1 nickel, 1 dime, and 1 quarter in any order without replacement.

A red, a green, and a yellow die are tossed. What is the probability that the following occurs?

5. All 3 dice show 4.

6. None of the 3 dice shows a 4.

7. The red die shows an even number and the other 2 dice show different odd numbers.

8. All 3 dice show the same number.

From a standard deck of 52 cards, 2 cards are selected. What is the probability that the following occurs?

9. 2 black cards; selection without replacement.

10. 2 black cards; selection with replacement

11. 1 red card and 1 spade in any order; selection without replacement.

12. 1 red card and 1 spade in that order; selection without replacement.

Glencoe Division, Macmillan/McGraw-Hill

NAME ______________________ DATE __________

15-7

Practice Worksheet

Multiplying Probabilities

There are 3 nickels, 2 dimes, and 5 quarters in a purse. Three coins are selected in succession at random.

1. Find the probability of selecting 1 nickel, 1 dime, and 1 quarter in that order without replacement. $\frac{1}{24}$

2. Find the probability of selecting 1 nickel, 1 dime, and 1 quarter in that order with replacement. $\frac{3}{100}$

3. Find the probability of selecting 1 nickel, 1 dime, and 1 quarter in any order with replacement. $\frac{9}{50}$

4. Find the probability of selecting 1 nickel, 1 dime, and 1 quarter in any order without replacement. $\frac{1}{4}$

A red, a green, and a yellow die are tossed. What is the probability that the following occurs?

5. All 3 dice show 4. $\frac{1}{216}$

6. None of the 3 dice shows a 4. $\frac{125}{216}$

7. The red die shows an even number and the other 2 dice show different odd numbers. $\frac{1}{12}$

8. All 3 dice show the same number. $\frac{1}{36}$

From a standard deck of 52 cards, 2 cards are selected. What is the probability that the following occurs?

9. 2 black cards; selection without replacement. $\frac{25}{102}$

10. 2 black cards; selection with replacement $\frac{1}{4}$

11. 1 red card and 1 spade in any order; selection without replacement. $\frac{13}{51}$

12. 1 red card and 1 spade in that order; selection without replacement. $\frac{13}{102}$

Glencoe Division, Macmillan/McGraw-Hill

NAME ________________________________ DATE ______________

15-8 Practice Worksheet

Adding Probabilities

An urn contains 7 white marbles and 5 blue marbles. Four marbles are selected without replacement. What is the probability that the following occurs?

1. all white or all blue

2. exactly 3 white

3. at least 3 white

4. exactly 3 white or exactly 3 blue

Two cards are drawn from a standard deck of 52 cards. What is the probability that the following occurs?

5. 2 spades

6. 2 spades or 2 red cards

7. 2 red cards or 2 jacks

8. 2 spades or 2 face cards

Three dice are tossed. What is the probability that the following occurs?

9. only two 5s

10. at least two 5s

11. three 5s

12. no 5s

Glencoe Division, Macmillan/McGraw-Hill

NAME ______________________ DATE ______________

15-8 **Practice Worksheet**

Adding Probabilities

An urn contains 7 white marbles and 5 blue marbles. Four marbles are selected without replacement. What is the probability that the following occurs?

1. all white or all blue $\frac{8}{99}$

2. exactly 3 white $\frac{35}{99}$

3. at least 3 white $\frac{14}{33}$

4. exactly 3 white or exactly 3 blue $\frac{49}{99}$

Two cards are drawn from a standard deck of 52 cards. What is the probability that the following occurs?

5. 2 spades $\frac{1}{17}$

6. 2 spades or 2 red cards $\frac{31}{102}$

7. 2 red cards or 2 jacks $\frac{55}{221}$

8. 2 spades or 2 face cards $\frac{47}{442}$

Three dice are tossed. What is the probability that the following occurs?

9. only two 5s $\frac{5}{72}$

10. at least two 5s $\frac{2}{27}$

11. three 5s $\frac{1}{216}$

12. no 5s $\frac{125}{216}$

Glencoe Division, Macmillan/McGraw-Hill

15-9

NAME ______________________ DATE ____________

Practice Worksheet

Simulation and Binomial Experiments

Six coins are tossed. What is the probability that the following occurs?

1. 3 heads and 3 tails

2. at least 4 heads

3. 2 heads or 5 tails

4. all heads or all tails

The probability of Chris making a free throw is $\frac{2}{3}$. If she shoots five times, what is the probability of the following?

5. all missed

6. all made

7. exactly 4 made

8. at least 3 made

When Mary and Sam play a certain board game, the probability that Mary will win a game is $\frac{3}{4}$. If they play five games, find the probability of each event.

9. Sam wins only once

10. Mary wins exactly twice

11. Sam wins at least two games

12. Mary wins at least three games

Glencoe Division, Macmillan/McGraw-Hill

NAME ______________________ DATE ____________

15-9 Practice Worksheet

Simulation and Binomial Experiments

Six coins are tossed. What is the probability that the following occurs?

1. 3 heads and 3 tails $\frac{5}{16}$

2. at least 4 heads $\frac{11}{32}$

3. 2 heads or 5 tails $\frac{21}{64}$

4. all heads or all tails $\frac{1}{32}$

The probability of Chris making a free throw is $\frac{2}{3}$. If she shoots five times, what is the probability of the following?

5. all missed $\frac{1}{243}$

6. all made $\frac{32}{243}$

7. exactly 4 made $\frac{80}{243}$

8. at least 3 made $\frac{64}{81}$

When Mary and Sam play a certain board game, the probability that Mary will win a game is $\frac{3}{4}$. If they play five games, find the probability of each event.

9. Sam wins only once $\frac{405}{1024}$

10. Mary wins exactly twice $\frac{45}{512}$

11. Sam wins at least two games $\frac{47}{128}$

12. Mary wins at least three games $\frac{509}{512}$

Glencoe Division, Macmillan/McGraw-Hill

NAME ______________________ DATE ______________

16-1

Practice Worksheet

Angles and the Unit Circle

Change each degree measure to radian measure.

1. $18°$

2. $-72°$

3. $-820°$

4. $6°$

5. $-250°$

6. $870°$

7. $347°$

8. $-165°$

9. $2\pi°$

10. $-\frac{4}{3}\pi°$

Change each radian measure to degree measure.

11. 4π

12. $\frac{5}{2}\pi$

13. $\frac{-7}{9}\pi$

14. $2\frac{3}{5}\pi$

15. $\frac{13}{30}\pi$

16. $-\frac{4}{7}\pi$

17. 4

18. $-\frac{5}{2}$

19. $\frac{5\pi}{4}$

20. $\frac{3\pi}{16}$

Glencoe Division, Macmillan/McGraw-Hill

NAME ______________________ DATE ____________

16-1 Practice Worksheet

Angles and the Unit Circle

Change each degree measure to radian measure.

1. $18°$ $\frac{\pi}{10}$

2. $-72°$ $-\frac{2\pi}{5}$

3. $-820°$ $-\frac{41\pi}{9}$

4. $6°$ $\frac{\pi}{30}$

5. $-250°$ $-\frac{25\pi}{18}$

6. $870°$ $\frac{29\pi}{6}$

7. $347°$ $\frac{347\pi}{180}$

8. $-165°$ $-\frac{11\pi}{12}$

9. $2\pi°$ $\frac{\pi^2}{90}$

10. $-\frac{4}{3}\pi°$ $-\frac{\pi^2}{135}$

Change each radian measure to degree measure.

11. 4π $720°$

12. $\frac{5}{2}\pi$ $450°$

13. $\frac{-7}{9}\pi$ $-140°$

14. $2\frac{3}{5}\pi$ $468°$

15. $\frac{13}{30}\pi$ $78°$

16. $-\frac{4}{7}\pi$ $-102\frac{6}{7}°$

17. 4 $\frac{720°}{\pi}$

18. $-\frac{5}{2}$ $-\frac{450°}{\pi}$

19. $\frac{5\pi}{4}$ $225°$

20. $\frac{3\pi}{16}$ $33\frac{3}{4}°$

NAME ______________________ DATE ______________

16-2 Practice Worksheet

Sine and Cosine Functions

For each of the following, find the least positive angle measurement that is coterminal.

1. $-74°$

2. $7\frac{2}{5}\pi$

3. $\frac{43}{5}\pi$

4. $-590°$

5. $-2\frac{5}{6}\pi$

6. $920°$

7. $1100°$

8. $-\frac{19}{10}\pi$

9. $\frac{85\pi}{6}$

10. $1426°$

Find each value.

11. $\cos \frac{7\pi}{4}$

12. $\sin -30°$

13. $\sin \left(-\frac{2}{3}\pi\right)$

14. $\cos (-330°)$

15. $\cos 600°$

16. $\sin \frac{9}{2}\pi$

17. $\cos 187\pi$

18. $\cos \left(-\frac{11}{4}\pi\right)$

19. $\sin (-225°)$

20. $\sin 870°$

Glencoe Division, Macmillan/McGraw-Hill

NAME ______________________ DATE ____________

16-2 Practice Worksheet

Sine and Cosine Functions

For each of the following, find the least positive angle measurement that is coterminal.

1. $-74°$ **286°**

2. $7\frac{2}{5}\pi$ $1\frac{2}{5}\pi$

3. $\frac{43}{5}\pi$ $\frac{3}{5}\pi$

4. $-590°$ **130°**

5. $-2\frac{5}{6}\pi$ $\frac{7}{6}\pi$

6. $920°$ **200°**

7. $1100°$ **20°**

8. $-\frac{19}{10}\pi$ $\frac{1}{10}\pi$

9. $\frac{85\pi}{6}$ $\frac{1}{6}\pi$

10. $1426°$ **346°**

Find each value.

11. $\cos \frac{7\pi}{4}$ $-\frac{\sqrt{2}}{2}$

12. $\sin -30°$ $-\frac{1}{2}$

13. $\sin \left(-\frac{2}{3}\pi\right)$ $-\frac{\sqrt{3}}{2}$

14. $\cos (-330°)$ $\frac{\sqrt{3}}{2}$

15. $\cos 600°$ $-\frac{1}{2}$

16. $\sin \frac{9}{2}\pi$ **1**

17. $\cos 187\pi$ **−1**

18. $\cos \left(-\frac{11}{4}\pi\right)$ $-\frac{\sqrt{2}}{2}$

19. $\sin (-225°)$ $\frac{\sqrt{2}}{2}$

20. $\sin 870°$ $\frac{1}{2}$

Glencoe Division, Macmillan/McGraw-Hill

NAME ______________________ DATE ____________

16-3

Practice Worksheet

Other Trigonometric Functions

Find each value.

1. $\tan 135°$

2. $\sec \frac{\pi}{6}$

3. $\csc -\frac{\pi}{6}$

4. $\cot 210°$

5. $\sec 210°$

6. $\csc\left(-\frac{3}{4}\pi\right)$

7. $\tan \frac{5}{3}\pi$

8. $\cot(-405°)$

9. $\csc(-390°)$

10. $\sec 270°$

11. $\cot(-87\pi)$

12. $\tan \frac{13}{6}\pi$

13. $\sec(-225°)$

14. $\csc 4\frac{2}{3}\pi$

15. $\tan(-720°)$

16. $\cot(-90°)$

17. $\sec 330°$

18. $\csc -\frac{11\pi}{6}$

19. $\cot \frac{9\pi}{4}$

20. $\tan -\frac{3\pi}{4}$

Glencoe Division, Macmillan/McGraw-Hill

NAME ______________________ DATE ______________

16-3 Practice Worksheet

Other Trigonometric Functions

Find each value.

1. $\tan 135°$ **-1**

2. $\sec \frac{\pi}{6}$ **$\frac{2\sqrt{3}}{3}$**

3. $\csc -\frac{\pi}{6}$ **-2**

4. $\cot 210°$ **$-\sqrt{3}$**

5. $\sec 210°$ **$-\frac{2\sqrt{3}}{3}$**

6. $\csc\left(-\frac{3}{4}\pi\right)$ **$-\sqrt{2}$**

7. $\tan \frac{5}{3}\pi$ **$-\sqrt{3}$**

8. $\cot(-405°)$ **-1**

9. $\csc(-390°)$ **-2**

10. $\sec 270°$ **undefined**

11. $\cot(-87\pi)$ **undefined**

12. $\tan \frac{13}{6}\pi$ **$\frac{\sqrt{3}}{3}$**

13. $\sec(-225°)$ **$-\sqrt{2}$**

14. $\csc 4\frac{2}{3}\pi$ **$\frac{2\sqrt{3}}{3}$**

15. $\tan(-720°)$ **0**

16. $\cot(-90°)$ **0**

17. $\sec 330°$ **$\frac{2\sqrt{3}}{3}$**

18. $\csc -\frac{11\pi}{6}$ **2**

19. $\cot \frac{9\pi}{4}$ **1**

20. $\tan -\frac{3\pi}{4}$ **1**

NAME ______________________ DATE ____________

16-4 Practice Worksheet

Inverse Trigonometric Functions

Find each value.

1. $\text{Cos}^{-1}\left(-\frac{\sqrt{3}}{2}\right)$

2. $\text{Sin}^{-1}\left(-\frac{\sqrt{2}}{2}\right)$

3. $\text{Arctan}\left(-\frac{\sqrt{3}}{3}\right)$

4. Arccos 1

5. $\sin\left(\text{Sin}^{-1}\frac{3}{8}\right)$

6. $\cos\left(\text{Sin}^{-1} -\frac{3}{5}\right)$

7. $\tan\left(\text{Cos}^{-1} -\frac{\sqrt{3}}{2}\right)$

8. $\sec\left(\text{Cos}^{-1}\frac{2}{9}\right)$

9. csc(Arctan −1)

10. $\cot\left(\text{Arcsin}\frac{12}{13}\right)$

11. $\text{Sin}^{-1}\left(\cos\frac{\pi}{3}\right)$

12. $\text{Cos}^{-1}\left(\tan\frac{3}{4}\pi\right)$

13. $\sin\left(2\ \text{Cos}^{-1}\frac{15}{17}\right)$

14. $\cos\left(2\ \text{Sin}^{-1}\frac{\sqrt{3}}{2}\right)$

15. $\sin\left(\text{Arctan}\frac{\sqrt{3}}{3}\right)$

16. $\text{Sin}^{-1}(\tan 45°)$

17. $\text{Cos}^{-1}\left(\text{Sin}\frac{\pi}{6}\right)$

18. $\sec\left(\text{Cos}^{-1}\frac{4}{5}\right)$

19. $\csc\left(\text{Sin}^{-1}\frac{9}{10}\right)$

20. $\cot(\text{Sin}^{-1} 0)$

Glencoe Division, Macmillan/McGraw-Hill

NAME ____________ DATE ____________

16-4 Practice Worksheet

Inverse Trigonometric Functions

Find each value.

1. $\text{Cos}^{-1}\left(-\frac{\sqrt{3}}{2}\right)$ **150°**

2. $\text{Sin}^{-1}\left(-\frac{\sqrt{2}}{2}\right)$ **−45°**

3. $\text{Arctan}\left(-\frac{\sqrt{3}}{3}\right)$ **−30°**

4. Arccos 1 **0°**

5. $\sin\left(\text{Sin}^{-1}\frac{3}{8}\right)$ $\frac{3}{8}$

6. $\cos\left(\text{Sin}^{-1} -\frac{3}{5}\right)$ $\frac{4}{5}$

7. $\tan\left(\text{Cos}^{-1} -\frac{\sqrt{3}}{2}\right)$ $-\frac{\sqrt{3}}{3}$

8. $\sec\left(\text{Cos}^{-1}\frac{2}{9}\right)$ $\frac{9}{2}$

9. csc(Arctan −1) $-\sqrt{2}$

10. $\cot\left(\text{Arcsin}\frac{12}{13}\right)$ $\frac{5}{12}$

11. $\text{Sin}^{-1}\left(\cos\frac{\pi}{3}\right)$ **30°**

12. $\text{Cos}^{-1}\left(\tan\frac{3}{4}\pi\right)$ **180°**

13. $\sin\left(2\ \text{Cos}^{-1}\frac{15}{17}\right)$ $\frac{240}{289}$

14. $\cos\left(2\ \text{Sin}^{-1}\frac{\sqrt{3}}{2}\right)$ $-\frac{1}{2}$

15. $\sin\left(\text{Arctan}\frac{\sqrt{3}}{3}\right)$ $\frac{1}{2}$

16. $\text{Sin}^{-1}(\tan 45°)$ $\frac{\pi}{2}$

17. $\text{Cos}^{-1}\left(\text{Sin}\frac{\pi}{6}\right)$ $\frac{\pi}{3}$

18. $\sec\left(\text{Cos}^{-1}\frac{4}{5}\right)$ $\frac{5}{4}$

19. $\csc\left(\text{Sin}^{-1}\frac{9}{10}\right)$ $\frac{10}{9}$

20. $\cot(\text{Sin}^{-1} 0)$ **undefined**

Glencoe Division, Macmillan/McGraw-Hill

16-5

NAME ____________________ DATE ____________

Practice Worksheet

Finding Values for Trigonometric Functions

Use a calculator to find each value. Round your answers to four decimal places.

1. $\sin 347°$

2. $\cos \frac{13}{5}\pi$

3. $\cot \frac{5}{8}\pi$

4. $\sec(-84°)$

5. $\csc -\frac{10}{7}\pi$

6. $\tan(-27452°)$

7. $(\sec 18°)(\tan -67°)$

8. $\left(\csc \frac{\pi}{8}\right)\left(\cot \frac{13}{8}\pi\right)$

9. $\dfrac{3 \cos 65° - \tan 11°}{\cot 5°}$

10. $\dfrac{\sec \frac{3}{5}\pi}{\sin \frac{4}{5}\pi + \cot \frac{1}{5}\pi}$

11. $\text{Cos}^{-1}\ 0.9347$

12. $\text{Tan}^{-1}\ 12$

13. $\csc(\text{Sin}^{-1}\ 0.8)$

14. $\cot(\text{Arccos}\ 0.321)$

15. $\cos 28°$

16. $\sin 18°30'$

17. $\tan 72°$

18. $\sec 12°12'$

Use a calculator to find the value of x, in degrees, for each trigonometric function. Round your answers to four decimal places.

19. $\sin x = 0.4899$

20. $\cos x = 0.8258$

21. $\cos x = 0.5240$

22. $\tan x = 0.2074$

Glencoe Division, Macmillan/McGraw-Hill

16-5

NAME ______________________ DATE ____________

Practice Worksheet

Finding Values for Trigonometric Functions

Use a calculator to find each value. Round your answers to four decimal places.

1. $\sin 347°$ **−0.2250**

2. $\cos \frac{13}{5}\pi$ **−0.3090**

3. $\cot \frac{5}{8}\pi$ **−0.4142**

4. $\sec(-84°)$ **9.5668**

5. $\csc -\frac{10}{7}\pi$ **1.0257**

6. $\tan(-27452°)$ **28.6363**

7. $(\sec 18°)(\tan -67°)$ **−2.4771**

8. $\left(\csc \frac{\pi}{8}\right)\left(\cot \frac{13}{8}\pi\right)$ **−1.0824**

9. $\frac{3 \cos 65° - \tan 11°}{\cot 5°}$ **0.0939**

10. $\frac{\sec \frac{3}{5}\pi}{\sin \frac{4}{5}\pi + \cot \frac{1}{5}\pi}$ **−1.6476**

11. $\mathrm{Cos}^{-1}\ 0.9347$ **20.8203°**

12. $\mathrm{Tan}^{-1}\ 12$ **85.2364°**

13. $\csc(\mathrm{Sin}^{-1}\ 0.8)$ **1.2500**

14. $\cot(\mathrm{Arccos}\ 0.321)$ **0.3389**

15. $\cos 28°$ **0.8829**

16. $\sin 18°30'$ **0.3173**

17. $\tan 72°$ **3.0777**

18. $\sec 12°12'$ **1.0231**

Use a calculator to find the value of x, in degrees, for each trigonometric function. Round your answers to four decimal places.

19. $\sin x = 0.4899$ **29.3340°**

20. $\cos x = 0.8258$ **34.3303°**

21. $\cos x = 0.5240$ **58.3991°**

22. $\tan x = 0.2074$ **11.7170°**

Glencoe Division, Macmillan/McGraw-Hill

NAME ______________________ DATE ____________

16-6 Practice Worksheet

Solving Right Triangles

Use the triangle below to state equations that would enable you to solve each problem. Then solve. Round measures of sides to the nearest tenth.

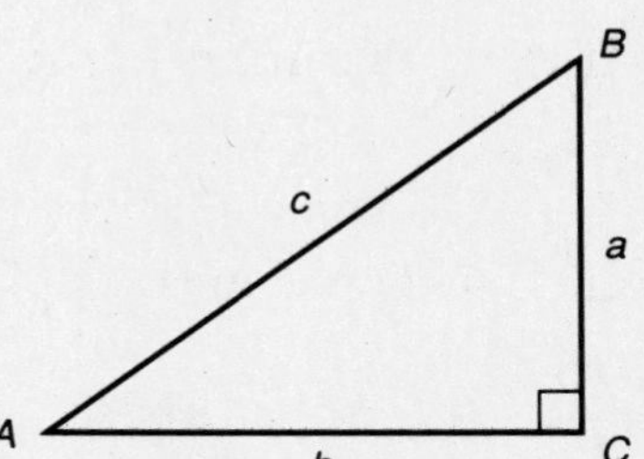

1. If $A = 20°$ and $c = 32$, find a.

2. If $A = 49°$ and $a = 17$, find b.

3. If $A = 27°18'$ and $a = 7$, find c.

4. If $a = 19.2$ and $A = 63°20'$, find b.

5. If $a = 28$ and $B = 41°$, find c.

6. If $A = 58°12'$ and $b = 34$, find c.

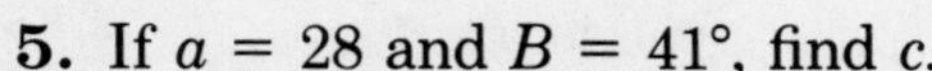

Solve each triangle described. Round measures of sides to the nearest hundredth and measures of angles to the nearest minute.

7. $a = 12, A = 35°$

8. $b = 25, B = 71°$

9. $a = 4, b = 7$

10. $b = 52, c = 95$

11. $A = 25°, c = 100$

12. $a = 7, c = 9$

NAME ____________________ DATE ____________

16-6 Practice Worksheet

Solving Right Triangles

Use the triangle below to state equations that would enable you to solve each problem. Then solve. Round measures of sides to the nearest tenth.

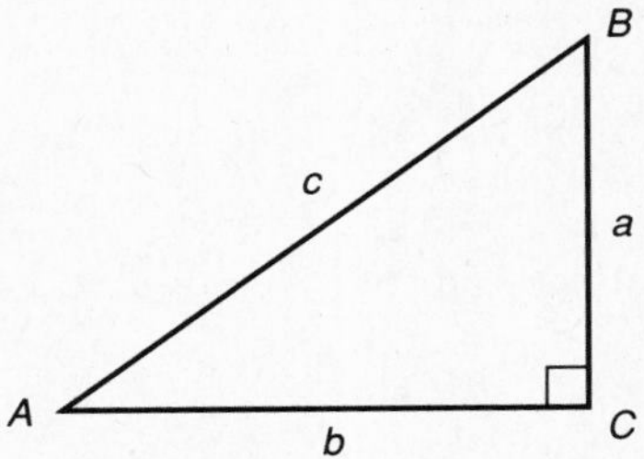

1. If $A = 20°$ and $c = 32$, find a.
10.9

2. If $A = 49°$ and $a = 17$, find b.
14.8

3. If $A = 27°18'$ and $a = 7$, find c.
15.3

4. If $a = 19.2$ and $A = 63°20'$, find b.
9.6

5. If $a = 28$ and $B = 41°$, find c.
37.1

6. If $A = 58°12'$ and $b = 34$, find c.
64.5

Solve each triangle described. Round measures of sides to the nearest hundredth and measures of angles to the nearest minute.

7. $a = 12$, $A = 35°$
$B = 55°$, $b = 17.13$,
$c = 20.92$

8. $b = 25$, $B = 71°$
$A = 19°$, $a = 8.6$,
$c = 26.44$

9. $a = 4$, $b = 7$
$A = 29°45'$, $B = 60°15'$
$c = 8.06$

10. $b = 52$, $c = 95$
$a = 79.50$, $A = 56°49'$,
$B = 33°11'$

11. $A = 25°$, $c = 100$
$a = 42.26$, $b = 90.63$,
$B = 65°$

12. $a = 7$, $c = 9$
$A = 51°3'$, $B = 38°57'$,
$b = 5.66$

Glencoe Division, Macmillan/McGraw-Hill

NAME ____________________ DATE ____________

16-7 Practice Worksheet

Applications of Right Triangles

Solve each problem. Round measures of lengths to the nearest hundredth and measures of angles to the nearest minute.

1. A highway has a 6% grade. That is, the highway rises 6 meters in each 100 meters measured horizontally. What is the angle that the highway is inclined to the horizontal?

2. Suppose a road makes an angle of 5° with the horizontal. What is the grade of the road?

3. Nancy shines a light from a window of Rocky Rococco's beachside mansion on a cliff 250 feet above the water level. Nick Danger, 10 feet above the water level in a ship off-shore finds that the angle of elevation of the light is 3°27′. Find the line-of-sight distance from the ship to Rococco's mansion.

4. An airplane is directly above a beacon that is 10,000 feet from an airport control tower. The angle of depression from the plane to the base of the control tower is 6°. How high above the beacon is the plane?

5. John views the top of a water tower at an angle of elevation of 36°. He walks 120 meters in a straight line toward the tower. Then he sights the top of the tower at an angle of elevation of 51°. How far is John from the base of the tower?

Glencoe Division, Macmillan/McGraw-Hill

NAME ______________________ DATE ____________

16-7 Practice Worksheet

Applications of Right Triangles

Solve each problem. Round measures of lengths to the nearest hundredth and measures of angles to the nearest minute.

1. A highway has a 6% grade. That is, the highway rises 6 meters in each 100 meters measured horizontally. What is the angle that the highway is inclined to the horizontal?
   3°26′

2. Suppose a road makes an angle of 5° with the horizontal. What is the grade of the road?
   8.75%

3. Nancy shines a light from a window of Rocky Rococco's beachside mansion on a cliff 250 feet above the water level. Nick Danger, 10 feet above the water level in a ship off-shore finds that the angle of elevation of the light is 3°27′. Find the line-of-sight distance from the ship to Rococco's mansion.
   3980.98 feet

4. An airplane is directly above a beacon that is 10,000 feet from an airport control tower. The angle of depression from the plane to the base of the control tower is 6°. How high above the beacon is the plane?
   1051.04 feet

5. John views the top of a water tower at an angle of elevation of 36°. He walks 120 meters in a straight line toward the tower. Then he sights the top of the tower at an angle of elevation of 51°. How far is John from the base of the tower?
   171.50 meters

Glencoe Division, Macmillan/McGraw-Hill

NAME ______________________ DATE ____________

16-8

Practice Worksheet

Law of Sines

Find the area of each triangle described below.

1. $a = 9, b = 11, C = 46°$

2. $a = 12, c = 15, B = 58°$

3. $b = 9, c = 9, A = 40°$

4. $a = 12.6, b = 8.9, C = 32°$

5. $a = 14.9, c = 18.6, B = 27°$

6. $b = 19.4, c = 8.6, A = 34°$

7. $a = 9, b = 7, C = 26°8'$

8. $b = 12, c = 19, A = 46°27'$

9. $a = 12, c = 14, B = 56°32'$

10. $b = 12, c = 14, A = 17°24'$

Solve each triangle described below.

11. $A = 50°, B = 30°, c = 9$

12. $a = 12, A = 56°, B = 38°$

13. $a = 14, b = 18, A = 36°50'$

14. $b = 20, c = 25, C = 70°10'$

15. $a = 25, b = 30, A = 46°18'$

16. $a = 40, A = 80°12', C = 14°12'$

17. $A = 80°, C = 40°, c = 30$

18. $c = 42, b = 56, C = 43°28'$

19. $b = 13, B = 46°38', C = 112°$

20. $A = 110°, a = 20, b = 8$

NAME ____________________ DATE ____________

16-8 Practice Worksheet

Law of Sines

Find the area of each triangle described below.

1. $a = 9, b = 11, C = 46°$
35.61

2. $a = 12, c = 15, B = 58°$
76.32

3. $b = 9, c = 9, A = 40°$
26.03

4. $a = 12.6, b = 8.9, C = 32°$
29.71

5. $a = 14.9, c = 18.6, B = 27°$
62.91

6. $b = 19.4, c = 8.6, A = 34°$
46.65

7. $a = 9, b = 7, C = 26°8'$
13.87

8. $b = 12, c = 19, A = 46°27'$
82.62

9. $a = 12, c = 14, B = 56°32'$
70.07

10. $b = 12, c = 14, A = 17°24'$
25.12

Solve each triangle described below.

11. $A = 50°, B = 30°, c = 9$
C = 100°, a = 7.00, b = 4.57

12. $a = 12, A = 56°, B = 38°$
C = 86°, b = 7.41, c = 14.44

13. $a = 14, b = 18, A = 36°50'$
B = 50°25′, C = 92°45′, c = 23.33

14. $b = 20, c = 25, C = 70°10'$
B = 48°49′, A = 61°1′, a = 23.25

15. $a = 25, b = 30, A = 46°18'$
B = 60°11′, C = 73°31′, c = 33.16

16. $a = 40, A = 80°12', C = 14°12'$
B = 85°36′, b = 40.47, c = 9.96

17. $A = 80°, C = 40°, c = 30$
B = 60°, a = 45.96, b = 40.42

18. $c = 42, b = 56, C = 43°28'$
B = 66°32′, A = 70°, a = 57.37

19. $b = 13, B = 46°38', C = 112°$
A = 21°22′, a = 6.52, c = 16.58

20. $A = 110°, a = 20, b = 8$
B = 22°5′, C = 47°55′, c = 15.80

NAME ______________________ DATE ______________

16-9 Practice Worksheet

Problem Solving Strategy: Examine the Solution

Solve. Use any strategy.

1. Marcia wants to form a triangle from some pieces of wood that she has. One piece of wood is 45 cm long. Another piece is 60 cm long with the angle opposite measuring 45°30′. What length should the third piece of wood be in order to form a triangle?

2. Simplify $\left[\left(\frac{1}{2}\right)^{-1} + \left(\frac{2}{3}\right)^{-1} + \left(\frac{3}{4}\right)^{-1} + \left(\frac{4}{5}\right)^{-1}\right]^{-1}$.

3. Robert made the four on a die into a six. On another die, he made the two into a three. What is the probability of rolling a sum of 7 with these two dice?

4. Insert operation symbols, +, −, ×, or ÷, and parentheses, as needed, to make a true equation from 9 3 6 4 2 = 8.

NAME ________________ DATE ________________

16-9 Practice Worksheet

Problem Solving Strategy: Examine the Solution

Solve. Use any strategy.

1. Marcia wants to form a triangle from some pieces of wood that she has. One piece of wood is 45 cm long. Another piece is 60 cm long with the angle opposite measuring 45°30′. What length should the third piece of wood be in order to form a triangle?

82.23 cm

2. Simplify $\left[\left(\frac{1}{2}\right)^{-1} + \left(\frac{2}{3}\right)^{-1} + \left(\frac{3}{4}\right)^{-1} + \left(\frac{4}{5}\right)^{-1}\right]^{-1}$.

$\frac{12}{73}$

3. Robert made the four on a die into a six. On another die, he made the two into a three. What is the probability of rolling a sum of 7 with these two dice?

$\frac{5}{36}$

4. Insert operation symbols, +, −, ×, or ÷, and parentheses, as needed, to make a true equation from 9 3 6 4 2 = 8.

Typical answer: (9 + 3) ÷ 6 + 4 + 2 = 8

NAME ________________________ DATE ____________

16-10 Practice Worksheet

Law of Cosines

Solve each triangle described below.

1. $a = 12$, $b = 7$, $C = 80°$

2. $a = 16$, $b = 20$, $C = 54°$

3. $A = 78°20'$, $b = 7$, $c = 11$

4. $B = 71°$, $c = 6$, $a = 11$

5. $a = 8$, $b = 6$, $c = 9$

6. $a = 16.4$, $b = 21.1$, $c = 18.5$

7. $a = 4$, $b = 5$, $c = 8$

8. $a = 4$, $b = 6$, $c = 3$

9. $A = 23°$, $b = 10$, $c = 12$

10. $C = 35°$, $b = 24$, $a = 18$

11. Two motorists start at the same point and travel in two straight courses. The courses diverge by 95°. If one is traveling at 50 mph and the other is traveling at 65 mph, how far apart will they be after 4 hours?

12. In problem 11, when will the motorists be 400 miles apart?

Glencoe Division, Macmillan/McGraw-Hill

NAME ______________________ DATE ____________

16-10 Practice Worksheet

Law of Cosines

Solve each triangle described below.

1. $a = 12, b = 7, C = 80°$
$c = 12.80, A = 67°24', B = 32°36'$

2. $a = 16, b = 20, C = 54°$
$c = 16.73, A = 50°41', B = 75°19'$

3. $A = 78°20', b = 7, c = 11$
$a = 11.78, B = 35°35', C = 66°5'$

4. $B = 71°, c = 6, a = 11$
$b = 10.68, C = 32°5', A = 76°55'$

5. $a = 8, b = 6, c = 9$
$A = 60°37', B = 40°48', C = 78°35'$

6. $a = 16.4, b = 21.1, c = 18.5$
$A = 48°23', B = 74°7', C = 57°30'$

7. $a = 4, b = 5, c = 8$
$A = 24°9', B = 30°45', C = 125°6'$

8. $a = 4, b = 6, c = 3$
$A = 36°20', B = 117°17', C = 26°23'$

9. $A = 23°, b = 10, c = 12$
$a = 4.80, B = 54°29', C = 102°31'$

10. $C = 35°, b = 24, a = 18$
$c = 13.87, B = 82°58', A = 62°2'$

11. Two motorists start at the same point and travel in two straight courses. The courses diverge by 95°. If one is traveling at 50 mph and the other is traveling at 65 mph, how far apart will they be after 4 hours?
341.56 miles

12. In problem 11, when will the motorists be 400 miles apart?
4.68 hours

NAME ______________________ DATE ____________

17-1

Practice Worksheet

Graphs of Trigonometric Functions

State the amplitude and period of each function.

1. $y = -4 \sin \theta$

2. $y = \cos 5\theta$

3. $y = \frac{1}{2} \sin \frac{3}{8}\theta$

4. $2y = -6 \cos 4\theta$

Graph each function.

5. $y = \sec 5\theta$

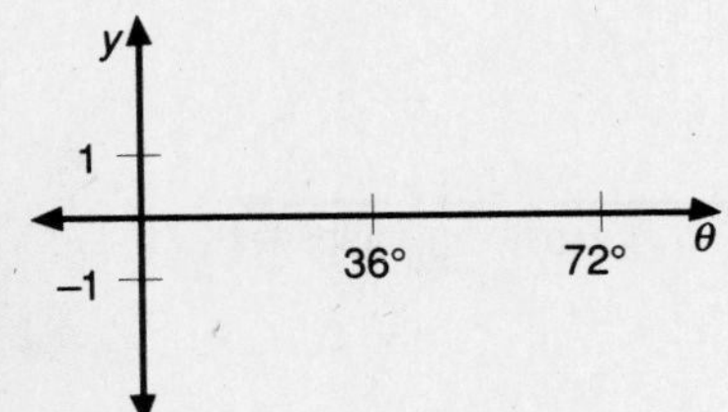

6. $y = \csc \frac{3}{4}\theta$

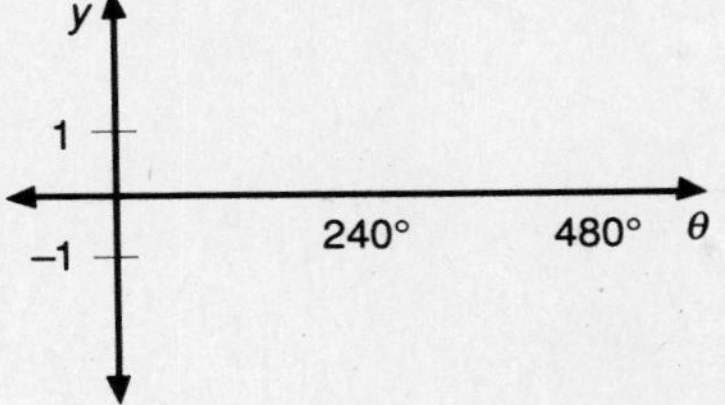

7. $y = \cot \frac{1}{2}\theta$

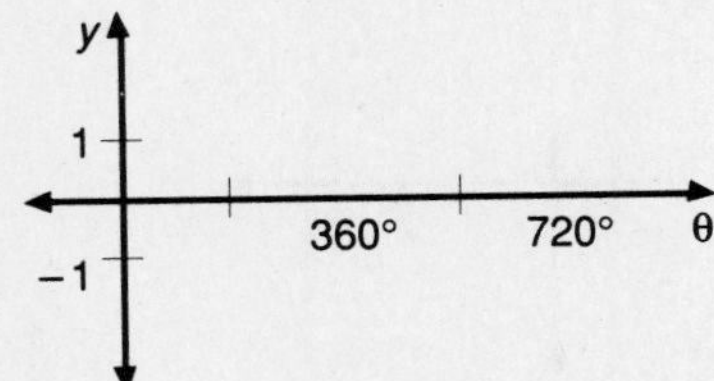

8. $y = \tan 10\theta$

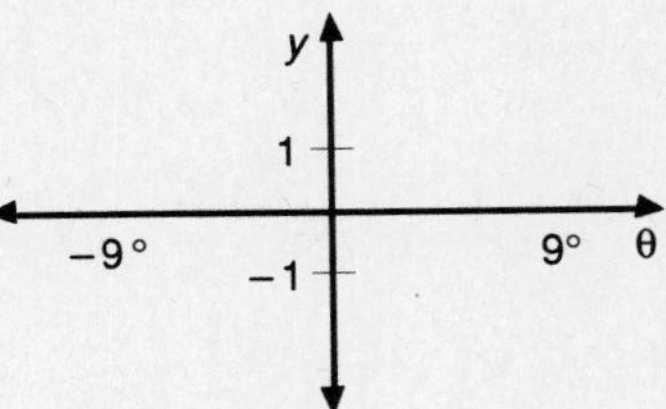

9. $y = 3 \csc 6\theta$

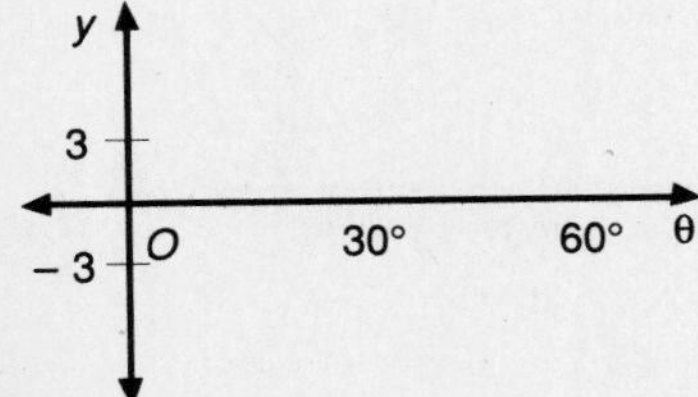

10. $y = \frac{1}{2} \sec 4\theta$

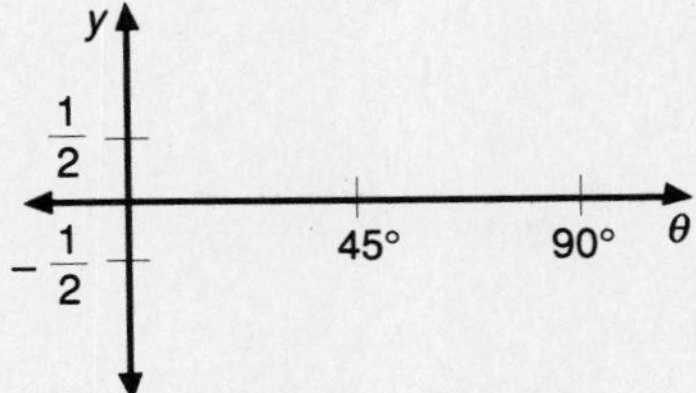

Glencoe Division, Macmillan/McGraw-Hill

NAME ______ DATE ______

17-1 Practice Worksheet

Graphs of Trigonometric Functions

State the amplitude and period of each function.

1. $y = -4 \sin \theta$ 4; 360° or 2π

2. $y = \cos 5\theta$ 1; 72° or $\frac{2\pi}{5}$

3. $y = \frac{1}{2} \sin \frac{3}{8}\theta$ $\frac{1}{2}$; 960° or $\frac{16\pi}{3}$

4. $2y = -6 \cos 4\theta$ 3; 90° or $\frac{\pi}{2}$

Graph each function.

5. $y = \sec 5\theta$

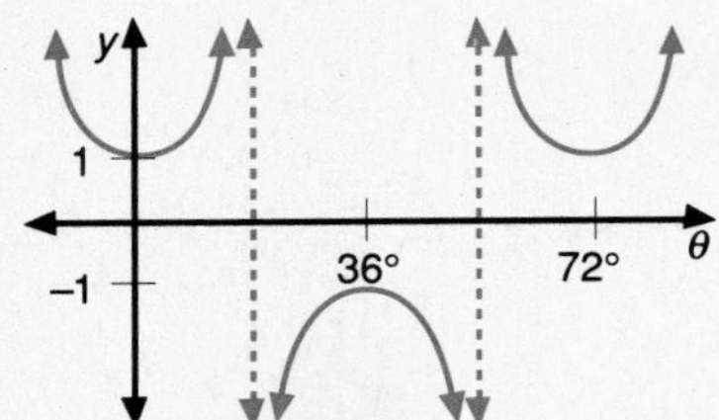

6. $y = \csc \frac{3}{4}\theta$

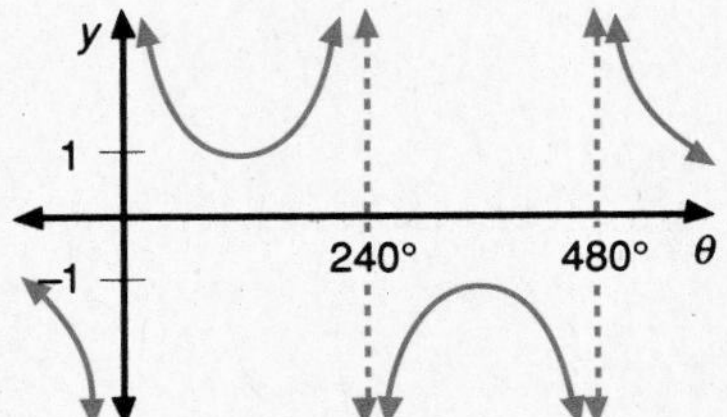

7. $y = \cot \frac{1}{2}\theta$

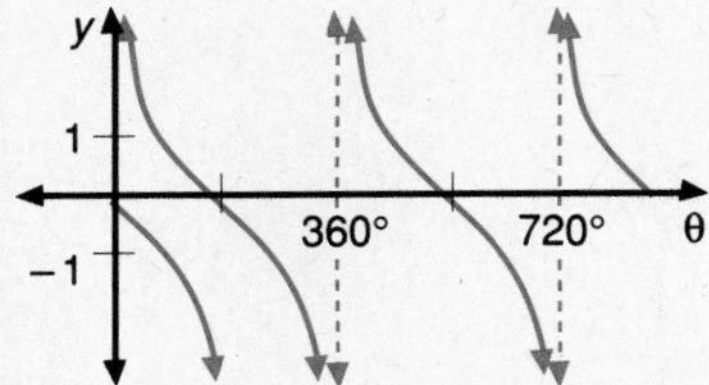

8. $y = \tan 10\theta$

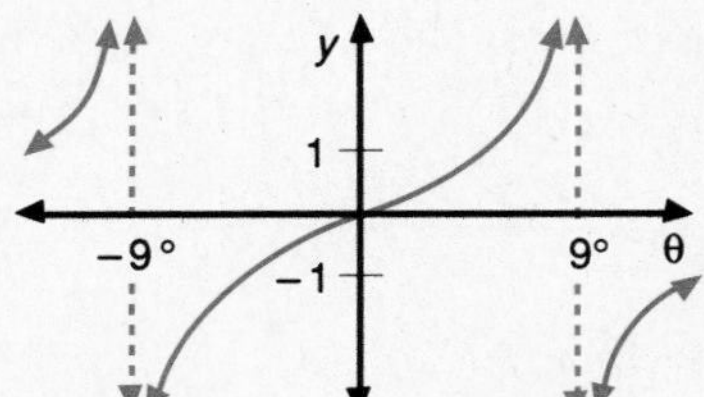

9. $y = 3 \csc 6\theta$

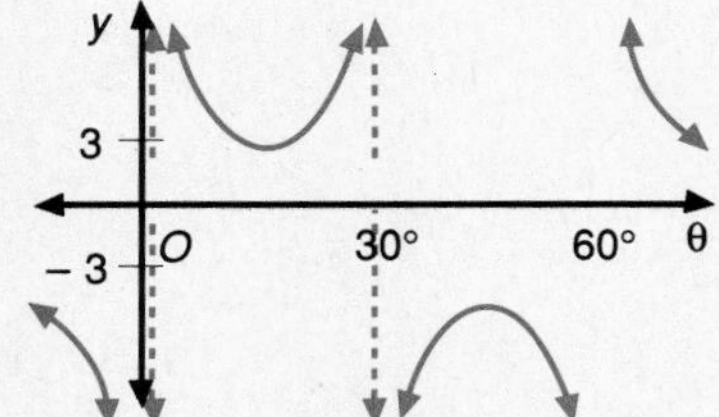

10. $y = \frac{1}{2} \sec 4\theta$

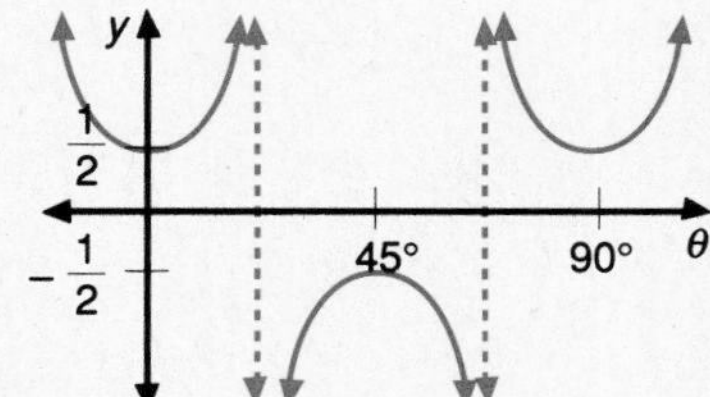

Glencoe Division, Macmillan/McGraw-Hill

NAME ______________________ DATE ____________

17-2 Practice Worksheet

Trigonometric Identities

Solve for values of θ between 0° and 90°.

1. If $\cos\theta = \frac{5}{13}$, find $\sin\theta$.

2. If $\sec\theta = 2$, find $\tan\theta$.

3. If $\cot\theta = \frac{1}{2}$, find $\sin\theta$.

4. If $\tan\theta = \frac{2}{5}$, find $\cot\theta$.

Solve for values of θ between 180° and 270°.

5. If $\sin\theta = -\frac{15}{17}$, find $\sec\theta$.

6. If $\tan\theta = 4$, find $\sec\theta$.

7. If $\csc\theta = -\frac{3}{2}$, find $\cot\theta$.

8. If $\sin\theta = -\frac{2}{9}$, find $\csc\theta$.

Solve for values of θ between 270° and 360°.

9. If $\cos\theta = \frac{3}{10}$, find $\cot\theta$.

10. If $\tan\theta = -\frac{1}{2}$, find $\sin\theta$.

11. If $\csc\theta = -8$, find $\sec\theta$.

12. If $\sec\theta = 3$, find $\cot\theta$.

Glencoe Division, Macmillan/McGraw-Hill

NAME ______________________ DATE ____________

17-2

Practice Worksheet

Trigonometric Identities

Solve for values of θ between 0° and 90°.

1. If $\cos\theta = \frac{5}{13}$, find $\sin\theta$. $\frac{12}{13}$

2. If $\sec\theta = 2$, find $\tan\theta$. $\sqrt{3}$

3. If $\cot\theta = \frac{1}{2}$, find $\sin\theta$. $\frac{2\sqrt{5}}{5}$

4. If $\tan\theta = \frac{2}{5}$, find $\cot\theta$. $\frac{5}{2}$

Solve for values of θ between 180° and 270°.

5. If $\sin\theta = -\frac{15}{17}$, find $\sec\theta$. $-\frac{17}{8}$

6. If $\tan\theta = 4$, find $\sec\theta$. $-\sqrt{17}$

7. If $\csc\theta = -\frac{3}{2}$, find $\cot\theta$. $\frac{\sqrt{5}}{2}$

8. If $\sin\theta = -\frac{2}{9}$, find $\csc\theta$. $-\frac{9}{2}$

Solve for values of θ between 270° and 360°.

9. If $\cos\theta = \frac{3}{10}$, find $\cot\theta$. $-\frac{3\sqrt{91}}{91}$

10. If $\tan\theta = -\frac{1}{2}$, find $\sin\theta$. $-\frac{\sqrt{5}}{5}$

11. If $\csc\theta = -8$, find $\sec\theta$. $\frac{8\sqrt{7}}{21}$

12. If $\sec\theta = 3$, find $\cot\theta$. $-\frac{\sqrt{2}}{4}$

Glencoe Division, Macmillan/McGraw-Hill

NAME ______________________ DATE ____________

17-3 Practice Worksheet

Verifying Trigonometric Identities

Verify that each of the following is an identity.

1. $(1 + \sin \theta)(1 - \sin \theta) = \frac{1}{\sec^2 \theta}$

2. $\cos^2 x \cot^2 x = \cot^2 x - \cos^2 x$

3. $\tan^4 w + 2 \tan^2 w + 1 = \sec^4 w$

4. $\sin^2 x(\csc^2 x + \sec^2 x) = \sec^2 x$

5. $\frac{\sin x + \cos x}{1 - \sin x} = \frac{1 + \cot x}{\csc x - 1}$

6. $\frac{1 - \tan x}{1 + \tan x} = \frac{\cot x - 1}{\cot x + 1}$

Glencoe Division, Macmillan/McGraw-Hill

NAME ______________________ DATE ____________

17-3 Practice Worksheet

Verifying Trigonometric Identities

Verify that each of the following is an identity.

1. $(1 + \sin\theta)(1 - \sin\theta) = \dfrac{1}{\sec^2\theta}$

$$(1 + \sin\theta)(1 - \sin\theta) \stackrel{?}{=} \frac{1}{\sec^2\theta}$$
$$1 - \sin^2\theta \stackrel{?}{=} \cos^2\theta$$
$$\cos^2\theta = \cos^2\theta$$

2. $\cos^2 x \cot^2 x = \cot^2 x - \cos^2 x$

$$\cos^2 x \cot^2 x \stackrel{?}{=} \cot^2 x - \cos^2 x$$
$$\cos^2 x \cdot \frac{\cos^2 x}{\sin^2 x} \stackrel{?}{=} \frac{\cos^2 x}{\sin^2 x} - \frac{\cos^2 x \sin^2 x}{\sin^2 x}$$
$$\frac{\cos^4 x}{\sin^2 x} \stackrel{?}{=} \frac{\cos^2 x(1 - \sin^2 x)}{\sin^2 x}$$
$$\frac{\cos^4 x}{\sin^2 x} = \frac{\cos^4 x}{\sin^2 x}$$

3. $\tan^4 w + 2\tan^2 w + 1 = \sec^4 w$

$$\tan^4 w + 2\tan^2 w + 1 \stackrel{?}{=} \sec^4 w$$
$$(\tan^2 w + 1)^2 \stackrel{?}{=} \sec^4 w$$
$$(\sec^2 w)^2 \stackrel{?}{=} \sec^4 w$$
$$\sec^4 w = \sec^4 w$$

4. $\sin^2 x(\csc^2 x + \sec^2 x) = \sec^2 x$

$$\sin^2 x(\csc^2 x + \sec^2 x) \stackrel{?}{=} \sec^2 x$$
$$1 + \frac{\sin^2 x}{\cos^2 x} \stackrel{?}{=} \sec^2 x$$
$$1 + \tan^2 x \stackrel{?}{=} \sec^2 x$$
$$\sec^2 x = \sec^2 x$$

5. $\dfrac{\sin x + \cos x}{1 - \sin x} = \dfrac{1 + \cot x}{\csc x - 1}$

$$\frac{\sin x + \cos x}{1 - \sin x} \stackrel{?}{=} \frac{1 + \cot x}{\csc x - 1}$$
$$\frac{\frac{\sin x}{\sin x} + \frac{\cos x}{\sin x}}{\frac{1}{\sin x} - \frac{\sin x}{\sin x}} \stackrel{?}{=} \frac{1 + \cot x}{\csc x}$$
$$\frac{1 + \cot x}{\csc x - 1} = \frac{1 + \cot x}{\csc x - 1}$$

6. $\dfrac{1 - \tan x}{1 + \tan x} = \dfrac{\cot x - 1}{\cot x + 1}$

$$\frac{1 - \tan x}{1 + \tan x} \stackrel{?}{=} \frac{\cot x - 1}{\cot x + 1}$$
$$\frac{\frac{1}{\tan x} - \frac{\tan x}{\tan x}}{\frac{1}{\tan x} + \frac{\tan x}{\tan x}} \stackrel{?}{=} \frac{\cot x - 1}{\cot x + 1}$$
$$\frac{\cot x - 1}{\cot x + 1} = \frac{\cot x - 1}{\cot x + 1}$$

Glencoe Division, Macmillan/McGraw-Hill

NAME ________________ DATE ________

17-4

Practice Worksheet

Problem Solving Strategy: Working Backwards

Solve. Use any strategy.

1. Find the difference of the reciprocals of two positive numbers whose difference is 6 and whose product is 16.

2. Consuelo earned some money doing odd jobs one weekend. She saved $\frac{1}{3}$ of what she earned. She gave half of what was left to her sister for a debt she owed. She then made purchases of $10.97, $8.42, $12.16, and $2.43. She had $18.60 left. How much money did she earn doing odd jobs?

3. Mrs. Grover picked some apples from her tree. She gave $\frac{1}{3}$ of what she picked to Mr. Anderson. Mr. Anderson gave half of his apples to Mrs. Miller. Mrs. Miller gave $\frac{1}{6}$ of her apples to Miss Paulson. If Miss Paulson received 10 apples, how many apples did Mrs. Grover pick?

Glencoe Division, Macmillan/McGraw-Hill

NAME ______________________ DATE ____________

17-4

Practice Worksheet

Problem Solving Strategy: Working Backwards

Solve. Use any strategy.

1. Find the difference of the reciprocals of two positive numbers whose difference is 6 and whose product is 16.
   $\frac{3}{8}$

2. Consuelo earned some money doing odd jobs one weekend. She saved $\frac{1}{3}$ of what she earned. She gave half of what was left to her sister for a debt she owed. She then made purchases of \$10.97, \$8.42, \$12.16, and \$2.43. She had \$18.60 left. How much money did she earn doing odd jobs?
   \$157.74

3. Mrs. Grover picked some apples from her tree. She gave $\frac{1}{3}$ of what she picked to Mr. Anderson. Mr. Anderson gave half of his apples to Mrs. Miller. Mrs. Miller gave $\frac{1}{6}$ of her apples to Miss Paulson. If Miss Paulson received 10 apples, how many apples did Mrs. Grover pick?
   360

NAME ______________________ DATE ____________

17-5 Practice Worksheet

Sum and Difference of Angles Formulas

Evaluate each expression.

1. $\cos 75°$

2. $\cos 375°$

3. $\sin (-165°)$

4. $\sin (-105°)$

5. $\sin 95° \cos 55° + \cos 95° \sin 55°$

6. $\cos 160° \cos 40° + \sin 160° \sin 40°$

7. $\tan (135° + 120°)$

8. $\tan (315° - \theta)$

Verify that each of the following is an identity.

9. $\cos (180° - \theta) = -\cos \theta$

10. $\sin (360° + \theta) = \sin \theta$

11. $\sin (45° + \theta) - \sin (45° - \theta) = \sqrt{2} \sin \theta$

12. $\cos \left(x - \frac{\pi}{6}\right) + \sin \left(x - \frac{\pi}{3}\right) = \sin x$

Glencoe Division, Macmillan/McGraw-Hill

NAME ______________________ DATE ____________

17-5 Practice Worksheet

Sum and Difference of Angles Formulas

Evaluate each expression.

1. $\cos 75°$ $\frac{\sqrt{6}-\sqrt{2}}{4}$

2. $\cos 375°$ $\frac{\sqrt{6}+\sqrt{2}}{4}$

3. $\sin(-165°)$ $\frac{\sqrt{2}-\sqrt{6}}{4}$

4. $\sin(-105°)$ $\frac{-\sqrt{2}-\sqrt{6}}{4}$

5. $\sin 95° \cos 55° + \cos 95° \sin 55°$ $\frac{1}{2}$

6. $\cos 160° \cos 40° + \sin 160° \sin 40°$ $-\frac{1}{2}$

7. $\tan(135° + 120°)$ $2 + \sqrt{3}$

8. $\tan(315° - \theta)$ $\frac{\tan\theta + 1}{\tan\theta - 1}$

Verify that each of the following is an identity.

9. $\cos(180° - \theta) = -\cos\theta$

$\cos(180° - \theta)$
$= \cos 180° \cos\theta + \sin 180° \sin\theta$
$= (-1)\cos\theta + 0 \cdot \sin\theta$
$= -\cos\theta$

10. $\sin(360° + \theta) = \sin\theta$

$\sin(360° + \theta)$
$= \sin 360° \cos\theta + \cos 360° \sin\theta$
$= 0 \cdot \cos\theta + 1 \cdot \sin\theta$
$= \sin\theta$

11. $\sin(45° + \theta) - \sin(45° - \theta) = \sqrt{2}\sin\theta$

$\sin(45° + \theta) - \sin(45° - \theta)$
$= \sin 45° \cos\theta + \cos 45° \sin\theta -$
$(\sin 45° \cos\theta - \cos 45° \sin\theta)$
$= 2 \cdot \cos 45° \sin\theta$
$= \sqrt{2}\sin\theta$

12. $\cos\left(x - \frac{\pi}{6}\right) + \sin\left(x - \frac{\pi}{3}\right) = \sin x$

$\cos\left(x - \frac{\pi}{6}\right) + \sin\left(x - \frac{\pi}{3}\right)$
$= \cos x \cos\frac{\pi}{6} + \sin x \sin\frac{\pi}{6} +$
$\sin x \cos\frac{\pi}{3} - \cos x \sin\frac{\pi}{3}$
$= \frac{\sqrt{3}}{2}\cos x + \frac{1}{2}\sin x + \frac{1}{2}\sin x - \frac{\sqrt{3}}{2}\cos x$
$= \sin x$

NAME ________________________ DATE ____________

17-6

Practice Worksheet

Double-Angle and Half-Angle Formulas

Find sin 2x, cos 2x, sin $\frac{x}{2}$, and cos $\frac{x}{2}$ for each of the following.

1. $\cos x = \frac{5}{13}$, x is in the first quadrant.

2. $\cos x = \frac{3}{7}$, x is in the fourth quadrant.

3. $\sin x = \frac{40}{41}$, x is in the second quadrant.

4. $\sin x = -\frac{4}{5}$, x is in the third quadrant.

5. $\sin x = -\frac{7}{8}$, x is in the third quadrant.

6. $\sin x = \frac{9}{10}$, x is in the second quadrant.

Evaluate each expression using the half-angle formulas.

7. $\tan 105°$

8. $\tan 15°$

9. $\cos 67\frac{1}{2}°$

10. $1 - 2\sin^2 15°$

11. $8 \sin(22.5°) \cos(22.5°)$

12. $\sin\left(-\frac{\pi}{8}\right)$

Verify that each of the following is an identity.

13. $\sin 2\theta = \frac{2\tan\theta}{1 + \tan^2\theta}$

14. $\tan x + \cot x = 2\csc 2x$

15. $\sin^2 \frac{x}{2} = \frac{\tan x - \sin x}{2\tan x}$

16. $\sin 4\beta = 4\cos 2\beta \sin\beta \cos\beta$

NAME ______________________ DATE ____________

17-6 Practice Worksheet

Double-Angle and Half-Angle Formulas

Find sin 2x, cos 2x, sin $\frac{x}{2}$, and cos $\frac{x}{2}$ for each of the following.

1. $\cos x = \frac{5}{13}$, x is in the first quadrant.
$\frac{120}{169}$, $-\frac{119}{169}$, $\frac{2\sqrt{13}}{13}$, $\frac{3\sqrt{13}}{13}$

2. $\cos x = \frac{3}{7}$, x is in the fourth quadrant.
$-\frac{12\sqrt{10}}{49}$, $-\frac{31}{49}$, $\frac{\sqrt{14}}{7}$, $-\frac{\sqrt{35}}{7}$

3. $\sin x = \frac{40}{41}$, x is in the second quadrant.
$-\frac{720}{1681}$, $-\frac{1519}{1681}$, $\frac{5\sqrt{41}}{41}$, $\frac{4\sqrt{41}}{41}$

4. $\sin x = -\frac{4}{5}$, x is in the third quadrant.
$\frac{24}{25}$, $-\frac{7}{25}$, $\frac{2\sqrt{5}}{5}$, $\frac{\sqrt{5}}{5}$

5. $\sin x = -\frac{7}{8}$, x is in the third quadrant.
$\frac{7\sqrt{15}}{32}$, $-\frac{17}{32}$, $\frac{\sqrt{8+\sqrt{15}}}{4}$, $\frac{\sqrt{8-\sqrt{15}}}{4}$

6. $\sin x = \frac{9}{10}$, x is in the second quadrant.
$-\frac{9\sqrt{19}}{50}$, $-\frac{31}{50}$, $\frac{\sqrt{50+5\sqrt{19}}}{10}$, $\frac{\sqrt{50-5\sqrt{19}}}{10}$

Evaluate each expression using the half-angle formulas.

7. $\tan 105°$ $-2-\sqrt{3}$

8. $\tan 15°$ $2-\sqrt{3}$

9. $\cos 67\frac{1}{2}°$ $\frac{\sqrt{2-\sqrt{2}}}{2}$

10. $1 - 2\sin^2 15°$ $\frac{\sqrt{3}}{2}$

11. $8 \sin(22.5°) \cos(22.5°)$ $2\sqrt{2}$

12. $\sin\left(-\frac{\pi}{8}\right)$ $-\frac{\sqrt{2-\sqrt{2}}}{2}$

Verify that each of the following is an identity.

13. $\sin 2\theta = \frac{2\tan\theta}{1+\tan^2\theta}$

$$\sin 2\theta \stackrel{?}{=} \frac{2\tan\theta}{1+\tan^2\theta}$$
$$2\sin\theta\cos\theta \stackrel{?}{=} \frac{2\tan\theta}{\sec^2\theta}$$
$$2\sin\theta\cos\theta \stackrel{?}{=} \frac{2\sin\theta}{\cos\theta}\cdot\cos^2\theta$$
$$2\sin\theta\cos\theta = 2\sin\theta\cos\theta$$

14. $\tan x + \cot x = 2\csc 2x$

$$\tan x + \cot x \stackrel{?}{=} 2\csc 2x$$
$$\frac{\sin x}{\cos x} + \frac{\cos x}{\sin x} \stackrel{?}{=} \frac{2}{2\sin x\cos x}$$
$$\frac{\sin^2 x + \cos^2 x}{\cos x \sin x} \stackrel{?}{=} \frac{1}{\sin x\cos x}$$
$$\frac{1}{\cos x\sin x} = \frac{1}{\sin x\cos x}$$

15. $\sin^2\frac{x}{2} = \frac{\tan x - \sin x}{2\tan x}$

$$\sin^2\frac{x}{2} \stackrel{?}{=} \frac{\tan x - \sin x}{2\tan x}$$
$$\frac{1-\cos x}{2} \stackrel{?}{=} \frac{\frac{\tan x}{\tan x} - \frac{\sin x}{\tan x}}{2\frac{\tan x}{\tan x}}$$
$$\frac{1-\cos x}{2} = \frac{1-\cos x}{2}$$

16. $\sin 4\beta = 4\cos 2\beta \sin\beta\cos\beta$

$$\sin 4\beta \stackrel{?}{=} 4\cos 2\beta\sin\beta\cos\beta$$
$$\sin 2(2\beta) \stackrel{?}{=} 4\cos 2\beta\sin\beta\cos\beta$$
$$2\sin 2\beta\cos 2\beta \stackrel{?}{=} 4\cos 2\beta\sin\beta\cos\beta$$
$$2\cdot 2\sin\beta\cos\beta\cdot\cos 2\beta \stackrel{?}{=} 4\cos 2\beta\sin\beta\cos\beta$$
$$4\cos 2\beta\sin\beta\cos\beta = 4\cos 2\beta\sin\beta\cos\beta$$

Glencoe Division, Macmillan/McGraw-Hill

NAME ______________________________ DATE ______________

17-7

Practice Worksheet

Solving Trigonometric Equations

Find all solutions if $0° \le x < 360°$.

1. $\sin 2x - \sqrt{3} \sin x = 0$

2. $\sqrt{2} \cos x = \sin 2x$

Find all solutions if $0 \le x < 2\pi$.

3. $\cos x + \cos (90 - x) = 0$

4. $\tan^2 x + \sec x = 1$

Solve each equation for all values of x if x is measured in degrees.

5. $\sin^2 x \cos x = \cos x$

6. $\csc^2 x - 3 \csc x + 2 = 0$

7. $\frac{3}{1 + \cos x} = 4(1 - \cos x)$

8. $\sqrt{2} \cos^3 x = \cos^2 x$

Solve each equation for all values of θ if θ is measured in radians.

9. $\cos^2 \theta = \sin^2 \theta$

10. $\cot \theta = \cot^3 \theta$

11. $\sqrt{2} \sin^3 \theta = \sin^2 \theta$

12. $\cos^2 \theta \sin \theta = \sin \theta$

NAME ______________________ DATE ____________

17-7 Practice Worksheet

Solving Trigonometric Equations

Find all solutions if 0° ≤ x < 360°.

1. $\sin 2x - \sqrt{3} \sin x = 0$

0°, 180°, 30°, 330°

2. $\sqrt{2} \cos x = \sin 2x$

90°, 270°, 45°, 135°

Find all solutions if 0 ≤ x < 2π.

3. $\cos x + \cos (90 - x) = 0$

$\frac{3}{4}\pi, \frac{7}{4}\pi$

4. $\tan^2 x + \sec x = 1$

$0, \frac{2}{3}\pi, \frac{4}{3}\pi$

Solve each equation for all values of x if x is measured in degrees.

5. $\sin^2 x \cos x = \cos x$

90° + 180n°

6. $\csc^2 x - 3 \csc x + 2 = 0$

30° + 360n°, 90° + 360n°, 150° + 360n°

7. $\frac{3}{1 + \cos x} = 4(1 - \cos x)$

60° + 180n°, 120° + 180n°

8. $\sqrt{2} \cos^3 x = \cos^2 x$

90° + 180n°, ± 45° + 360n°

Solve each equation for all values of θ if θ is measured in radians.

9. $\cos^2 \theta = \sin^2 \theta$

$\frac{\pi}{4} + \frac{\pi n}{2}$

10. $\cot \theta = \cot^3 \theta$

$\frac{\pi}{2} + n\pi, \frac{\pi}{4} + \frac{n\pi}{2}$

11. $\sqrt{2} \sin^3 \theta = \sin^2 \theta$

$\frac{\pi}{4} + 2\pi n, \frac{3\pi}{4} + 2\pi n$

12. $\cos^2 \theta \sin \theta = \sin \theta$

$0 + n\pi$

Glencoe Division, Macmillan/McGraw-Hill

NAME ______________________ DATE ____________

17-8 Practice Worksheet

Trigonometric Notation for Complex Numbers

Write each number in polar form.

1. $\sqrt{2} + \sqrt{2}i$

2. $1 - \sqrt{3}i$

3. $3 - 3i$

4. $\sqrt{3} + 3i$

Write each number in rectangular form.

5. $2\left(\cos \frac{\pi}{2} + i \sin \frac{\pi}{2}\right)$

6. $5\left(\cos \frac{\pi}{6} + i \sin \frac{\pi}{6}\right)$

7. $4\left(\cos \frac{3\pi}{4} + i \sin \frac{3\pi}{4}\right)$

8. $2\left(\cos \frac{5\pi}{4} + i \sin \frac{5\pi}{4}\right)$

Find each product. Then express the result in rectangular form.

9. $2\left(\cos \frac{5\pi}{4} + i \sin \frac{5\pi}{4}\right) \cdot 3\left(\cos \frac{7\pi}{4} + i \sin \frac{7\pi}{4}\right)$

10. $3\left(\cos \frac{2\pi}{3} + i \sin \frac{2\pi}{3}\right) \cdot 4\left(\cos \frac{\pi}{6} + i \sin \frac{\pi}{6}\right)$

11. $2\left(\cos \frac{4\pi}{3} + i \sin \frac{4\pi}{3}\right) \cdot 6\left(\cos \frac{5\pi}{6} + i \sin \frac{5\pi}{6}\right)$

12. $3\left(\cos \frac{3\pi}{4} + i \sin \frac{3\pi}{4}\right) \cdot 5\left(\cos \frac{7\pi}{6} + i \sin \frac{7\pi}{6}\right)$

Find each power. Express the result in rectangular form.

13. $\left[2\left(\cos \frac{\pi}{2} + i \sin \frac{\pi}{2}\right)\right]^3$

14. $\left[3\left(\cos \frac{3\pi}{4} + i \sin \frac{3\pi}{4}\right)\right]^4$

NAME ______________________ DATE ____________

17-8 Practice Worksheet

Trigonometric Notation for Complex Numbers

Write each number in polar form.

1. $\sqrt{2} + \sqrt{2}i$
   $2\left(\cos \frac{\pi}{4} + i \sin \frac{\pi}{4}\right)$

2. $1 - \sqrt{3}i$
   $2\left(\cos\left(-\frac{\pi}{3}\right) + i \sin\left(-\frac{\pi}{3}\right)\right)$

3. $3 - 3i$
   $3\sqrt{2}\left(\cos\left(-\frac{\pi}{4}\right) + i \sin\left(-\frac{\pi}{4}\right)\right)$

4. $\sqrt{3} + 3i$
   $2\sqrt{3}\left(\cos \frac{\pi}{6} + i \sin \frac{\pi}{6}\right)$

Write each number in rectangular form.

5. $2\left(\cos \frac{\pi}{2} + i \sin \frac{\pi}{2}\right)$
   $0 + i\sqrt{2}$

6. $5\left(\cos \frac{\pi}{6} + i \sin \frac{\pi}{6}\right)$
   $\frac{5\sqrt{3}}{2} + \frac{5}{2}i$

7. $4\left(\cos \frac{3\pi}{4} + i \sin \frac{3\pi}{4}\right)$
   $-2\sqrt{2} + 2\sqrt{2}i$

8. $2\left(\cos \frac{5\pi}{4} + i \sin \frac{5\pi}{4}\right)$
   $-\sqrt{2} - \sqrt{2}i$

Find each product. Then express the result in rectangular form.

9. $2\left(\cos \frac{5\pi}{4} + i \sin \frac{5\pi}{4}\right) \cdot 3\left(\cos \frac{7\pi}{4} + i \sin \frac{7\pi}{4}\right)$
   $6(\cos \pi + i \sin \pi)$; $-6 + 0i$

10. $3\left(\cos \frac{2\pi}{3} + i \sin \frac{2\pi}{3}\right) \cdot 4\left(\cos \frac{\pi}{6} + i \sin \frac{\pi}{6}\right)$
    $12\left(\cos \frac{5\pi}{6} + i \sin \frac{5\pi}{6}\right)$; $-6\sqrt{3} + 6i$

11. $2\left(\cos \frac{4\pi}{3} + i \sin \frac{4\pi}{3}\right) \cdot 6\left(\cos \frac{5\pi}{6} + i \sin \frac{5\pi}{6}\right)$
    $12\left(\cos \frac{\pi}{6} + i \sin \frac{\pi}{6}\right)$; $6\sqrt{3} + 6i$

12. $3\left(\cos \frac{3\pi}{4} + i \sin \frac{3\pi}{4}\right) \cdot 5\left(\cos \frac{7\pi}{6} + i \sin \frac{7\pi}{6}\right)$
    $15\left(\cos \frac{23\pi}{12} + i \sin \frac{23\pi}{12}\right)$; $15\left(\frac{\sqrt{6} + \sqrt{2}}{4}\right) + 15\left(\frac{\sqrt{2} - \sqrt{6}}{4}\right)i$

Find each power. Express the result in rectangular form.

13. $\left[2\left(\cos \frac{\pi}{2} + i \sin \frac{\pi}{2}\right)\right]^3$ $0 - 8i$

14. $\left[3\left(\cos \frac{3\pi}{4} + i \sin \frac{3\pi}{4}\right)\right]^4$ $-81 + 0i$